ARE THE RUSSIANS
TEN FEET TALL?

ARE THE RUSSIANS TEN FEET TALL?

WERNER KELLER

Translated and with an introduction by
CONSTANTINE FITZGIBBON

with 67 illustrations in halftone
109 in line and 6 maps

THAMES AND HUDSON
LONDON

TRANSLATED FROM THE GERMAN
'OST MINUS WEST = NULL'
BY CONSTANTINE FITZGIBBON
AND SYBIL WELCH

914.7
K29αXf

THIS EDITION © THAMES AND HUDSON LONDON 1961
© DROEMERSCHE VERLAGSANSTALT MUNICH/ZURICH 1960
PRINTED IN GREAT BRITAIN BY EBENEZER BAYLIS AND SON, LTD
THE TRINITY PRESS, WORCESTER, AND LONDON

Contents

INTRODUCTION

PART ONE
FROM RURIK TO THE REVOLUTION

PART TWO
FROM LENIN TO GAGARIN

6

Introduction

THIS BOOK is part of the Cold War. Those who are too fastidious, too frightened, too frivolous or too stupid to join in the struggle that is now taking place to decide humanity's future, and even more those who desire a totalitarian victory, will dismiss it. But for those of us who are interested and engaged it states an important thesis.

Dr Keller's argument, briefly, is that the Russians, coming late into the world of history, were still technologically in Western leading-strings when the Communists seized power. Imaginatively the Russians were, of course, our equals, as were pre-dynastic Egyptians and presumably Cro-Magnon man too, and no intelligent person, least of all Dr Keller, would presume to say that a Pushkin, a Dostoievski, a Mayakowski or a Pasternak was in any way inferior to his Western peers. But whereas the arts are produced by individuals who may on rare occasions be uneducated, stupid or even mad, the sciences, and even more so the applied sciences, can only flourish well in a society that is itself deeply imbued with skills and techniques which have been developed and passed on over the generations. A man of genius may have the 'idea' of a house, but it takes many men with very varied knowledge to build and furnish it. And this is, of course, even more so in the case of sustained laboratory work, of creating an industry, of constructing a technology. On the other hand any reasonably intelligent and educated man can be taught a simple technique. Therefore the Russian method, in the four centuries before 1917, was to import the technicians and copy their techniques. This of course was a practice also followed by other countries determined to catch up with their neighbours, but nowhere in Europe to the same extent as in Russia, for no other land was so lacking in a craftsman-artisan class. And since Western techniques were constantly being improved, this was not an operation that could ever be completed unless and until such an indigenous class came into existence. And this in turn implied the existence of a certain social stability and a certain measure of freedom for the artisans. Since all this was lacking, new technicians had to be imported with each new generation. On the occasions when Russian xenophobia won the day, and the foreigners were excluded or driven out, Russian technology immediately fell badly behind that prevailing in more civilized lands.

When Lenin seized power in Russia as the head of a small minority party with a conspiratorial past, he was confronted with two, among many, problems. He and his friends were committed to the Marxist analysis of the past which Marx had extended into a prophecy for the future as well. And Lenin held absolute power in a backward, primarily agrarian country. But the Marxist interpretation was already proved false by this very fact, for Marx had postulated revolution in advanced, industrialized societies. Therefore the sensible, indeed the honest, conclusion for the Russian Communists to draw would have been that Marxist theory was not applicable to, and should not be applied in, Russia. A liberal régime in Russia, which had then existed in embryonic form for a dozen years and had come to birth in the spring of 1917, might have given that great country the opportunity of developing into a healthy, happy and unique society. However it was this régime that the Bolsheviks had destroyed, and any return to a Kerensky-type government would have meant the end of absolute power for the Soviets. The Bolsheviks were men of violence, of the political underworld where crime, deceit, murder and the secret police are the order of the day. Therefore after waiting hopefully for the 'German October' that should have justified Marx but never came, and meanwhile subsisting on Western charity and Western trade, they chose what was for them the inevitable, the violent solution. If the theory did not fit the facts, then the facts must be changed.

Stalin presided over the great 'betrayal' of the revolution which was, as we can now see, inevitable if Marxist-Leninism was not to be simply and quietly scrapped. The facts, so stubbornly at variance with the theory, had to be remodelled, if the theory were to survive. This was done in two ways.

The facts could *apparently* be altered by the substitution of lies for truth. This has always been a major weapon in the hands of the Bolsheviks. They are not, in their jargon, inhibited by any sentimental bourgeois morality, and part of that morality involves a respect for truth. They have none. Unlike Marx, the latter-day Marxists regard words as mere weapons in their unending conspiracy to rule the world. To call this propaganda is to underestimate its power and extent: it is a basic readjustment of what we call thinking into what they call dialectical materialism. Whatever forwards the conspiracy is truth: whatever does not is either irrelevant or must be crushed and silenced by force. The world saw this in its purest form in the farrago of nonsense that the Old Bolsheviks spouted out, against themselves, in the purge 'trials' of the middle thirties.

But that was not all. If Marxism postulates an industrial society as a pre-requisite to socialism and communism, and if Russia were not then an industrialized country, it must be transformed into one with all speed. Thus would the facts be made to fit the theory. And this was done, regardless of the cost in human suffering. The liquidation of the kulaks to provide slave labour was perhaps the largest act of human brutality then seen, only to be surpassed by Auschwitz and the Chinese massacres of a dozen years ago. Millions of peasants were murdered or shut away in concentration-camps, while the country starved, and all because Stalin was determined to industrialize Russia with all speed. The series of Five Year Plans began. And as Dr Keller points out with a mass of confirming evidence, the West was called in to provide the skill and the knowledge to get industrialization under-way. We provided it.

Russia survived the onslaught of Stalin's ally, Adolf Hitler; whether she could have done so without American help in the form of massive lend-lease shipments is doubtful. Once that war was nearly won America, and to a lesser extent Britain, believed naïvely that the Russian leaders must surely have learned from their past mistakes and would now pursue the paths of welfare and peace along which the West was prepared to help them. But such gentle and sensible ambitions have no place in dialectical material- ism, save in so far as their enunciation may be used tactically to forward the conspiracy aiming at total, permanent domination of the globe. Nor could the Russian leaders learn any fundamental lessons from the past, for such lessons inevitably run counter to the dogma which, with each passing year, becomes more and more remote from the reality.

Russia therefore resumed industrialization at once, with the same violence and using the same methods as before. The immediate objective was and is to achieve a military position of such strength that absolute global power can be obtained, either with or without war. Dr Keller describes in detail how they have set about achieving it: on the one hand was the vast war booty from industrial Germany, in the form of plant, technique and highly skilled labour: on the other their enormous espionage apparatus, both military and industrial: subsidiary to these were such minor sources of profit as the anxiety of Western businessmen to trade with their mortal enemies: and behind it all was the mass of the Russian people, gelded by an omnipotent police force and compelled to work for purposes that are inhuman and often in conditions that were and are bestial. Industrialization has always, and in all lands, been a painful and even a disgusting business. Its justification, in free countries, is that it ultimately produces a higher living standard. But the Russian and Chinese industrializations have only inciden- tally and partially produced such a result, for the purpose of the Bolsheviks is and remains to achieve world power through military might.

Much was, indeed, achieved. Atom-bombs were made, then hydrogen- bombs: satellites have circled the globe and the moon; huge numbers of submarines apparently prowl the oceans, and rockets are poised to destroy foreign cities. At vast cost Russia became the second most powerful military nation in the world. All this had and has nothing to do with humanity's dream of peace, prosperity and freedom.

But it did give the Russians a marvellous weapon for their propaganda armoury. See, they say, we can circle the globe: therefore we are the most advanced country; therefore communism, the real communism that will bring you peace, prosperity and freedom is just around the corner. And a lot of people, not least in the highly industrialized West, fall for this type of argument. It is, of course, a lie: Russia is neither closer to, nor further from, true communism because of the Sputniks than Hitler was because of the *Autobahnen* or than Franco is because he has built hydro-electric installations in the Pyrenees. But the argument is not meant to be true in our sense. Its dialectical-materialistic 'truth' lies in the fact that if the world is sufficiently terrified of Russia's industrial-military might, it may surrender its liberties, and the conspiracy will thus have achieved total power.

And the purpose of this book is to expose the lie behind the argument. That Russia is a mighty power goes without saying. Russia was a mighty power in 1914, in 1815, in 1712. But as Dr Keller explains in such lavish detail, Russian power now as then is relatively weak when compared with that of the West as a whole, precisely because the West was and is the prime source of Russian power. And since Russia lacks the basic potential— educated, that is to say free, men in numbers approaching our own—it can never catch up on its own, though by devoting vast effort and energies to specific projects it may occasionally lead the West in certain fields.

This is a heartening and valuable contribution to understanding the world of today and tomorrow. It is not, however, any sort of encouragement to complacency. If Russia can now threaten us as she does, we have only our-selves to blame. We gave her the arms and the technical knowledge, even as we threw away our own arms and allowed our technical skills to stagnate in unnecessary economic depressions or wasted them on the creation of useless and ugly objects. It was traitors from our side, not agents from theirs, who won them our most closely guarded military secrets. And it is our news-papers that naïvely swallow their propaganda open-mouthed before passing it on, unwittingly to confuse and deceive our people.

Nevertheless, it is we in the West who are the more powerful, and not only because we have greater native skill and greater industry. Permanent and continuing achievements in science and technology depend, as they also and more obviously do in the humanities, upon intellectual freedom. And freedom is indivisible. In the absence of government by consent, and when the liberty of the individual is denied over a broad sector of his life, the springs of intellectual vitality gradually run dry. A tyranny, itself fundamentally unstable, ultimately destroys the ability and the will of its citizens to serve it creatively. Once the gloss has worn off, the outside world sees its material achievements as the barren tokens of a society which has ceased to serve humanity. If this book should lead a few more people to be less frightened, more determined, and more sceptical about Russian claims, it will have contributed to the future welfare of all mankind, including the large and unhappy numbers that now live in the darkness and fear which threaten us all.

CONSTANTINE FITZGIBBON

to the people of the free world

Spitzbergen

Bear Island

Murmansk

Kola Pen.

Novaya Zemlya

Liepaja

Dorpat

Riga

Kronstadt

L. Ladoga

St Petersburg

Pleskau

Novgorod

Volkhov

L. Onega

Archangel

Kholmogory

Vitebsk

Smolensk

Dniepr

Vologda

Kiev

Kaluga

Jaroslavl

Kostroma

Kotlas

Tula

Moscow

Vladimir

Pechara

Poltava

Kolomna

Nijni-Novgorod

Odessa

Krivoi Rog

Kharkov

Lipetsk

Ob

Dniepropetrovsk

Zaporozhe

Voronezh

Volga

Simferopol

Yuzovka

Kazan

Perm

Sevastopol

Taganrog

Saratov

Kerch

Rostov

Don

Ufa

Tobolsk

BLACK SEA

Tsaritsyn

Maikop

Omsk

Tomsk

Astrakhan

Batum

Novosibirsk

Tiflis

CASPIAN SEA

Irtysh

Aral Sea

Baku

Balkhash

L. Balkhash

Alma Ata

Tashkent

Samarkand

Part One · From Rurik to the Revolution

New Siberian Is.

iye

Kolyma

Petropavlovsk

Okhotsk

Yakutsk

Lena

Krasnoyarsk

Angora

L. Baikal

Amur

Khabarovsk

Irkutsk

Ulan Ude

Vladivostok

I   'Come to our Country'

DURING THE LAST CENTURY large numbers of coins were unearthed in Sweden which caused a considerable sensation. They had been buried in an ancient settlement near Uppsala, the country's first royal capital. These coins—there were about 40,000 of them in all—must have travelled a long way one thousand years ago, for they originated in Arabia.

Abu Mohammed Harun Ibn al Mahdi al Rashid, the 'law-giver', whom we call Haroun al Rashid, sat at that time upon the glittering throne of the oriental Caliphate. He was a dangerous enemy to his neighbour in the east, the great Eastern Roman Empire of Byzantium-Constantinople, but his relations with the mighty ruler of the West, Charlemagne, were friendly.

As the ninth century dawned upon the glory and rivalries of these three empires, the eastern Caliphate, the Byzantine Empire and the Western Empire of Charlemagne, the whole of Eastern Europe still slumbered in the darkness of prehistory. Yet even then the West had already begun to explore the vast and almost uncharted territories of the East. From the far north northern seamen, warriors and traders and those Swedish Goths known as the Varangians were establishing the first links between Scandinavia and the Orient. It was along their trade routes that the Arabian coins had travelled to southern Sweden.

By the year 800 there were already two of these important international shipping routes. It took a thousand years for the Russians to re-create such a route, linking the Baltic to the Black Sea and the Caspian: indeed, it was only done by Stalin when he built the great canals.

Coming from the Gulf of Finland through the Karelian Isthmus the dragon ships of the Varangians succeeded in reaching the Volga, which is linked by no natural waterway with the north. A land barrier then blocked all access to the great river's headwaters. But the resourceful seamen knew how to master this natural obstacle. They built 'ships' rollers', or roads of logs, along which they pulled and pushed their longboats across mile after mile of dry land until at last they came to the upper reaches of the Volga. Thus did these warrior-merchants from the north establish a nautical trade route over two thousand miles in length, and a very flourishing one at that. Itil, at the mouth of the Volga and not far from the present-day Astrakhan, was then the capital of the Khazar empire; this became the principal tranship-ment port for the Varangian traders. Arabian writers have described meeting the men from the north in the great Khazar market. 'They are tall as palm-trees, rosy-cheeked and with red hair. They wear neither blouse nor *kaftan*, but are dressed in coarse cloaks, which they throw over one shoulder, thus leaving their right hand free. Each man carries an axe, a dagger and a sword. They are never to be seen unarmed . . .'

For a long time this Volga route remained the main trade artery to the distant south, which stretched as far as Baghdad.

A second north-south water-route established by the northerners was to have world-wide political importance. For this was to open a way, for the first time, through the territory where lived the Eastern Slavs.

It, too, relied on 'ships' rollers'. From Lake Ladoga a natural waterway is provided by the River Volkhov to Lake Ilmen and then by the River Lovot to join up with the River Dvina. Thence the ships had to be pulled over dry land, until, at a point north of where Vitebsk now stands, they could be launched upon the upper reaches of the Dniepr.

In the period about the year 800, each summer saw great convoys of Scandinavian boats sailing upon these twelve hundred miles of water. At Zaporozhe they navigated the nine notorious Porogi, those dangerous whirlpools and rapids of the lower Dniepr, and then with oar and sail made their way along the shores of the Black Sea as far as the Bosphorus and the Sea of Marmora. This Dniepr route was famous throughout the East, and was known as the 'Varangians' Road to Greece', in the Arabic chronicles of the time. Rare and valuable goods from the far north travelled along it: honey, beeswax, splendid furs, the pelts of beaver, otter and sable, black fox and—a popular item—the winter furs of squirrels.

The Imperial City on the Golden Horn—known to the northern peoples as *Miklagard* ('the shining city')—was then the transhipment centre for goods from all over the world. Like a spider's web, its trade routes spread outwards to all the points of the compass. Through Turkestan caravans brought silks overland from China; up the Red Sea and through Alexandria spices and drugs, ivory, pearls and precious stones came from the Indies to the Bosphorus. Thus were priceless wares interchanged between two worlds: one, the almost unknown world in the far north, the other the great and famous world of antiquity. And all this trade moving up and down the shallows and rapids of the mighty Dniepr passed through the lands of the Eastern Slavs. Depots were first created, then small trading-posts, finally fortified market towns.

The Eastern Slavs, across whose lands the Varangians travelled, had neither the ability nor the desire to combine politically and thus to create a state of their own. External teachers had to be called in before this could be achieved.

When one examines the lives and customs of these Slavs, and studies their previous history, it seems as though time for them had stood still. In those centuries they remained, as it were, rooted in prehistory, a strange contrast to the rest of the world.

Italian architects under Ivan III (15th century) completely changed the appearance of the Kremlin. In place of a fortress surrounded by a wooden palisade (above) they built the cathedrals and palaces we know today, surrounded by stone walls. (Russian drawings by Vasnekov.)

One of the magnificent bronze doors of the St Sophia Cathedral, Novgorod, built 1045–52. Attributed to Master Ruffin of Magdeburg.

The church of Spas na boru (Redeemer in the forest), built 1380, one of the few stone buildings in Moscow until the arrival of the Italian architects at the end of the 15th century. The great palace of the Kremlin, in the background, was built by Konstantin von Thon in the 19th century.

The Varangians used ships' rollers for their shipping routes through Russia from the Baltic to the Black Sea and the Caspian.

All that they could produce was honey and wax, skins and furs from the forest. Thus did the fruit-pickers and hunters live, who inhabited all the world in prehistoric times. They also practised agriculture and kept cattle, but only in the most primitive fashion.

All forms of political organization were unknown to them. 'These people,' the Byzantine chronicler Procopius wrote in the sixth century, 'are not subject to any man, but have lived since earliest times in a state of democracy.'

What Procopius meant by 'democracy' was their social organization. The Eastern Slavs recognized no loyalties, beyond those due to the family and the tribe, and later to the village community and to a loose clan system. It was the family which collectively made all the important decisions; to the family belonged all the arable land tilled by its members; there was no private ownership or occupation of this land, which was common property. There was absolute equality between all members of the family living this tribal life; but personal freedom could not exist in such conditions.

Temples and priests were both unknown. The Slavs worshipped the sea and the waves, the forests, trees and animals. Their principal gods were the sun god, Dashbog, and the god of cattle, Veles; the god of fire, Svarog, and

Perun, the god of thunder. The forests and the streams were inhabited by *Russalki*, that is to say by demons and nymphs, water-spirits and woodland sprites, which still live on in Slav songs today.

The Eastern Slavs are described as courageous and resourceful, as hospitable and—what is characteristic—'uncontrolled and quick to anger'. Should hostilities break out or should they stumble upon an enemy, it never led to open combat; a disciplined battle array was completely unknown to them. Lightning-quick surprise attacks from ambush—such was their method of fighting.

They could neither read nor write, were totally ignorant of astronomy and mathematics, medicine and engineering, were familiar neither with philosophical, moral nor religious teachings, had never seen a stone house, temple or palace. They knew nothing of seamanship nor the casting of iron— in fact they stepped upon the stage of history with empty hands. As Herder, after many years' study of the Slav people, wrote in the eighteenth century, 'They take up more space on the map than they do in history.'

Like a giant walking in his sleep, his muscles still untested, the Slav masses entered the spotlight of history. After the Slavs no other great race appears upon the world stage—they were the last to emerge from the darkness. This was not an automatic disadvantage to them, though no cultivated nation has had so insignificant a past. In the life of a people late development is not unusual nor is it a disgrace; the Slavs' western neighbours, the Germanic races, came next to last in the long cavalcade of history. And were not all peoples raw, unskilled savages once upon a time, before they took over the heritage of other races, usually by plunder and violence?

Such late development for so young, fresh, gifted and exceptionally strong a race could have meant a great opportunity. For the Slavs appeared at exactly the right moment of history, at a transition period when something completely new was coming to birth. In those centuries, when the Slav hordes first pounded upon the gates of the civilized world and clamoured for admission, the Middle Ages had already begun in the West. The peoples of Europe had laid the stupendous foundation stones upon which humanity was to build. They had begun to pave the great highway which would lead steeply into the new age. Incalculable energy—physical, mental and spiritual —was to be needed for all this, and any who wished to join in the great work of the future were sure to be welcomed with open arms.

Would the Slavs answer this call? Would they understand and join in the struggle up the steep, laborious path that has led from early feudalism to the twentieth century?

All roads lay open to the Slavs. It was only a question of which they would take; of how they would co-operate among themselves; and of whether they would learn to combine their own gifts with those of other peoples in order to create something positive and new.

The initial process of crystallization was to take place in the north, where the trade routes began. From their ancestral home between the Vistula and the Dniepr the Slavs had pushed upstream through the territories inhabited by the Finns and the Lithuanians as far as the Gulf of Finland. This led to friction and endless bloody feuds, not only with the foreigners but between themselves.

Incapable of solving these quarrels themselves, the Slavs called for foreign help.

'We must get ourselves a king,' they said, 'who can rule over us, and lead us properly.' So says the *Nestor Chronicle*, the most valuable of the old Russian histories, written by the Monk Nestor about A.D. 1100.

What more obvious than to turn to those Nordic warrior-merchants who for so many years had been sailing their ships southwards through the country of the Slavs, who had built trading-posts, with whom they had bartered, and who had even provided bodyguards for their chieftains?

So the Slavs sent messengers across the Baltic to the country of the Varangians. They went to see the chieftain of the 'Rus'; for the Varangians were called by the Finns *Ruotsi*, or oarsmen, which in Slavonic became *Rus*. In Roslagen, Sweden, they made their request, which Nestor has recorded as follows:

'Our land is large and rich, but we have neither law nor order. Come to us, rule us, and command us.'

The Varangians, as we know, answered the call of the Slavs. Three brothers came, with their warriors, to rule the country, which was henceforth called 'Rus-Land': they were Rurik, Sineus and Truvor—in old Swedish, Hrörekr, Signjotr and Thorvardr. They began by building strong fortified towns as centres of the three territories over which they ruled. The most powerful of these capitals, which they called Holmgard, was Novgorod on the shores of Lake Ilmen. It was the seat of Prince Rurik, and on the death of his brothers he took over their lands as well.

The story of Rurik's call to the throne has been much embellished by myth and legend. One fact, however, is beyond dispute: Varangian overlords brought law and order to the Slavs. The birth of an eastern state coincides with the moment that their rule began.

The *Nestor Chronicle* gives the date that Rurik was summoned as 862. The Russia of the Romanov Tsars later recognized this as a great historical event, and in 1862 the thousandth anniversary of the founding of the Russian Empire was celebrated with much pomp and splendour.

The new empire of the Swedish rulers was rapidly extended towards the alluring south, following the old trade route from the north, by way of the Dniepr down which the Varangians' boats still sailed. The successors of

Rurik, Askold and Dir, soon controlled the Kiev region, where Dnaparstadir, the capital of the old Eastern Gothic kingdom, must once have stood. Shortly after Rurik's death, Helge (in Russian, Oleg, who from 879 to 912 reigned as regent for Igor, Rurik's son) consolidated the two areas north and south of the Dniepr into one kingdom which he further extended in victorious campaigns.

Eastwards, he and his men pushed forward as far as the upper reaches of the Volga and the Don, westwards to the Bug and the Dniestr, and southwards to the Ukraine. The fortresses of Tchernigov and Pereyaslavl were built. With a great horde of warriors, known as the *Drushina*, Oleg made a triumphant entry into the fortress of Kiev.

'This shall be the Mother City of all Russia!' Oleg is quoted by Nestor as pronouncing. And so Kiev became the new capital of the Rus, while Novgorod in the north sank into the background.

Thus within a few decades the Ruriki had performed a remarkable feat: they had organized and unified the Slav peoples.

Fortified trading-ports had now been built from Lake Ladoga in the north to the Lower Dniepr in the south; the nomadic clans had been conquered and compelled to unify: and thus the Slavs, under their Scandinavian rulers, became a state. It is to these invaders from the north that they owe their unification.

Scarcely had the Slavs acquired the status of a major power, scarcely had their political organization, administration and their armed forces begun to take shape, before they embarked, quite characteristically, upon the first of a long series of aggressions against the West.

Kiev was the jumping-off place. The tempting target, which beckoned from across the Bosphorus, was the mighty, golden city of Byzantium, the city which was to ordain the fate of Russia.

The attack was powerfully mounted. Without warning, a flotilla of two thousand boats, manned by fighting seamen, appeared off Byzantium in the year 907. The Grand Duke of Kiev, as Oleg now called himself, had an ambitious aim. He wished to compel the Byzantine Emperor to recognize him as a ruler of equal rank with himself. And he pulled it off. In 911 a pact of friendship was signed. Written in purple on two pages of parchment, it stated that 'everlasting peace' should reign between the two states. Furthermore, Byzantium was to open its gates to the Dniepr trade and to give all help and protection to the foreign traders.

Oleg might well be satisfied. Without his having to make the slightest political or military concession, his unexpected attack had produced all the results for which he had hoped. But despite the fine phrases the 'everlasting peace' did not last long. It was broken by the East, after Oleg's death. His

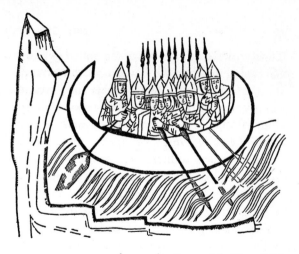

Rurik's warriors on the Dniepr. (10th Century.)

successor, Igor, began to prepare a new attack on the Imperial City. This time, however, Slav surprise tactics were destined to misfire.

When in 941 Igor's forty thousand warriors in a thousand rowing and sail boats suddenly appeared in the Bosphorus and began to attack both banks, Byzantium was ready and launched a furious and immediate counter-attack. The Imperial Fleet was engaged elsewhere. The Emperor therefore made a quick decision, and ordered fifteen ships which were out of commission to go into action at once.

This meant the end for the men from Kiev. For every Byzantine ship carried on board, disguised as its figurehead, equipment which constituted the first 'super-weapon of the West'. At the bow of each ship there towered a bronze lion's head. Its open jaws concealed a pipe. From a large, hidden metal container at the base of this tube, a fluid was pumped up, and the lion's head began to spew out fire. This was the terrible and terrifying 'Greek Fire'.

This 'super-weapon', invented by the Byzantine shipbuilder Kallinikos, was a carefully guarded state secret: a mixture of petroleum, brimstone, rock-salt, resin, asphalt and calcinated lime, the fluid continued to burn even on the water, and the lion could hurl his flames far across the waves.

When the thousand boats of the Kiev fleet met the fifteen ships of the Imperial squadron the outcome was soon decided. Greek fire defeated and in part destroyed the fleet of the Rus.

The pact signed in 945 plainly shows the magnitude of the defeat sustained by Kiev. Freedom to trade in Byzantium was now limited, and it was agreed that Kiev should give military aid to the Emperor, whenever he might demand it.

The immensely superior military skill of the Byzantines had saved the Imperial Capital and forced the Kiev Rus back behind their own boundaries.

The Kiev Rus could not even contemplate any attempt to produce Greek fire themselves, as the Russians, after 1945, were to copy the A-bomb and H-bomb which had been developed in the USA. They were still too uncivilized, technically too backward.

They therefore embarked upon a new policy—and one that is still favoured at such times by their descendants today: the policy of coexistence. The Russian Princess Olga—the Russian version of the name Helga—widow and successor of Igor, made the first official state visit to Byzantium in 956.

All that happened at this important first meeting between 'West' and 'East', all that was displayed before the astonished eyes of the princess from the eastern state, still in the first springtime of its youth, the subtle but powerful administration, the glitter and glory and splendour which so impressed her—all this is symbolic of the great influence that Byzantium was to exercise over the whole of Russia.

In their attacks upon the Imperial Capital on the Golden Horn, the Kiev Russians had learned to know the highly developed equipment and military strength of Byzantium. That, however, was only one aspect. They were now seeing how infinitely superior Byzantium was to Kiev in political, cultural and spiritual matters—not to mention the importance of the city as the second centre of Christendom. All this acted like a magnet upon Olga. She was drawn to copy their administrative techniques, first in the Kiev district, an act of imitation in which all Russia was later to join. What a difference between the Royal Palace at Kiev (built of wood and located in a fortified trading-post amidst the forests that flanked the Dniepr) and the glittering Imperial metropolis upon the Golden Horn!

We can read in a very detailed protocol exactly how, on 9th September of the year 956, the Emperor Constantine VII Porphyrogenitus received the Princess Olga of Kiev as the first Russian sovereign to set foot inside the Imperial Palace of Byzantium.

On this day the entire Senate—at its head the highest state officials, the Treasurer, the Minister in Charge of Home Affairs throughout the vast Empire, the Postmaster-General, who acted also as Minister for Foreign Affairs, the Commander of the Imperial Bodyguard, the Prefect of the City and the Chief of the Security Police which dealt with foreigners, beggars and vagrants—all repaired to the Magnaura Palace, which stood high upon the Seraglio Peak near Hagia Sophia, the Church of St Sophia. The members of the Senate took their places dressed in the splendid robes which the strictest etiquette demanded. Thus they sat, awaiting their Emperor. Lord Chamberlains and Chamberlains, as well as lictors who, as in a previous age, carried the bundle of fasces with the axe, and guards recruited from foreign countries in glittering armour and magnificent uniforms were meanwhile conducting the Emperor into the Church of Christ which adjoined the palace. There candles were lit as an act of worship. After a brief service they all moved on, towards the Triklinon of the Magnaura, the great audience-chamber.

The Imperial choirs and representatives of the Circus factions intoned songs of praise as the monarch entered his palace. The Emperor first went

St Sophia Cathedral, Novgorod—a copy of the Hagia Sophia, Byzantium.

to an ante-room, to await the completion of the preparation for the audience. At a sign from the Kuropalat, the equivalent of the Court Chamberlain, the Emperor entered the great hall. He donned the Imperial robes and the diadem, and while cries of welcome echoed through the hall, and the choirs resumed their chanting, the Emperor walked up the porphyry steps to his throne, which was surmounted by a canopy and draped in soft purple, and sat himself upon it. In front of the throne, on a dais, stood a tree of gilt bronze, in the branches of which were perched golden birds of every sort. As if to guard the Imperial presence, golden lions and chimeras flanked the throne. Soldiers in the white uniform of the *Candidi* stood to either side, against a background of brilliantly-coloured banners and pennants.

Amid total silence one soft word of command was spoken by the Master of Ceremonies: '*Keleusate!*' This summoned the Ostiarii, who entered the hall, their golden, jewel-studded staffs in their hands; they were followed by the courtiers of the highest rank across a mosaic floor strewn with fragrant roses.

Over the rich Persian carpets which muffled every sound the Princess Olga and her entourage at last approached the presence. She was dressed in robes of great splendour, previously presented to her by the Court. The Russians in her train prostrated themselves before the Emperor. The Princess walked up to the throne, and exchanged formal words of greeting with the Postmaster-General. The Emperor meanwhile remained silent upon his throne: it would have been beneath his dignity either to speak or otherwise to greet his guest.

Time seemed to stand still in the breathless silence. Then with a sudden outbreak of deafening sound the curtain rose on a fascinating spectacle presented to the foreigners.

The notes of an organ pealed forth, and the strange animals grouped about the throne began to stir. The tails of the lions lashed the marble floor, their jaws opened, their tongues rolled out and a great roar issued from their throats. The bodies of the chimeras began to twitch, and they made a hissing noise. The birds in the tree beat their wings and from their golden beaks, which opened and shut, there poured forth a loud twittering. When all those present had bowed low three times, the movement of the golden creatures stopped as suddenly as it had begun, and the noise with it. And the great monarch, the Emperor himself, had vanished—a hidden mechanism had carried him upwards, out of sight, still seated upon his throne.

The audience was over. The Princess walked away, followed by the courtiers in order of rank.

We have a contemporary eye-witness account of such an audience. The ambassador of the German King Otto I, a certain Liutprand who later became Bishop of Cremona, has described it all in detail.

No chronicler tells us what else took place during the visit to Byzantine of Olga of Kiev. Staying in the Imperial guest-rooms which were assigned to her would alone have sufficed to show the Princess what overwhelming splendour prevailed in the glittering metropolis.

The buildings of the Imperial Palace consisted of a single gigantic complex of open courts, galleries and halls, of long flights of stairs and terraces, paved with superb shining marble or gilded or inlaid with fabulous mosaics or covered with gorgeous oriental rugs which shone in the sunlight by day and at night were lit by countless chandeliers, hanging lamps and torches. The central block, the sacred palace of the Emperor, consisted of seven buildings and boasted an unbelievable luxury; in its gardens between the pavilions and the pergolas, fountains of fragrant rose-water played. For the maintenance of the concert halls, art galleries, the audience-chambers and women's quarters, chapels and churches, twenty thousand servants were required.

A wide view, an unequalled panorama, was visible from the Seraglio Peak. Immediately behind the Palace of the Senate towered the mighty domed roof of the Church of St Sophia, the Hagia Sophia built by Constantine the Great. The columns of Constantine rose up, and from the Augusteion, only a few yards away, ran the centuries-old *Via Triumphalis* of the Byzantine emperors, flanked by splendid buildings hung with tapestries, down to the Golden Gate. Near the cliffs that led down to the Sea of Marmora was the colossal Hippodrome, arena for the great chariot-races which formed part of the state ceremonies. Far below in the harbour of the Golden Horn, protected by iron chains, lay the squadrons of the Imperial Navy. Moored to marble terraces the great purple Dromona ships lay at anchor, built for the Emperor's sea voyages; in their midst lay the Imperial Ship of State, with its gilt wood carving. When the monarch visited his Water Castle on the Asiatic shore of the Bosphorus to attend the wine-harvest, he travelled in this vessel, seated on a silver throne, shaded by a purple canopy, while great silken banners fluttered overhead.

Olga of Kiev, after her audience with the Emperor, became the guest of his consort. The Empress Helena had invited the Princess to join her ladies in the Triklinon of Justinian. This reception concluded with an elaborate banquet, at which, according to protocol, spectacles were mounted to accompany each course; these began with music, mime and ancient Greek dances during the first course, and ended with displays by Chinese acrobats and Hindu jugglers during the dessert.

Deeply impressed with the pomp and splendour, the power and plenty of Byzantium, and with its high standard of culture, the Russian Princess returned to her own small, drab castle on the banks of the Dniepr. The results of this first encounter with superior Western culture were to be considerable. For shortly after the Russian state visit the first steps were taken upon a path which, for over a millennium, was to be pursued by the eastern state. It was then that a policy was formulated which has not changed to this day, a policy of acquisition from the West in order to assist Russian development, of constant endeavour to 'catch up and overtake'.

A year later Olga visited the Imperial City a second time, to be baptized by the Patriarch. Thus she showed the road her country must take, if it wished ever to emerge from its backwardness. The far-sighted Princess from Kiev had recognized that the key to advancement lay in Christianity, that it was Christianity which opened the way to the possessions and achievements of a progressive world.

Four decades later Olga's grandson forcefully continued her work. In Kherson on the Black Sea in the year 990 the Grand Duke Vladimir and his followers were baptized. The Prince then married the Byzantine Princess Anna, and introduced Christianity as the state religion. He ordered that all idols be destroyed, and issued a decree that all his subjects without exception must be baptized. Any person who refused would be arraigned as an enemy of God and of the Grand Duke. The Slavs gathered in crowds and were baptized in the Dniepr. In place of the overthrown idol representing their god, Perun, a Christian church was built.

Thus the door to the West was opened.

'Saint Vladimir is the beginning, the cause and the motive of everything here in Russia.' This remark was made many years later by Feofan Prokopovich, court theologian to Peter the Great.

*St Sophia Cathedral,
Kiev, built c. 1000 by
Greek architects, which
served as a pattern for
Russian church archi-
tecture. (Front and rear
views.)*

With the introduction of Christianity and the arrival of the Imperial
bride from Byzantium, both the organization of government and the way of
life of the people were radically transformed, and a strong and influential
current began to flow through the eastern territories. Within a hundred
years this second—and far more significant—assimilation of foreign influences
began to affect the Russians.

In 900 the Slavs had adopted with unusual speed all that the Varangians
had brought them—a state organization, law and order, an efficient military
force. Similarly at the beginning of the next century Imperial Byzantium
became the great example, the model to be followed and copied. Christianity
provided the first major bridgehead to what was then the 'modern world',
and the gates to the West were unlocked. For the under-developed and still
uncivilized eastern state this provided a unique opportunity for development
and for the acquisition of power and status.

Foreign influence flooded into the country. For the first time the Russians
learned to read and write, to build in stone, to paint and to compose music.

In Vladimir's own lifetime the first large stone building was begun, under
the supervision of skilled Greek architects. Built on the model of the famous
Hagia Sophia, the Cathedral of St Sophia at Kiev arose on the banks of the
Dniepr.

'The Church of St Sophia at Kiev,' according to an authority on ancient Russian art, N. Brunov, 'was the first large building with a central construction in Russian architecture. In order fully to understand the significance of this fact, one should not forget that the central dome remained up till the end of the nineteenth century the only form of church construction practised in Russia.'

This new, foreign art must have fascinated the Eastern Slavs, for with surprising speed it spread over the length and breadth of the land. From Kiev, Byzantine dome-building and stonemasonry travelled to the far north. On Lake Ilmen the Cathedral of Sophia at Novgorod, built in the years 1045 to 1052, shows this, though it also contains the first evidence of architectural, technical and cultural influences reaching Russia from Central

Byzantine craftsmen made silver coins for Yaroslav the Wise of Kiev. The obverse (left) reads 'Georgi', the prince's name in Greek; the reverse, 'Yaroslav's silver', in Cyrillic.

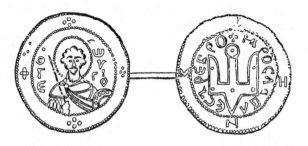

and Northern Europe. The magnificent ornamentation of the Novgorod Cathedral included the wonderful bronze gates attributed to Master Ruffin of Magdeburg and superb church doors executed by Swedish artists.

'It is only the wooden churches in Russia which owe nothing to Byzantine architecture,' the French art historian Louis Réau tells us. 'They are derived directly from peasant huts and are mere enlargements of these. This is the only strictly indigenous style of building; before, and since, all architecture in Russia has been Byzantine and Western-classical in derivation.'

Vladimir's son, Yaroslav, who consecrated the Cathedrals of St Sophia in Kiev and in Novgorod, opened the first schools, with teachers imported from Byzantium. As soon as he had recognized the importance of books, he bought many volumes in the Imperial Capital. He also imported numerous translators and transcribers into the country. The Greek texts were translated into Slavonic, using the Cyrillic script which is derived from the Greek alphabet.

In the Cathedral of St Sophia, the first library was formed. The earliest chronicles were now written, modelled exactly on those of Byzantium, their pages illuminated with pictures and monograms according to the Greek or Bulgarian pattern. Even the technique of bookbinding was copied in all its splendour.

As with architecture and literature, painting was also imported from Byzantium. The Greek icons, austere at that time, were copied. Vladimir had destroyed, along with the Perun idols, all heathen musical instruments—horns, flutes and drums—but now there was Byzantine choral church music in the land of the Slavs, and the Russians were learning those wonderful cantatas for eight voices which they enjoy so much even to the present day.

The first monasteries were established. Greek masters created the world-famous Lavra monastery at Kiev, which is hollowed out of the rock-face.

Under these powerful influences from the 'West', the eastern territories flourished. South German traders who visited Kiev at this time have recorded their astonishment at such progress. The Russian market suddenly began to deal in the choicest goods from the entire Orient, transported across the Black Sea. There were even Chinese silks, and the rich women of Kiev wore Greek dresses and were adorned with costly jewellery from the Imperial City on the Bosphorus.

A hundred years later, however, the first symptoms of decline were already in evidence. After the death of Vladimir Monomakh (1113–25) the power of the Grand Duchy on the Dniepr started to decline.

At the beginning of the thirteenth century the Mongol onslaught hit the west, and Kiev was no longer capable of offering any serious resistance to the savage attack. The eastern territories fell to the Khan of the Golden Horde, and vanished for a long time from the eyes and even from the consciousness of Europe.

Genghis Khan. The Eastern State disappeared from the consciousness of Europe with the victory of the Mongols at the beginning of the 13th century.

2 The Kremlin's Italian Builders

THREE HUNDRED YEARS had passed since the Mongol hurricane had obliterated the East from Europe's consciousness. Then, in 1549, a book was published in Vienna, which was to be read with burning interest and discussed at great length in all Europe.

Sigmund, Freiherr von Herberstein was the author of this work: *Rerum Moscoviticarum Commentarii*. In it he recounted his own experiences and observations in Moscow. It was illustrated with a number of woodcuts. He had twice visited Russia on behalf of the Archduke Ferdinand, in 1517 and 1526, and he had also acted as ambassador for the Emperor Maximilian at the Kremlin.

Few books have ever caused such a sensation as did Herberstein's report about that distant land far away in the east. It sold many copies, and was, indeed, a 'best-seller'. First appearing in Latin, it was later translated into German, French and Italian. Throughout most of Europe in the 1550's people were astonished to learn of the existence of a Muscovite state. Nobody guessed that the first steps of the development of that distant land had begun quietly during the previous century, with the help of European experts.

Where the Russian capital now stands, the wooded banks of the Moskva river describe an arc like the Thames at London. But in the year 1450 a visitor to those banks would have searched in vain for any trace of cathedrals towering to the sky, mighty castles or shining palaces.

A fortified earthwork—which bore the Tartar name of *Kremlin*, meaning strongpoint or fortress—rose to a height of 120 feet above a collection of primitive log-cabins and unpaved tracks, all encircled by a further wood-and-earth wall as an outer defence. Such was Moscow when the Grand Duke Ivan III became its ruler in 1462.

Compared with the magnificent royal residences of other sovereigns at that time, this fortress was an insignificant blot on the landscape, unknown to the rest of the world. Yet from this seed was to grow the great power that today governs more than one-sixth of the earth's surface. Over five hundred years after the founding of the first principality by the Varangians, long after the springtime of Kiev's flowering under Byzantine influence, there began again under the third Ivan that process of ceaseless, relentless effort to assimilate and appropriate the technical genius of the West, a process which runs like a thread through the whole history of the Russian state.

It was then that the Muscovites opened their doors to men from abroad— '. . . very much earlier,' according to the Italian historian Lo Gatto, 'than is generally supposed, if one recalls the statement that it was Peter the Great who opened the window of Russia to Europe.'

Emulating his predecessors, Ivan Kalita and Ivan II, Ivan III carried on a vigorous policy of incorporating the Eastern Slav principalities into his realm. He won fame as the 'Collector of Russian Soil'. In the south, after more than two hundred years, the kingdom of the Tartars, the old empire of the 'Golden Horde' to whom the Muscovites had had to pay tribute, was in process of disintegration. In the north Ivan set out to conquer all the hitherto independent principalities. The Princes of Tver, of Rostov, and of Yaroslavl were deprived of their rights by Ivan in his capacity of *Gosudar* or *Samoderzhets*, 'Supreme Ruler of all the Russias' or 'Autocrat' as he had styled himself since 1478. He subordinated the free Republic of Great Novgorod (a Hansa town hitherto governed according to the so-called Lübeck Laws) to the central government. The German trading offices within its walls were closed down and the great trading area of this once powerful Hansa town, stretching from the White Sea to the Urals, passed under Moscow's control. Novgorod's famous bell, the *Viechevoi Kolokol*, which for centuries had tolled to summon the Assembly of the People together, was silenced by his orders for ever. Novgorod's bronze symbol of freedom and democracy was later removed to Moscow as a victory trophy by Ivan III's grandson, Ivan the Terrible, after he had razed Novgorod to the ground.

In the years that Ivan III was ruthlessly laying the foundations on which the Russian state was to be built, another event occurred which was to be of great importance in its history. This originated from abroad—in the form of a proposal of marriage.

In 1468, just one year after Ivan III had become a widower, a confidential emissary of Cardinal Bessarione arrived from Italy on a special mission to Moscow. He proposed to the Grand Duke that he take the Princess Zoë Paleologa to be his wife. This Princess was a niece of the last Byzantine Emperor, Constantine XI. The Emperor had been killed in the defence of Constantinople. When in 1453 the Turks captured the capital on the Bosphorus, Zoë, who was still a child, fled with her parents to Florence. Since then her father, the Emperor's brother, had also died.

The Grand Duke was delighted to accept this proposal, and took all the necessary steps so that the wedding might be solemnized as soon as possible. He ordered the Italian, Gianbattista della Volpe, who was in charge of the Mint in Moscow, to visit Rome on his behalf. And in November 1472, the Princess arrived in Moscow where she was married to Ivan III. Zoë Paleologa became the Grand Duchess Sophia.

St Vladimir had also wed an emperor's daughter, Anna, and now once again a Byzantine princess had married a Russian Grand Duke. However, the hopes of the Papal Court in arranging this family link between the

Grand Duke Ivan III of Muscovy who commissioned Italians to build the Kremlin, and adopted the Byzantine double-headed eagle (above) as the Russian crest. The portrait is from 'Cosmographie universelle' by A. Thevet.

Byzantine Imperial family and that of the Muscovite Grand Duke were not to be realized. The cardinal had secretly planned to use the Grand Duchess in order to enrol the Muscovites against the Turks who were advancing into Europe from Constantinople. Exactly the reverse took place.

Everything that has ever gone to Russia from Europe, whether it be technical skills or theoretical ideas, has eventually been used against the West. This was the case with the marriage contrived in Italy. Soon enough Rome itself had to pay the bill.

Ivan III, as husband of a princess from the proud house of the Paleologi, not only took the two-headed eagle for his national emblem, but also adopted the Byzantine court ceremonial and hierarchy, with its strict distinctions of rank. And Sophia called herself Tsarevna of Tsargrad, Empress of the Imperial City (Byzantium). Thus Moscow staked its claim to be the 'rightful heir' of Byzantium, and was henceforth to regard itself as the capital of the 'Holy East Roman Empire of Russia'.

It was a splendid and fascinating idea that the monks had brought with them when the Turkish advance into the Danube basin compelled them to emigrate to Russia; it was the concept of a Third Rome. The idea that after the conquest of Bulgaria (1393) and the sack of Constantinople (1453) by the Turks a new home and seat for the Patriarch of the Orthodox Church must be found elsewhere was born in the ancient cloisters in Bulgaria. It is to be found in the ecclesiastical literature of Bulgaria, written as the Turkish menace drew steadily closer.

Moscow did not hesitate to accept this idea and indeed to make it particularly her own. As early as 1547 Ivan IV, the grandson of the famous marriage, had himself crowned 'Emperor of all the Russias', and consciously adopted as his constitutional role that of the Byzantine absolute monarchs. Henceforth, until 1917, all the Russian rulers bore the title of Tsar.

'He is the only ruler of the Christians in all the world.' Thus did the monk Philotheos of Pleskau (Pskov) in his famous letter to Ivan IV, 'The Terrible', interpret the Bulgarian idea of 'the leader of the Apostolic Church, who is in the Holy City of Moscow and not in Rome or Constantinople. He alone is the light of the whole world, brighter than the sun. Then know, ye devout one! All the Realms of Christendom are dissolved and reunited in the Realm of our Sovereign, as is laid down in the books of the prophets; such is the Russian Empire. For two Romes have fallen, but the third stands, and there will be no fourth.'

Even folk-songs describe Russia as the 'third Rome'. 'Historical' fairy tales endeavoured to give a 'factual' foundation to the claim. The claim that 'Russia leads the world' was then made theologically, even as for the inventors it was to be made technologically when the 'Wave of Inventions' claim was launched after 1945.

A document entitled *The Genealogy of the Russian Grand Dukes*, which was widely read, regaled the Russian people in all seriousness with a string of unbelievable historical gibberish. 'The glorious Rurik, and through him all the Russian Grand Dukes,' it says, 'are descendants of the Roman Emperor Augustus. He had a brother called Prus, to whom the dying Augustus gave that territory which, in honour and memory of Prus, came later to be called Prussia. This Prus, however, was none other than the ancestor of Rurik and therefore also of all the Russian autocrats since Rurik.'

Moscow's dream of becoming the heir and successor of Byzantium remained, however, unfulfilled—inevitably, for the Russians lacked every quality for the role, in particular that of creative endeavour. The parchment rolls bearing the works of the great Greek poets and philosophers, the spirit of which burnt bright in the libraries of the European monasteries until it poured forth into the world in modern times, slumbered unread and dusty in the Orthodox monasteries of the Slav Empire. No one examined them, to no one did they come as a revelation. Spiritual inflexibility was characteristic of Russian monastic life; such immobility of mind had prevailed in the Byzantine monasteries during the period about the year 1000, when Christendom was embraced by the State of Kiev, and thence it spread throughout Russia.

Moscow was remarkably ill-equipped to lay claim to imperial status and to adopt the Byzantine arms. The royal palace was built of wood. There was not a single school. Scarcely one of the nobles could read or write. Yet at that time the Universities of Paris, Bologna and Oxford were already in a position to celebrate their two-hundredth and three-hundredth anniversaries.

Nobody was more aware of the discrepancy between these bombastic claims and the obvious facts of cultural backwardness and lack of civilization than the Princess Sophia. She had spent her youth in Florence, in the city of Dante, that treasure-house of Italian art and culture. It must all have sounded

Interior of the Uspenski Cathedral in the Kremlin, built by Aristotele Fioraventi (1475–79). All the Tsars were crowned here from the 16th century.

The Spassky Gate, Red Square, built in 1491 by P. Antonio Solari. The belfry is the work of the Englishman Christopher Galloway (1625).

The magnificent cathedral of the Archangel Michael, Archangelsky Sobor, built by Alevisio Novi of Milan.

The dome of the Coronation Chamber in the Granovitaya Palace, supported by a single column and built by the Lombards P. Antonio Solari and Marco Ruffo, 1487–91.

like a fairy-tale to Ivan, when the Greek princess and her noblewomen told him of the great world far away, of the palaces and capitals, of the art schools and universities.

From them the Grand Duke gained, for the first time, real insight into the high technical standard that prevailed abroad in such industries as shipbuilding and mining, of many crafts hitherto unknown in Muscovy— and of the power of modern weapons. Their tales aroused so passionate an interest in Ivan III that he resolved to put out feelers towards Europe. Contact must be established, he decided, so that his people might benefit from the advancement of others. He therefore sent Muscovite ambassadors to Denmark, Italy and Germany, a totally new departure.

Ivan III resolved simultaneously that Moscow must no longer lag so grotesquely far behind foreign capitals, and must be architecturally beautiful. The beginning was to be a magnificent stone church. Two Russians, Peter Kryvtsov and Mishkin, were ordered to build it. But it came to naught. Even the attempt to lay the foundations and to build the base-walls had to be abandoned. Nobody in Moscow, nobody in the whole of Russia (an urgent appeal was carried through Russia by the Tsar's couriers) possessed at this time the necessary knowledge of how to build. In Muscovy there was quite literally no possibility of building in stone, as ordered by Ivan III. Neither experienced architects nor skilled craftsmen were to be found, neither masons nor stone-cutters. There were no building tools, nor even anyone who understood how to mix mortar.

Advised by Sophia, Ivan III decided to engage foreign master builders. The building of a cathedral, and the grandiose reconstruction of Moscow, would have to be done by foreigners. There was no alternative. With instructions to bring back everything necessary for the building of a new and splendid capital, the Grand Duke's emissaries set off for distant Italy.

In the year 1475 the urgently needed help arrived in the form of a team of specially selected master builders, the best available. This was the first large group of Western experts; later they were to pour into Russia in their tens and hundreds of thousands.

At the head of these elegantly-dressed foreigners, whom the Grand Duke had brought to the Kremlin, and at whom the astonished Muscovites gaped with distrust, was 61-year-old Aristotele Fioraventi degli Uberti. He came from Bologna, whose walls shelter the oldest university in Europe, founded in 1119. With him were master builder Pietro Antonio Solari and Alevisio Novi, as well as Antonio Fryazin—as the Russians called him, 'Fryazin', 'the Frank', being a general nickname given to all foreigners at the time. Skilled craftsmen, masons and stone-cutters, each a master of his craft, came with them.

With the arrival of Aristotele Fioraventi a true genius of the Western type entered the service of Russia.

Fioraventi's reputation was then at its peak: he was honoured and revered in his own country as a brilliant architect. The Bolognese was—like so many artists and architects of the age—a mechanic and an engineer as well, and, in addition, an expert on metal-casting, copper-engraving and the minting of coins.

The Grand Duke entrusted Fioraventi with the task that had had to be abandoned: the building of a cathedral in stone. This was done, and in the Kremlin the Uspenski Sobor, the Cathedral of the Ascension of the Virgin, is much admired today and is visited by people from all over the world. Before the actual building could start, however, certain important preliminary work had to be done. The great Bolognese architect set up a building school. Its purpose was to instruct the Muscovites in the, to them, completely unknown techniques of stonemasonry. Southern Italian craftsmen began to teach the natives how to carve stone, mix mortar and bake bricks.

At the suggestion of the Grand Duke, the foreign master builders meanwhile went on a tour of the country. They travelled to Vladimir and Suzdal. Ivan III wanted the Italians to study some of the 'original prototypes'. At these places there still existed 'native' stone churches from Russia's earlier period.

To their great surprise the Italians found, in Vladimir and Suzdal, what they had not imagined could exist in Muscovy, exquisite churches and beautiful stone buildings; in Moscow, the capital, there was nothing of that sort. What they now found dated from the twelfth century.

Minting and casting coins (contemporary miniature, about 1535). Ivan III's master minter was the Italian della Volpe.

Uspenski Cathedral in the
Kremlin where all the Tsars
were crowned. Built by Aristotele
Fioraventi, 1475–1479, under
Ivan III.

A fact quite unsuspected by Fioraventi and his colleagues was that in addition to the Greek-Byzantine influence, other elements from the West had been at work at this earlier epoch too. About 1200, according to the old chronicles, 'Lombard masters' were working at Vladimir. The famous Cathedral of the Ascension of the Virgin bore witness to their skill. But their knowledge, if the Russians ever acquired it, had been lost in the chaos of the Mongolian invasion.

In five years the Uspenski Cathedral, Fioraventi's masterpiece, rose above the ancient fortifications of the Kremlin. It was to be the Coronation Church of all the Tsars from the sixteenth century onwards. Built in the Lombard-Byzantine style, it forms a square, almost equilateral. In the centre towers a mighty onion dome over one hundred and twenty feet high, and at the four corners are smaller domes. It was consecrated in the year 1479.

What evoked the particular delight of Ivan III, and no less of the Muscovites, were the Italian mouldings and window-frames with their profusion of lavish stone-work carved by the Lombard sculptors. From that time forth these were to be regarded as an essential ingredient of Russian architecture. Ever since then, Lombard mouldings and window-frames have decorated churches, palaces and private houses everywhere throughout the Slav state.

The day came when the colony of Italian craftsmen could have the pleasure of welcoming a fellow-countryman in Moscow. In 1476 an envoy of the Venetian Republic, Ambrogio Contarini, on his way back from an embassy to the court of the Shah of Persia, visited the Kremlin. Ivan III did not, of course, neglect this opportunity of giving a commission to his honoured guest. The Grand Duke was anxious that more artists, and also more engineers, should be persuaded to come to Moscow. The foreigners already in the country were not nearly enough to carry out his ambitious plans. From a report by the Venetian Ambassador, we learn that Contarini met many other Europeans, in addition to his own countrymen, in Moscow. Among the Italians whose services Contarini enlisted for Ivan III, was the architect Marco Ruffo, known as Mark Fryazin, the 'Foreigner', to the Russians.

As the splendid cathedral neared completion, the old fortress of Moscow was also completely changing its appearance thanks to the skilled guidance of the foreigners.

According to the plans and under the supervision of Marco Ruffo and Pietro Antonio Solari, who came from an old and respected family of Ticino architects, the Granovitaya Palace was built between the years 1487 and 1491. It was modelled on the famous Florentine Palazzi Strozzi and Pitti. The influence of the Bevilacqua Palace at Bologna is also in evidence.

The stones used for the façade were carved by the Italian master builders in the form of diamonds, with facets; thus did the palace get its nickname, 'The Diamond Palace'.

Inside, the Granovitaya Palace contained a vast throne-room, the vaulted roof of which was supported by a single massive central pillar. If those walls could speak, they could tell the names of the countless foreign experts who, throughout the centuries, have there been received by successive Russian rulers since the completion of the palace in the year 1491.

The primitive earth-and-wood enclosing walls of the fortress, which although built quite recently were already almost in ruins, were replaced by strong stone fortifications. Sketches and plans show that the model was the castle at Milan, and so the familiar picture of the Kremlin as we now know it started to grow. A mighty sixty-foot reinforced wall, almost two miles long, formed an irregular pentagon, broken by only five gates and eighteen splendid turrets. These ramparts and gates with their superstructure of turrets were solidly built by the recently trained Russian workers, using bricks for the first time. On the open ground inside the fortress they built stone barns for the storing of grain, the second-storey rooms being used as winter quarters for the garrison.

The first tower of the new fortifications, the Troinitskaya Bashnya, was built as early as 1485 by Antonio Fryazin, and he too was responsible for the Vodovosnaya Bashnya, the Kremlin's water-tower.

On the Red Square today two main entrances lead into the Kremlin, on either side of the Red Mausoleum. Above one of these, Byzantine arches support a heavy tower, surmounted by the Byzantine double eagle. The Spasskaya Vorota, the Gate of the Redeemer, was built by Pietro Antonio Solari. Only the final belfry was added later, to the design of the English architect Christopher Halloway in 1625.

At the same time Pietro Antonio Solari drew up plans for the second gate-tower leading to the Red Square, the Nicholas Gate. It was later rebuilt, after the French invasion of 1812, by Carlo Rossi, an architect from

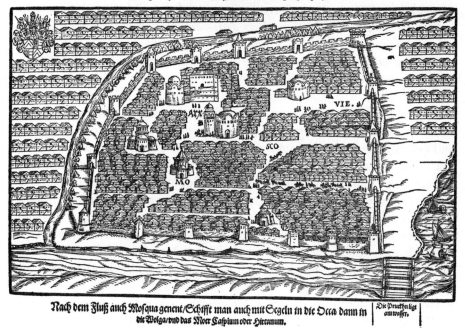

View of Moscow showing the walls of the Kremlin with its palaces and cathedrals built by Italians. (From the travelogue of Sigmund von Herberstein.)

Lugano. This great architect gave it its present-day form; it was inspired by the beautiful Church of St Mary, at Stargard in Pomerania.

By the end of the century—before 1500 that is—the grandiose building projects in Moscow had been completed; the talented Italians had created the pride of Russia, the Moscow Kremlin, which was to be the symbol of the strength and greatness of the Slav state. 'Above Moscow,' the saying goes, 'there is only the Kremlin, above the Kremlin only Heaven.' Unfortunately, this saying omits to mention to whom the Russians owe their much-prized Kremlin.

The Italians brought in by Ivan III were succeeded in the following century by other craftsmen in large numbers, who added building after building to the Kremlin. Contrary to the usual custom of the West, there are no memorial plaques in the Kremlin bearing the builders' names. But were the architects and master builders to be honoured in the normal fashion, what about the makers of the Kremlin's contents? In order that the Kremlin might take on its new splendour, furniture and ornaments were imported to make a lavish display of magnificence at the Moscow court. Even today the

museums are overflowing with the treasures which poured into the country
from all over Europe. In the Kremlin Treasure-house alone—and it contains
only a fraction of the foreign *objets d'art*—are housed objects of immense
value of Dutch, Danish and English origin, as well as the most valuable
extant collection of work by the German goldsmiths who lived in Nuremberg, Augsburg and Danzig.

Stories about the astounding beauty of the Kremlin spread rapidly
throughout Russia, and many provincial cities copied the buildings in
Moscow. In doing this they were assisted by master builders from the West,
and especially from Italy, whose names are often unknown to us.

Despite the admiration evoked by the stone Kremlin beside the River
Moskva, the populace continued, for some considerable time, to build as
they had always done, that is to say in wood. In 1555 an Englishman, who
had recently visited Russia, wrote:

'Moscow is a bigger city than London but it is grey and without any sort
of order in its building. All the houses are of wood. . . .' Even rich and
noble Russians were to continue for centuries to live in these ancient
wooden cabins.

Now that Moscow had been rebuilt with such magnificence, the next
project was to transform it into an important centre of trade since the great
market at Novgorod had been abolished. Such, at least, was the ambition of
Ivan III. But nothing came of it. 'Inns' were built, where the 'guests'—as the
Russians called the foreign merchants—could be accommodated when they
came to offer their goods for sale. But none came, for what had this remote
place to offer them? The journey was both long and wearisome. Fine
examples of craftsmanship did not exist, for the Russians could not even
carry out skilled leather-work. 'On the ice on the Moscow river,' a foreigner
commented on the winter bazaar, 'the merchants set up their booths with
all their different wares displayed. Here each day throughout the winter can
be seen grain, meat, pigs, firewood, hay and other commodities. At the end
of November the country folk slaughter their cows and pigs and bring them
into the city to sell. It is a great joke to see these enormous quantities of
slaughtered cattle lying skinned on the ice.'

Of all the intelligence which Ivan III received from his new envoys, what
interested him most were the reports and particularly sketches dealing with
technical matters. And he was interested above all else in weapon development as it was being carried out abroad. For in the West a completely new
age had begun, a technological revolution which was affecting every field
including that of warfare and of armaments. Gunpowder had been invented
in the second half of the fourteenth century, followed almost at once by
portable firearms, and by now there was in existence a complete arsenal of
cannons and muskets. With these new firearms the last hours of the feudal
system had struck.

Winter transport in Russia at the beginning of the 16th century. (Drawing from the travelogue of Sigmund von Herberstein.)

In contrast to all this, how archaic the Muscovite methods of warfare must have seemed! The army consisted of levies of knights, equipped with bows and arrows, even as they had been in the days of Tartary. Nothing new had been invented, no techniques or weapons evolved in all Russia.

Even before that prestige edifice, the Kremlin, was completed, Ivan III embarked upon a large-scale armaments programme in which Western models he had bought were copied exactly. A number of South German master armourers came to work in the Russian service. From Venice, too, Ivan III imported technical experts, from Sweden metal and foundry workers, and gunsmiths. The Grand Duke sent quantities of mining experts to the Urals, in search of iron ore.

North-west of the Kremlin, on the banks of the Neglinka Stream (nowadays built over), the versatile Fioraventi, who had also put up the first modern bridge in Russia across the Volkhov, and who had minted coins for Ivan III, built the *Liteiny Dvor*, the first foundry. It was not long before the first cannons were being forged on Russian soil, within sight of the Kremlin battlements, by the skilled hands of master craftsmen from the West.

3 Ivan the Terrible and the Beardless Men

THAT QUARTER of Moscow which then hummed with activity has nowadays lost its name and has, indeed, been totally forgotten. Here were centred the vital impulses and the technical knowledge without which the development of the Slav state could never have taken place, nor Russia ever have become a great power. These events are therefore of immense importance. Yet no street sign shows this, nor can the facts be found in any Intourist guide.

Before the First World War, this quarter of the city was not difficult to find. Only a few steps from the Red Square beside the Kremlin a No. 3 horse-tram would take you, for ten kopeks, to a street called the *Nyemetskaya Ulitsa* or 'German Street'. This street, less than one mile in length, and running due south to the little stream called the Yausa, used to be the centre of the former *Nyemetskaya Sloboda* or 'German Quarter'. The Germans were indeed not the only foreigners who lived in this much admired part of the city—much admired because it was so clean, well kept and well laid out. But for the Russians, who as yet knew practically nothing of the different nations of the West, every foreigner was simply a *Nyemets* or German.

The name of the *Nyemetsky Rynok* or 'German Market' has also vanished, though until quite recently it was the principal market-place in the eastern part of Moscow; similarly the name of the 'German Cemetery', which lay on the far side of the Yausa, has also gone, and the Lutheran Church of St Michael, built in the Gothic style near the southern end of the *Sloboda* in 1576, today houses a Soviet educational institute.

Ivan IV's father, Vassily III, laid the foundations of this 'Little Europe', outside Moscow's gates, and three miles to the east of the Kremlin. The flood of foreign specialists had so increased during his reign that they could no longer be accommodated in the Kremlin as had been the case with the Italian engineers and architects brought in by Ivan III.

Throughout the reign of Ivan IV—nicknamed *Grozny* or 'the Terrible' (1534–84)—the woods above the Yausa River were steadily felled as the foreign quarter grew ever larger.

Besides the many Germans, the 'sausage-eaters', there were colonies of Dutchmen, Lithuanians, Italians and Danes—'the beardless men', as the Russians indiscriminately called all foreigners. For foreigners in transit comfortable inns were built, the most famous being the 'Danish Inn'.

So the *Nyemetskaya Sloboda* grew and flourished, much favoured and supplied with all it needed by the new ruler. Ivan IV continued the policy that his grandfather, Ivan III, had inaugurated, and imported specialists, technical equipment and above all weapons from the West.

Ivan IV, the 'Terrible', who summoned scores of European craftsmen, master engineers and cannon forgers.

In the new lives led by the 'beardless men' in the Yausa quarter, the great receptions at the Kremlin played an important part. Technicians and teachers, merchants, even master craftsmen were more or less regular guests at the Tsar's table. This much annoyed the Boyars, who despised and hated the 'foreign devils', and who were angry that their ruler should sit at table with simple craftsmen, metal-workers and gunsmiths, with whom he was happy to talk for hours on end. Among the natives only the highest and most respected dignitaries of Russia were bidden to this table where the festivities were conducted with all the sumptuous pomp and splendour associated with oriental rulers; Ivan's court was modelled on the old Imperial Byzantine court at Constantinople. The Boyars and the distinguished courtiers may have grumbled, but Ivan IV knew well what he was doing. His talks with the inhabitants of the *Nyemetskaya Sloboda* were worth a fortune to him. There were countless matters the foreigners could tell him about which were still completely unknown to the Russians. They knew about astronomy and algebra and geometry, they understood something of church building and fortifications, of modern methods of warfare, of metal-casting and the latest firearms. The Tsar listened to them and questioned them about it all.

He gave them his entire attention. A secretary was often employed to make notes of the long conversations, writing down word for word his questions and the answers of the foreign experts. 'After these conversations with the foreigners the Tsar would frequently summon his officials to a secret conference,' remarks W. Kostyliov in his book *Ivan Grozny*.

Among the Tsar's closest advisers was a certain Joachim Krummhausen, from Narva, said to be one of the richest merchants of the age. He was known all over Germany, and was an important figure in the Hanseatic port of Lübeck. He had seen much in his lifetime, had lived long in Moscow, where he had even brought up his children, as had another friend of the Tsar's, the German merchant Hans Pennedos. Through them Ivan IV made many friends among the German merchants and the members of the Hanseatic League: Georg Liebenhauer from Augsburg, Hermann Bisping from Münster, Veit Seng from Nuremberg (whose protector was Albrecht, Duke of Bavaria), and the merchants, Hermann Stahlbruder and Nikolaus Pacher from Prussia. There were many other foreigners in close personal contact with the Tsar.

Johann Schlitte from Goslar played a special role in Moscow as a sort of Man Friday. The Tsar was for ever sending him to the West to fetch specialists. Schlitte was perhaps his best procurer of large-scale traders and his best recruiting officer of technicians.

Ivan IV even begged the German Emperor Charles V to let him have skilled men to help in the development of Russia. The Livonian Ambassador at the Emperor's court implored Charles V to impose his supreme 'veto' against any further 'export' of German technicians and to prevent those already enlisted from leaving the country. He entreated the Emperor to save the Livonians 'from the great and terrible power of Muscovy, which is filled with lust to conquer Livonia and to achieve supremacy about the Baltic, and whose power would lead to the inevitable subjugation of all the peoples living about that sea—Lithuanians, Poles and Swedes'.

The ambassador begged in vain, and his words of warning passed unheeded. On the contrary, the Emperor even allowed Johann Schlitte to draft an official Imperial decree recommending service in Russia.

The text of the Emperor's announcement shows quite clearly what exactly it was that Russia wanted. There is still in existence the four-page *Import List* which Schlitte had drafted. It states:

'On the basis of this letter We allow the said Johann Schlitte to travel through Our entire Empire and all Our principalities in order to seek out and enlist the services of

Doctors, masters of all the free arts, metal-workers, master-miners, goldsmiths, carpenters, stone-masons and particularly such as are skilled in the building of fine churches, master bridge-builders, paper manufacturers and physicians

with a view to visiting the Russian Grand Duke without further ado or permission, and of agreeing to work for him.

This is the result of requests to Us from the present Grand Duke and from his father, of blessed memory, the Grand Duke Vassily Ivanovich, to Our predecessor.'

'Metal-workers' meant the specialists of every sort whom Russia then needed most urgently in order to create an armaments industry. In the

Banquet in Granovitaya Palace where Ivan IV regularly entertained foreigners.

West the last few years had witnessed tremendous developments in the armaments field. Italians, French and Germans were competing in the production of new weapons. It was extremely hard for Russia to keep up with them, to discover which was the best to copy, or even to obtain the latest prototype quickly enough. Ivan IV was confused by the tremendous tempo of development in Western Europe.

A century ago his grandfather had set up the *Liteiny Dvor*, his great foundry, with foreign help. These works had in the meantime been enlarged and improved, and Russia was now capable of producing her own armaments. But technically she was still far behind the West. So Ivan IV was delighted to put a skilled and trusted foreigner in charge of the foundry. This was Ole Petersen, a Swede.

Ole Petersen had been taken prisoner by Ivan IV's soldiers and brought to Moscow, where he was immediately put to 'forced labour'. It had been customary in the Tartar period for specialists to be considered as spoils of war. Woe to anyone who hurt a hair of the head of any artist or teacher or craftsman, no matter what his craft, during a foreign campaign! With silken gentleness the eagerly awaited experts and skilled workers were transported eastwards over the steppes; such was the strict command of the two great Khans, Genghis Khan and Kubla Khan. The reason for such gentleness was that every item of intellectual booty was urgently needed in Russia.

'You shall proclaim in Novgorod, and in all the districts thereabouts,' states a command of Ivan the Terrible, dated 24th February 1556, to the Government clerk at Novgorod, 'that the sons of Boyars and others must not sell German prisoners to the Germans in Livonia nor in Lithuania, but only in the cities of Muscovy.'

'Ivan the Terrible,' says the Russian historian Grigor Alexinsky in his *La Russie et l'Europe*, 'used the enemy soldiers captured in his European wars as teachers in his own lands.' 'Just as this Tsar had used his German-

Baltic prisoners of war, so Peter the Great employed his Swedish prisoners to create a Slav culture; they were compelled to teach young Russians the crafts of the smithy. The prisoners included locksmiths, saddlers, sword-cutters and others more highly educated,' writes B. Ischchanian.

Ivan IV was often to be seen at the foundry, beside the narrow Neglinka River, among the teeming throng of 'beardless men'. He observed every new sort of casting. He was present, too, when the Swedish master craftsman, Petersen, instructed his Russians in the casting of cannons and cannonballs, and in range calculation. A complete arsenal of captured or imported fire-arms from the West was at the disposal of the instructors, heavy pieces and mortars, field-guns and muskets. One day after many years of effort, and to the Tsar's great delight, the very newest model from abroad arrived at the foundry—a 'falconet'. This six-foot-long piece, which fired four pounds of iron or lead, had been brought from Italy by Prince Lykov, a close and trusted friend of Ivan IV.

In 1552 Ivan IV ventured for the first time to put the growing production of his foundry to the test. He met with success. In a campaign in the south, Kazan fell, the powerful citadel of the Volga Khanate, the key to the Volga route to the Caspian, and to all the roads to the Urals. The Russians, how-ever, did not owe their victory to their numerical superiority; for the siege only succeeded after 'Kazan, with the help of foreign engineers, was sur-rounded by a ring of trenches and ditches; movable turrets were rolled up to the walls and the walls themselves undermined'. This is a quotation from

A movable siege tower built by Western engineers and used for the conquest of Kazan in 1552.

Foreign building labourers under Ivan the Terrible. (Contemporary miniature.)

the official *History of the USSR*. The successful campaign in the south encouraged Ivan IV, in the same decade, to move towards the Baltic, which meant an attack on Livonia. Narva and Dorpat fell. Scarcely a soul in Europe could guess what a fateful precedent had been established. For the first time the weapons and technical skill of the West had been used successfully by Russia against the West.

Twenty years later foreign arms enabled the Russians to win another victory against the same enemy they had defeated at Kazan. In 1572 the Tartars suddenly and unexpectedly advanced northwards with the object of capturing Moscow itself. When Ivan IV heard of the approach of the enemy, he immediately left the Kremlin and hid in the forests. Nobody knew where he had gone. Yet despite his absence, Moscow was preserved, though he could claim no credit for the saving of his capital. A German, Colonel von Fahrenbach, who commanded seven thousand mounted soldiers in the Tsar's service, pushed the enemy back and finally routed them some thirty-five miles from the city. The Tsar returned to the Kremlin as soon as he had heard the glad news and celebrated the victory of Lopassnya among his people.

As a memorial to the victory over Kazan the famous Vassily Blashenny Cathedral was built in the Red Square in 1552. The master builders, Barma and Postnik, of whom Barma was certainly no Russian, put up a central edifice, surrounded by seven wooden chapels. This structure does not appear to have pleased the Tsar. The art historian, Tamara Talbot Rice, who was herself Russian-born, has said of this incident:

'It is supposed to have been rebuilt by an Italian architect almost immediately afterwards. In its final form it became an irregular construction,
consisting of eleven chapels.'

Ivan IV now realized how correct was the policy he had been following.
He redoubled his efforts and concentrated more than ever on his plans to
exploit Europe in the interests of Russia.

In the sixteenth century, English trade was flourishing, but the English
merchants were competing for new markets with two determined adversaries
—the Spanish and the Portuguese. In the age of discovery Spain and Portugal
had won all the early triumphs. It was they who had taken all the risks, who
had discovered the New World and the route round the Cape of Good Hope
to India and who had finally proved, by Magellan's voyage, that the world
was round. And what they had, they held. But would it not be possible to
discover an alternative sea route to India and China? Perhaps 'over the top',
across the Arctic? This idea appealed to the English.

Sebastian Cabot, an Italian navigator and explorer, had first suggested a
search for this 'North-East passage'. An expedition was fitted out, and in
1553 three ships put to sea in the direction of North Cape. Two of them, in
one of which was the leader of the expedition, Sir Hugh Willoughby, went
down in a terrible storm off the coast of Lapland. The third, the *Edward
Bonaventura*, commanded by Richard Chancellor, was driven across the
White Sea and made landfall near the mouth of the Dvina. The Englishmen
had not, as they hoped, discovered a new direct sea route to India and China,
but they had found their way to the state of Muscovy.

As soon as Ivan IV heard of this from his governor in Kholmogory, he
ordered Chancellor brought at once to Moscow—some fifteen hundred miles
over land. The Englishman was given a princely reception. Then Ivan compelled
the navigator to return to England as his envoy, for the Tsar was determined
to seize without delay the opportunity that fate had placed in his hands.
He saw a chance of breaking the trade monopoly hitherto enjoyed by the
Hanseatic League. That was why he wished to open trade with that distant
country, England. He commissioned Chancellor to send one hundred and
twenty of his compatriots to Moscow to instruct his Russians in 'every sort
of craft'.

A year later a large group of English master craftsmen arrived in Moscow.

Regularly, and in ever larger convoys, the keels of English merchant
ships ploughed their way through the waves of the Polar Sea. In the god-
forsaken town of Kholmogory a flourishing trading-post came into existence.
A Londoner, Richard Grey, set up the first hemp factory on the banks of
the Dvina. Russia received from England much-needed 'cloth and other
woven goods', and, most important of all, 'iron and iron by-products',
and 'lead, sulphur, firearms and munitions'. For 'her own industry was
still not sufficiently developed'.

For England, the Muscovite kingdom was a new market, and one which depended on the advice of experts. Ivan IV set down his requirements in a letter to Queen Elizabeth herself:

'From Italy and England we need master builders, who can construct for us fortresses, bastions and palaces, also surgeons and apothecaries, also master craftsmen who understand how to prospect for and mine gold and silver. We have sent letters of privilege asking your favour for all those who may wish to come here and serve Us, whether they wish to remain in Our service for a few years only or for ever, that those people, master builders, surgeons and apothecaries may be allowed to come to Us and serve Us. We shall repay you for your great kindness according to your wishes, and as for those who wish to serve Us all their lives, We shall ensure a good living to them, and shall supply them with all that they may need. Those who may later wish to give up their allegiance to Us shall be rewarded for their services; should they desire to return to their mother-land, We shall not retain them, but shall let them go with handsome remuneration, as We have stated in our letters of privilege. Written in Moscow, capital of this Our empire.'

This letter is dated 1566. A little later the Tsar sent a second communication to Elizabeth of England in which he requested that the English Queen permit her merchants to supply him in Narva with cannons, ammunition and all other weapons of war; above all, he requested that she send him shipbuilders.

England fulfilled Russia's demands. With the Queen's reply there arrived in Russia the people so eagerly awaited by Ivan. There were Reynolds the surgeon, Thomas Carver the apothecary, Humphrey Lock the engineer, accompanied by his assistant John Finton, the goldsmith and 'prospector' (that is to say, metallurgist), Thomas Green, and many other skilled masters of their art or craft.

Technicians and scholars continued to arrive in Moscow. Two English doctors were appointed court physicians. The English scientist, Standish, appeared to lead the group. Like many of his compatriots he had permanent apartments in the Kremlin.

The English thus followed the Italians, Germans, Dutchmen and Swedes as a new and valuable source of information to Ivan IV.

From contemporaries we learn: 'For hours on end in the Kremlin the Tsar would discuss such matters as the seas, the nature of water, the stars and firearms with the English scientist, Standish. No matter whom he might be talking with, Ivan Vassilievitch always saw to it that every conversation, no matter how it had started, always ended with the subject of shot, saltpetre and gunpowder.'

Stories of the great careers that were to be made in Russia reached Scotland. A group of experts from that land, led by a certain Johnny Lingelt, set off for Moscow via Sweden. The gaily dressed group were

Relief from Ivan IV's throne in Uspenski Cathedral. (Foreign artist.)

received by Ivan IV in the Kremlin. He had already learned that they included architects, engineers, gunners and experienced soldiers. He received them with great pomp, and as soon as the introductions were completed and the formalities exchanged, he got down to business.

'He wished to know,' says W. Kostyliov, 'what sort of light field-gun was in use abroad, of the six-or-seven pounder variety with a good range and yet transportable on horseback.' The Tsar talked so fast that the interpreter could scarcely manage to translate, thus incurring the displeasure of the monarch. A second interpreter was summoned, and they both bombarded the Scots with questions. As it turned out, the Scots were experts in this field, and were able to tell the Tsar all about the new guns they had seen in various countries. Ivan was especially interested in those cannons with inner jacket casing such as were made in Sweden; their leather-bound copper barrels were capable of firing two or three rounds simultaneously. At the Tsar's command the Scotsmen took paper and charcoal and drew a blueprint of the cannon in question. The Tsar thanked them and ordered that they be taken into his service.' This 'pumping' of foreigners, even down to the smallest details, was considered by Ivan IV as part of the royal prerogative.

One striking fact is to be found in every report about the Muscovy of Ivan IV, and that is the Tsar's passionate interest in artillery. In order to astound his people Ivan IV organized an annual display of artillery in action. He wished to show what his iron foundry could now do. A long column marched out from the gunsmiths' forge. First came enormous siege-guns on long gun-carriages, pulled by dozens of horses. They were followed by large numbers of cannon, field artillery, double-barrelled pieces, howitzers and shot-cannons, and mortars with gaping muzzles.

Andreas Winius from Holland, who started the famous iron and munitions factories in Tula.

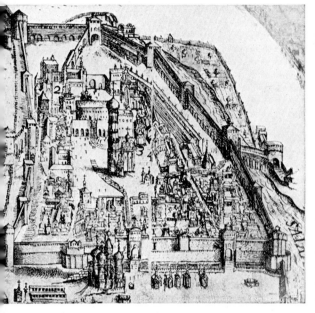

A drawing for King Sigismund III of Poland, 1610, of the Kremlin, showing in the foreground the Vassily cathedral on Red Square. On the right Spassky and Nicholas gates in the Kremlin wall, built by Pietro Antonio Solari. In the centre the Ivan Veliky bell tower.

German gunnery captain moving a gun across the Dniepr. (16th century painting.)

Nyemetskaya Sloboda—the "German suburb"—outside the gates of Moscow, after a drawing of 1711. This settlement of Europeans dated back to Vassily III (1505–34).

Domenico Trezzini, the great planner and architect of St Petersburg, built the cathedral on the island of St Peter and St Paul.

This display of gunnery took place before the Kremlin. The Muscovites were agape, the foreign specialists astounded. Such was the purpose of the display, which was therefore an exact equivalent of the May Day Parades of today. Then, as now, the foreigners were able to see exact copies of weapons from foreign countries.

If England supplied goods and manpower, she received in exchange the following very considerable benefits:

'We give you complete freedom and the full right to carry out every kind of trade without let or hindrance, without customs duties, taxes or other restriction.' Thus, in a document signed by the Tsar's own hand, the newly founded Muscovy Company received permission to trade freely as far as Kazan and Astrakhan, in Narva and Dorpat and even in Bulgaria.

In addition to the Muscovy Company, the German Hansa also traded in Moscow. For both of them this was a profitable business with a distant empire, far removed from the great world.

Ancient prototype of today's May Day parades: artillery made by foreign cannon forgers assembled in the Kremlin in Moscow. (Drawing from the Palmquist Album, 1674.)

A very few people realized that the equipping, and hence the arming, of this Eastern Empire, and the help given in its development by the West, might one day be used against the West itself. Among these few were the men who controlled Prussia, Courland and Livonia. This was not surprising, for Muscovite pressure against the Baltic countries was becoming ever stronger and more threatening. Not infrequently the lords of Dorpat would obstruct whole cargoes of goods and men—master craftsmen and technicians—on their way to Moscow. Even Johann Schlitte, on his way to bring yet another group of experts to Russia, was once held prisoner in Lübeck, despite his letter from Charles V. Sweden and Denmark also tried to dam the stream of goods flowing to Russia, and their privateers were active in the Baltic. It availed nothing. Nobody in Europe listened seriously to the warning voices of countries which, being Muscovy's neighbours, obviously knew most about what was going on there. One such neighbour was King Sigismund II Augustus of Poland, the last of the Jagiellos (1548–1572).

This monarch's letters to the Queen of England are filled with dark forebodings. To the Polish king the position was clear.

'We must state plainly that the Muscovite—the hereditary enemy of all free peoples!—has made exceptional progress in the training and arming of his forces as a result of the recent increase in sea-borne traffic, and this is true not only of firearms, munitions, and strategy . . . but also of other matters which can be of great service to him. I am here referring to those master craftsmen who are ceaselessly making guns, ammunition and similar products for the enemy, products hitherto unknown in his barbarous land. It is essential that we realize that our intentions—even our most secret ones—are known to him, so that he is fully aware of all we lack, and is in a position to send all our allies to their doom . . .

'Your Most Serene Highness will surely agree that we cannot allow this shipping traffic to Muscovy. . . . The enemy, thanks to the free trading permitted English merchants—and this is the crux of the matter!—is enabled to learn how to use weapons hitherto unknown in his barbarous land, and of course—and this is the essence!—to learn from its master craftsmen themselves. It is now clear, even if there be no further importations of such persons, that with the help of such persons as already are there and with the continuing freedom of the seas for the importation of the material he needs, he can produce for himself all that is necessary for the waging of war, and which, hitherto, he neither had nor knew how to use.'

Sigismund carefully explained the urgency of the situation in another letter, dealing with this irresponsible sending of men and materials into Russia from the West.

'. . . We have already written, and now write to Your Majesty again. We are informed from reliable sources that the enemy of world freedom, the Muscovite, is daily growing stronger thanks to the valuable cargoes of various materials arriving at Narva; there he receives not only goods, but also weapons hitherto unknown to him, and furthermore masters of all the arts and crafts; this is enabling him to arm himself with the intention of subjugating all other rulers. . . . Therefore, We, who know this enemy better than others, since our lands abut upon his own, are bounden as a Christian ruler to warn the rulers of all other Christian realms lest they surrender their freedom and dignity and the lives of their subjects to this . . . enemy. For we fear that if other Christian rulers do not heed this warning, the Muscovite, who is already overweening with the materials delivered at Narva, and making use of these to equip himself with weapons and ships of war, will do all in his power to overthrow

Christendom, and to enslave and exterminate all those peoples who resist him—from which God protect us all!'

The words of King Sigismund of Poland found no echo. Elizabeth of England ignored his warning. Indeed, she encouraged her English merchants to increase their trade with the Slav Empire. In one letter, marked in her own hand as 'secret' and known only to her Privy Council and herself, she assured Tsar Ivan IV: 'And We promise that We . . . shall observe the agreements described in this letter down to the least details, so long as God grants Us life, and to this We give our royal word.'

The outlet to the Baltic and the ports of Narva and Dorpat remained in Russian hands only for a few years. Ivan IV soon had to vacate the area again. The great push westwards to the Baltic was not to take place for a hundred years, when Tsar Peter I had completed the arming and equipping of Russia thanks once again to European skill and materials. But Ivan IV had carried out the policy inaugurated by his grandfather, the third Ivan. He had continued the laying of the foundations of a great Muscovite State on Western lines, and on these others could continue to build.

By the time that Ivan the Terrible died in 1584 a steady stream of finished goods and raw materials was flowing into Russia across the Baltic and the Polar Sea, all of which a backward, under-developed country needed urgently in order to 'catch up'.

For many years now thousands of Europeans had been working in the Tsar's service, prospecting for mines or building fortifications, as gunsmiths, architects, armourers or military instructors. The first foreign physicians and apothecaries had arrived. Since the year 1569 English-built ironworks in the Vologda District had been in production, while mines sunk by Englishmen at Perm were yielding precious ore. Industrial undertakings introduced into Russia by Europeans then included the production of potash, soap and hemp-seed oil, as well as the distillation of alcohol. Under Western instruction the goldsmith's craft was now practised for the first time, and clockmaking was introduced by a Serbian monk named Lazarus.

In cultural matters, too, foreign influences were noticeable. According to a Lutheran Pastor, Elias, who lived in the German Quarter, a library of foreign volumes was collected in the Kremlin. Meanwhile, Pastor Westermann arranged and catalogued for the first time the totally neglected Library of the Patriarch, which contained over one thousand valuable Greek and Slavonic manuscripts, some dating from the seventh century. He then translated the works of Livy and Suetonius, which he had found in that collection, into Russian.

There were only very few people, of course, who could read or write; Ivan IV had not yet succeeded in setting up a single school. But there was already the *Pechatny Dvor*, the 'Printing Works', which stood out among Moscow's wooden houses, being one of the very rare two-storied stone buildings. Ivan IV's command ('the Tsar's coffers will meet the cost') that a printing press be built, and his determination to reward lavishly all those who promoted the art of printing in his land, had sufficed to procure even this 'instrument of the devil' (as his subjects called it) from the West. By 1564 the inks, paper and printing presses had arrived from Holland, and under the supervision of Danish, German and Dutch master printers the first printed Russian book was launched upon the world—*The Acts of the Apostles.*

'Tipografiya', 16th-century Russian printing press. Danes and Dutchmen built the first printing works in Moscow for Ivan IV.

4   Prelude to the Age of Peter

IN 1565 the Antwerp merchants, envious of British commercial successes in Moscow, sent an enterprising native of Brussels, one Olivier Brunel, to the White Sea area. In his search for a suitable harbour he explored the Dvina, as far as the River Ob, which flows into the Arctic, east of the Urals, and also made favourable trade agreements with Moscow. As a result Johann Lippen of Alkmaar sailed direct to the Dvina in 1578. The English-men had chosen Kholmogory some distance up river as their trading-post, but the Dutchmen settled nearer the mouth of the Dvina. Some thirty miles from the estuary stood the lonely *Archangelsky Sobor*—the Monastery of the Archangel Michael. Nearby was a log cabin surrounded by a thick palisade, the so-called 'German House', then still the centre of the flourishing trade which the Hanseatic merchants had been carrying on here for centuries.

With the Dutchmen new life came to this ancient and forgotten trading-post. They established a regular, thriving shipping route, in which an important merchant house, Moucheron of Middelburg, played an important part. Huge warehouses were built at the mouth of the Dvina, markets were set up, quays erected for the loading and unloading of ships. The Dutch-built modern dock installations were the first on Russian soil. The founda-tions were thus laid for the rapid development of the town of Archangel.

Even more than the Dutch imports of lead, iron and tin, copper wire, sulphur and cast-iron, bellows, small bells for use in falconry and so forth, it was the spices and sweet things that they brought which aroused the wonderment of the Russians. In addition to saffron, ginger and raisins, there were—most delectable of all—the first dried plums.

The Dutch now repeated the attempts of the British and adopted Sebastian Cabot's idea of finding a north-easterly sea route to China, to distant Cathay 'with its golden roofs' as described by Marco Polo. The firm of Moucheron were able to interest the provincial towns of Holland and Zeeland in the undertaking.

In 1594 three ships put to sea, in search of the North-East Passage. In June, Willem Barents sailed his ship to the northern latitude of 72°25′ off the west coast of the island of Novaya Zemlya, which he actually discovered, and skirted its coast as far as the North Cape. Impenetrable ice-floes forced him to turn back on the 1st of August, when he had reached latitude 77° north.

The other two ships of the expedition, under command of Cornelis Nay van Enkhuizen, steered a more southerly course as far as the Kara Sea. He there decided that it was impossible to push farther east before the onset of winter, and therefore turned back.

A second expedition, in which both navigators took part—this time with seven ships—set out again in 1595 for the Kara Sea, but no further results were achieved. The Dutch municipalities henceforth ceased to subsidize these voyages of discovery directly, but did offer a reward of 25,000 guilders to the man who should first discover the northern sea route to China.

In that same year the city of Amsterdam fitted out two ships, commanded by Jan Corneliszoon Rijp and Jakob Hendrikzoon Heemskerk; Barents joined the expedition as chief navigator. It was Rijp's opinion that the route to China lay across the Pole—this was the logical conclusion to be drawn from the first terrestrial globe designed by the Nuremberg geographer, Martin Behaim, and used in Europe since 1492—and he hoped to find an ice-free Polar Sea.

The port of Archangel at the mouth of the Dvina on the White Sea, constructed by Dutchmen. (17th-century Dutch drawing.)

They sailed their ships almost due north, past Norway. They discovered Bear Island and on the 17th of June they saw the snowy peaks of Spitzbergen. Here Heemskerk and Barents separated from Rijp, according to plan, in order to attempt the circumnavigation of Novaya Zemlya. After a hard struggle through the ice they doubled the North Cape for the first time and reached the 'longed-for promontory' (Hoek van Begeerte—today, Cape Zhelaniye) and continued as far north as latitude 80°10′. There, fearsome ice-packs forced them back southwards towards the east coast of the island. At latitude 76°7′ their ship stuck fast in the ice and was crushed. For the first time Europeans spent the winter in a log hut in the Arctic wastes, from the 26th of August 1596 to the 14th of June 1597.

On 14th June they were ready to set off. In five open boats the men started in search of the way home via the North Cape. Barents and Heemskerk died

Dutch ships in the Arctic off the Russian coast. (Engraving from Gerrit de Veers' book.)

while circumnavigating the Cape. The others survived a journey of sixteen hundred nautical miles across the Polar Sea in open boats. When the exhausted men, almost dead from hunger and cold, finally reached the Kola peninsula, a ship sighted them and took them on board—it was the other ship of the expedition, under the command of Rijp.

On the 1st of November 1597 the survivors, who had long been assumed dead, came ashore amid the rejoicings of the burghers of Amsterdam.

The primitive huts made of driftwood and sealskins and used by the Dutch expedition during their winter on Novaya Zemlya were found by the Norwegian explorer, Ellins Carlson, in 1871, untouched and in perfect condition. Inside them were diaries containing entries concerning the Polar night, exact geographical summaries, and descriptions of the Arctic fauna. There was also a tattered book about Cathay, or China. Those 'Barents Huts' are today in the Nautical Museum at The Hague.

The distant target at which Barents had aimed was not to be reached until almost three centuries had passed, and then by another man from Western Europe, the Swede Adolf Erik Nordenskjöld in 1878–79. For his success in

Construction of hut for winter quarters at Novaya Zemlya. (Drawing from the report of the expedition by Barents.)

completely circumnavigating Northern Asia from the White Sea by way of the East Cape as far as the Sea of Okhotsk in his ship *Vega*, Erik Norden-skjöld received, in 1879, the prize of twenty-five thousand Dutch guilders first offered in 1595. He was also ennobled by his King.

Many other Westerners—including the famous navigator, Henry Hudson, in 1607, 1608 and 1609, and his compatriots, Abraham Wood and Flawes, in 1676—searched in vain for a North-East Passage. But though their voyages were failures from this point of view, they permitted the charting of the Arctic with ever greater accuracy. German sailors also took part in this, though they were more interested in hunting and fishing than in discovering the route to China. Men from Hamburg and Bremen started whale-fishing—in the four years beginning in 1670 they killed more than ten thousand whales—and also hunted walruses, seals and polar bears as well as other valuable furred beasts. In 1671 the first collection of Arctic flora was brought to Germany by Friedrich Martens, Bader and Feldscher, who had sailed to the far north in the ship *Jonah in the Whale*; they also brought back descriptions of the local fauna, and particularly of bird-life in the Arctic.

Meanwhile what were the contributions of the Slav Empire to knowledge of this Arctic region upon their very doorstep?

Far away in the east, Siberian Cossacks undertook a series of voyages of discovery, starting in 1633. They sailed along the coast from mouth to mouth of the great rivers, the Lena, the Yana, the Indegirka and the Kolyma. In 1648 the Siberian Cossack, Semyon Ivanov Deshnev, setting off from the Kolyma and hugging the coast eastwards, came to a river at the mouth of which his ship was dashed to pieces. This river is called the Anadyr and flows into the Bering Sea. Deshnev was thus the first man to circumnavigate the East Cape. Neither he nor his contemporaries had any idea of the importance of this perilous undertaking and of the discovery he had made—if, indeed, he did make it, for even today the facts are not quite sure. His report was only published nearly a century later, in 1736, and from his description of the *Great Promontory* (no exact navigational or geographical data were given) it was reckoned that the Cossack Deshnev had achieved the amazing feat of circumnavigating the outermost cape of Asia.

It is to the Dutchman Barents that the world owes the first accurate charts of those parts of the Polar Sea over which he sailed. He had plotted the geographical latitude of his winter quarters during the dark Polar night, using five astral measurements, with such accuracy that his huts could be found, at 76°7', three hundred years later. No great progress in this work of discovery in high latitudes took place during the eighteenth century, until a Dane, Vitus Bering, produced the first scientific charts of Polar Siberia and the North-East Passage, a work continued by the great English navigator, James Cook, in the southern part of the Bering Straits.

So much for the facts. In the Russian State publication, *History of Modern Times*, the student learns something quite different. This book was compiled for the Faculties of History in Soviet universities and educational institutions, and a long list of professors from the USSR Academy of the Sciences have given their names to it. It says:

'As early as the first half of the seventeenth century Russian geographical knowledge had assumed a leading place in international science. The great discoveries of Deshnev, who explored the northern coasts and waters of Russia, found the passage from the Polar Sea to the Pacific and drew the first chart of that region [where is it?]; the journey described by Nicolai Spafari [who was no Russian, being a native of Moldavia] through Siberia and China [since Marco Polo's report of his travels in China and his life in Peking, 1271–95, dozens of Europeans had gone to China both by land and by sea, and during the Mongol Period a French Mission had even flourished in that country, together with an Archbishopric of Peking, 1307–68!], the maps and descriptions of the western [!] and eastern portions of Russia—all this constituted a very major contribution to the geography of the age.'

And millions of Russian schoolchildren are today taught by their *History of the USSR* (Moscow, 1947) the following fantastic account of Deshnev's 'expedition':

'In the year 1648 a group of Russian merchants and trappers planned to investigate the coast of the Arctic Ocean eastwards from the mouth of the Kolyma. They were after walrus, having realized how valuable their tusks were. The leader of the expedition was the Cossack, Semyon Deshnev, from Yakutsk. The expedition put to sea from the mouth of the Kolyma in seven ships, and sailed along the coast. The ships of this brave seaman had been built very hastily with planks [planks, that is to say sawn wood, were first used in Russia after the compulsory introduction of saws from Europe by Peter I] and soon sank. Only the ship in which Deshnev himself sailed was driven far eastwards by the storm, into the strait which divides Asia from America [the Bering Straits]. At this time nobody in Europe yet knew that Asia was divided from America by a narrow channel. This question was settled by Deshnev's voyage of discovery.'

Nevertheless, the stretch of water that divides America from Asia and the Arctic from the Pacific is called today, as it has always been, not the Deshnev Straits but the Bering Straits, for such was the name of its real discoverer.

The story of the Tsar Peter I, who started with nothing, 'opened his windows on the West', defeated the Swedes, at that time the greatest power on the

Two worlds meet.
Reception of envoys from
Holstein (centre) in the
Duma by Michael, the first
of the Romanov Tsars.
(Drawing by Olearius.)

Continent, raised Russia to the status of a great power, and frightened all Europe, is a legend known to all. Only the proper prologue is lacking to this story. Those historians who fill their books with the dates of reigns and battles have so far neglected to throw any light on the technical and administrative background to the reign of Peter I. Hitherto little has been written about the vast influence which the tremendous cultural and technical developments in other European countries had exercised upon Russia since 1600. This contribution by the West to the development of the East is the key to any real understanding of Russia's apparent leap from nothingness to the status of a great power.

What Peter I, known as 'the Great', had to open was not a 'window' to the West, but a huge door, that stood ready to be swung back, thanks to the policy of his predecessors, the rulers of the Rurik dynasty, the last two Ivans, their Tartar successor, Boris Godunov, and subsequently, since 1613, the Romanovs.

The effects of this process of infiltration from the West, which touched every aspect of Russian life in the seventeenth century, are easily recognizable even today.

It first becomes clearly evident in the setting up of the *Prikazi* or administrative departments, through which the central government could function. Over forty of these *Prikazi* were established, with a Boyar at the head of each.

These included the *Inozyemny Prikaz*, the 'Foreign Department', which handled the foreign technicians and experts resident in Moscow, the *Reytarsky Prikaz* or 'War Department (Cavalry)' which was responsible for all the musket-equipped cavalry units trained according to foreign models, and the *Pushkarsky Prikaz*, or 'War Department (Gunnery)', which dealt with the making and maintaining of the artillery.

Boris Godunov, the Tartar Tsar (1598–1605), had first decided to employ foreign bodies of troops in the service of Moscow. Mikhail Feodorovich, the first Romanov, who reigned from 1613 to 1645, also strengthened his army with 'foreign' regiments. His basic reorganization of the army began about 1630. The Scottish mercenary leader, Lesley, was able to procure him five thousand men, as well as arms, and also German master armourers and a well-known Dutch gunsmith named Coyet. Russia's own production of weapons was nothing like adequate. Lesley bought, among other items, 10,000 muskets and 5,000 sabres. The Tsar Alexei Mikhailovich, the second Romanov, continued the policy which his father had inaugurated, and brought it to completion. Regiments of Russian recruits and volunteers were formed and in order to train these men on 'foreign lines', large numbers of instructors were brought to the country from abroad. The troops thus trained were formed into horse and foot regiments under foreign officers. The 'Foreign' and 'Cavalry' *Prikazi* must have had very considerable duties to perform. For by the time Alexei Mikhailovich died there were sixty-three permanent, Western-European-trained regiments in Russia; excluding the Cossacks, they accounted for 60 per cent of all the troops in the country. Under this Tsar, foreign master craftsmen also built the first Russian warship, the *Orel*.

As far as industry goes, the picture is much the same. Since the end of the Middle Ages new industries had been emerging in the West independent of the old trade guilds. Some factories still used the traditional craft

The Orel, *the first Russian man-of-war, built by Dutchmen in Archangel.*

*European techniques in the
East: a 17th-century forge.*

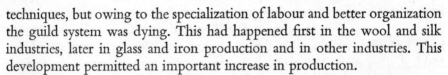

techniques, but owing to the specialization of labour and better organization
the guild system was dying. This had happened first in the wool and silk
industries, later in glass and iron production and in other industries. This
development permitted an important increase in production.

The *Inozyemny Prikaz* or 'Foreign Department' wasted no time in
granting concessions to foreigners experienced in these advanced techniques.
In the year 1632 the Dutch merchant, Andreas Winius, was given the iron-
ore mining concession at Tula. He began the production of iron and built
the first gun factory as well as four ironworks, which were called *Gorodi-
shensky*. This energetic innovator thus laid the foundations of the Tula
ironworks and munitions factories, which were later to become world
famous.

The first glassworks was founded by Covit, a Swede, near Moscow. In
1644 a Dutchman, Peter Marselis, was given a concession to build iron
foundries on the Volga, the Sheksna and the Kostroma. As early as 1626
the Foreign Department had already enlisted the services of an English
engineer, Bulmer, to prospect for and develop iron ore in Russia. Throughout the country glassworks and potash works, gold refineries, cloth and other
factories were being built by foreigners. The Foreign Department saw to it
that these concessionary industries received the necessary labour force; in
each area where such a factory was built a large number of peasant serfs
were designated 'factory serfs'.

Clockmakers, stonemasons, metal-workers and hydraulic engineers
flocked to the service of the Tsar of Russia. In 1639 Adam Olearius, a
Holstein mathematician and librarian, was invited to pass through Russia
on his way to Persia where he planned to carry out geographical and
astronomical research. We have to thank this highly cultured man for a
description of the people of Russia which is well worth reading even today.
It is called: *A Description of a Journey to Muscovy and Persia* (1647). In Russia
Olearius was known as 'the magician from the West'.

The large number of instructors from Western Europe is shown by the fact that the *Nyemetskaya Sloboda* on the Yausa River at Moscow was then flourishing once again, as in the time of Ivan the Terrible, though now the 'German Quarter' outside Moscow's walls was bigger and better than ever before—after having been partly depopulated during the period of confusion before the Romanovs came to power. On the 4th of October 1652, it was officially designated, by special order of the Tsar, as the 'Foreign Quarter'. The bells of many churches were soon tolling throughout the 'Quarter'; there were three Lutheran and two Reformed churches, one Dutch and one English. The streets between the solid stone houses, their front gardens filled with flowers, were paved and kept properly repaired. The foreign quarter had its own school and a theatre, something hitherto unknown in Moscow. The theatre in the *Nyemetskaya Sloboda* was to be the seed from which all Russian theatres were to grow.

The German clergyman Johann Gottfried Gregory installed the first theatre in Russia under Tsar Alexei.

A German clergyman, Magister Gregory, and Rinhuber, a physician, produced religious plays, in which there was also singing; these were immensely popular and so they started a drama school, which Russian children also attended. One day the Tsar Alexei, who had heard tell of this theatre, visited the German quarter. In a wooden building sixty-four young 'foreigners' acted before their distinguished guest. For ten hours they entertained the Tsar with their performance, and he was delighted and charmed by it all.

Hitherto all that the sovereign, like his predecessors and the Russian people as a whole, had ever seen were primitive entertainments with buffoons, jesters, wrestlers and dancing bears. The Tsar was so impressed by what he now saw that he had a proper theatre built in the suburb of Preobrazhenskoye, only a few hundred yards from the *Sloboda*. The enterprising Lutheran pastor was made director of this, and instructed to produce suitable plays from the West. The Tsar rewarded him with forty priceless sables. Performances started in that same year, the year in which the Tsarevich Peter was born, who later became Tsar Peter the Great. The date was 1672.

On 17th October of that year the first play officially to be produced upon the Russian stage was put on in German. Pastor Gregory, director, producer and author, had written a play which was originally called *Esther and Ahasuerus*. For the opening performance the author changed the title to *The Transformation of Artaxerxes*. He hoped that this would please the Tsar, for he thought that the name Artaxerxes would sound better to Russian ears than that of the biblical King Ahasuerus. During the intervals the guests were delighted by the playing of the German musicians whom Gregory had engaged.

On 9th February 1673 the first performance in Russia of *Orpheus and Eurydice* was also greeted with thunderous applause. The text of this had been written by Professor August Buchner of Württemberg. After the prologue, which Gregory had composed as a hymn in praise of the Tsar, the curtain rose to reveal paper pyramids upon the stage. The audience gasped with surprise and delight when these pyramids broke into a dance!

Tsar Alexei proved himself to be one of the Russian rulers most interested in the arts, although he was for a long time under the influence of the strict Patriarch Nikon. When he married for the second time, in 1671, he defied the Church's opposition to 'music-making', and even 'played a German organ, while trumpets were blown and drums beaten', according to court chronicles. In the year after the birth of the Tsarevich Peter, Alexei dispatched Colonel Nikolaus von Staden in great haste to Courland, there to 'procure the best and most popular trumpeters, and other performers who can act in any kind of play'. It is true that Felten, the actor, and the famous singer from Copenhagen, Anna Paulsen, refused to come to Moscow. Colonel von Staden did, however, bring back one trumpeter and four other musicians and they played at the cradle of Peter the Great.

With the Tsar Alexei's death, the story ends; the brief hour of the Muses, scarcely begun, came to a close. His successor, Feodor Alexeyevich (1676–1682), his son by his first marriage, ordered the theatre to be razed.

'Russia in the second half of the seventeenth century,' according to a distorted book by the Soviet professors, Biryukovich, Porshnev and Skazkin, entitled *A History of Modern Times*, 'was one of the more important centres of European cultural life. . . . This period was for Russia an age of soaring development in literature, the arts and in architecture.'

It was then five hundred years since the founding of the first universities of Western Europe, in Italy, France, England and Germany. It was a very

Copper coin of the Tsar Alexei Mikhailovich's period.

long time since the great spiritual examination of the heritage of antiquity had begun, first by the monks of the Middle Ages, then by the laymen of the Renaissance. Plato and Aristotle, Archimedes and Euclid, Hippocrates and Galen had long formed part of the intellectual wealth of the West.

Unknown and unread, similar manuscripts from the hands of the great thinkers of the past had meanwhile lain rotting for centuries in the monasteries of Russia. Nobody had ever thought of translating them into the vernacular, for Russian monasteries were never seedbeds of culture nor were Russian monks' cells ever used for study or learning of any sort. Furthermore, whatever was printed in Russia up to the end of the seventeenth century—exclusively church literature, dealing in the most specialized manner with the church and monastic matters—was written in the ecclesiastical old Slavonic, using the ecclesiastical Cyrillic script.

'At the end of the seventeenth century,' writes Ernst Freiherr von der Brueggen, 'the Slavonic [i.e. Cyrillic] script had already been in use for seven hundred years. Up to the time of Peter I, however, its use was limited to men handling the affairs of Church and State. And even there the knowledge of writing was employed only in the day to day business of essential administration. The limitation of the use of the written word prevented all cultural development not only in the people as a whole but also in the civil and ecclesiastical ruling class. How incredible must have been their intellectual apathy and inertia to make such a state of affairs possible! For hundreds of years this script was used by officials, yet never artistically nor for the purpose of self-expression. This startling phenomenon displays a characteristic intellectual inertia not to be found anywhere else in Europe, and shows in glowing colours the fundamental difference between the way of life of the Russian people before Peter and that of the Western peoples.'

As it happens, the father of the first Romanov Tsar knew Latin owing to the fact that an Englishman, Horsey, had written a Latin-Russian grammar. In 1649, when it was decided that the Bible should be translated, two Greek monks had to be brought to Moscow for this purpose. In 1655 the first Latin school was founded in the *Spassky Monastyr*, the Abbey of the Redeemer, in Moscow. And in 1681 something resembling a university, but also under ecclesiastical control, was established in Moscow. In 1686 it had two hundred and thirty-three students. This was not precisely an Orthodox theological college, as the Russian historian, O. Klyuchevsky, states, but rather an ecclesiastically-disciplined educational establishment founded with the object of preserving Russian Orthodoxy from the inroads of 'Latin', i.e. Roman Catholic, heresies.

Just as knowledge had stagnated, so the plastic arts had petrified. The ancient religious paintings were copied and recopied century after century. The icons remained unchanged in every detail—colour, shape, size and form—from the original designs brought to Kiev from Byzantium. Nothing new had been introduced, nor was there any sign of change or of life, except among the masters of the Great Novgorod school. There something had been attempted, and a start had been made to get away from the lifeless, stereotyped formulas—on Western lines. Almost realistic faces now appeared on the Novgorod icons, portraits of the artists' patrons.

Many difficulties confronted the second Tsar of the House of Romanov, Alexei Mikhailovich, when he wished to have his portrait painted. Oil paintings did hang on the walls of the Kremlin, but these were portraits of Western European sovereigns and their daughters painted in Western Europe. Ivan IV had sent for these when he was toying with the idea of marrying a European princess.

The best-known artists in Russia were summoned to the Tsar's palace to paint the Tsar Alexei. But the results were disappointing, lifeless features in the usual icon style. Therefore, as on so many other occasions, he had recourse to the 'Foreign Department'.

The two best-known Russian painters of that period, Abramov and Stepanov, had received some instruction in their art from the gifted German, Hans Detterson. But now an art school was established for the first time in the Kremlin, under a Dutchman, Daniel Vuchters, assisted by Hans Walter and G. E. Grube from Hamburg, the decorator Peter Engels and the Swedish landscape painter, Gul. In the years 1667 to 1694 they collaborated with painters of the Eastern school, including an Arab named Sasha Yakovlev, an Armenian painter by the name of Saltanov and two Greek artists called Yuryev and Salomonov.

A much greater impression, however, was made by the introduction of copper-plate engravings. In 1650 there was published, in Amsterdam, an illustrated edition of the Bible by the Reform Church theologian, Johann Fischer; following the custom of the age, he called himself Johannes Piscator. About three hundred works by the greatest artists of the West were here reproduced as engravings. These engravings opened a new and unknown world to the Muscovites, and showed them all the living beauty of Western painting.

The impression made by the pictures in the Piscator Bible was so strong that traces of their influence were soon to be discerned everywhere. Even in

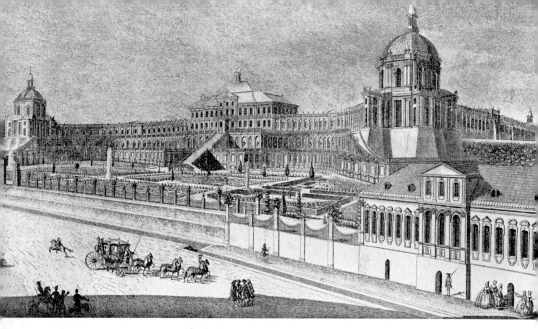

Oranienbaum, the pleasure palace built for Prince Menshikov by Johann Gottfried Schädel in 1714.

The St Petersburg palace of Prince Apraxin, designed by Andreas Schluter.

Leonhard Euler of Basle, one of the most important mathematicians and physicists of his time, who worked at the St Petersburg Academy of Sciences in the 18th century.

Johann Georg Gmelin of Tubingen, 1727–47, member of the Academy, who wrote Flora Sibirica.

Vitus Bering, the Danish leader of the Great Northern Expedition of 1734–41.

Peter Simon Pallas of Berlin (1768–1810), member of the St Petersburg Academy who explored the ethnology, zoology and botany of Russia, Siberia and Mongolia.

Aug. Lud. Schlözer of Göttingen who designed the school programme for Catherine II. His idea of parish registers was to constitute the first census.

The Ambassadors'
courtyard in the Moscow
Kremlin. (Copper
engraving of 1656.)

provincial cities, such as Yaroslavl and Kostroma, motifs from the Piscator Bible appeared in church murals. And despite all the opposition from the Orthodox clergy a spark was kindled in the field of icon-painting. The cold, dead, stylized tradition began to break down. A living and hitherto unknown manner of painting was introduced into Russian art by no less a man than Simon Ushakov, the court painter at the Kremlin. He attempted, with great success, to portray biblical incidents realistically. 'The Virgin of Vladimir' (1652), 'Christ' (1657) and 'The Annunciation' (1659) glow with un-mistakable passion and humanity.

An icon-painter named Josef has left us a document, which he wrote in memory of Ushakov, and which contains a series of discussions on painting between the two of them. In it he accuses the clergy of destroying the inspiration of creative artists, and of encouraging only paid hacks and daubers:

'Do you wish to ensure that only Russians be allowed to paint religious pictures, and that only Russian icons be worshipped? Do you want to see Western painting trampled underfoot and never employed for the greater glory of God? . . . Learn, then, that in foreign lands not only are Christ and the Holy Virgin realistically represented, but such works of art are also cleverly reproduced on paper; and whenever or wherever we icon-painters see engraved or beautifully painted pictures of Christ or the Virgin, whether they be by foreigners or by our fellow-countrymen, we are filled with love and reverence. Thus are we not consumed by envy, nor do we hate the foreigners, when we learn that they possess such finely painted religious pictures. On the contrary, we treasure these blessed works more than all earthly goods and chattels, and are filled with love when we buy them or beg them as gifts beyond price. We accept such representations of Christ, whether printed on paper or painted on wood, with holy awe. Why, then, are we compelled to reproduce all sacred faces as dark-brown and gloomy? Is the whole human race moulded in a single form? Were all the Saints mournful and sickly?'

This was a call for freedom, for fresh air, such as can be heard again today. For just as art, at the time of the icon-painter Josef, was hidebound by Church dogma, so today it is tied hand and foot by the inflexible doctrine of 'Socialist Realism', which portrays a whole people as monotonous, robot-like Stakhanovs, mindless factory hands and tractor-drivers. But what man in power in the East, then or now, has ever been interested in the living development of the individual, in the colossal complexity of each and every human being? All that counted then, all that counts now, is the appropriation and exploitation of technical and materialistic skills. And this acquisition of knowledge is itself merely a means to an end—the strengthening of the power of the State. It was not for true educational and humanitarian reasons that schools were established after the reign of Peter I, and an attempt made to make ten years' school attendance compulsory. The real reason was that it had been realized at last that illiterates are simply incapable of working complicated machines, let alone of building them.

5   Peter's Window to the West

WAS IT COINCIDENCE or destiny? Peter Alexeyevich, later known as 'The Great', spent his Russian childhood in the closest personal contact with Europe. His first impressions, which were to influence his whole life, all his knowledge and his very considerable learning derived from Western Europeans.

Between the royal residence in Preobrazhenskoye, the eastern district of Moscow, where Peter lived with his mother, the Tsarina Natalya, and the Kremlin in which, in 1689, Peter Alexeyevich was to be crowned Autocrat lay the *Nyemetskaya Sloboda*, the German Quarter. The young prince then followed a road which runs geographically from east to west. The small oasis of Westerners was a sample of life in busy, progressive Europe, and it gave to young Peter the idea of turning his backward and undeveloped Russia into a huge *Nyemetskaya Sloboda*. Peter's knowledge of the *Sloboda* was to be Russia's destiny.

It was all so strange, so new and unfamiliar. This little town of foreign soldiers and engineers, merchants and craftsmen—the Barbarians, as his countrymen called the Germans, Dutch, English, Scottish and French who lived there—constituted another world. Between the homes of the rich merchants abutting on the only paved streets in Moscow stood the taverns, the houses of officers, doctors, chemists and craftsmen, many in the style that prevailed in their homelands, with ornamented gables, gardens and birdbaths. Fountains splashed among the flowers, and the wind turned the sails of many windmills. A colony of over a thousand families here led lives utterly different from those of the Russians all about them. Nobody here wore the cumbersome, trailing *kaftan* or long, shapeless, fur garments. The men went about in black knee-breeches, white stockings and buckled shoes, and beneath tight-fitting, snuff-coloured jackets they sported white cravats. The women wore aprons and brightly coloured caps, and did not have to spend their lives in the shuttered *terem*, as did the wives and daughters of the Boyars.

Peter's visits to the *Sloboda* were for him voyages of discovery. With astonishment he examined, for the first time in his life, a saw. Later he ordered saws in large quantities from abroad, and it was a great struggle before he could persuade the Russians to use this completely unfamiliar tool, and this despite the fact that they lived in the most richly wooded country of the Old World.

Peter was filled with a consuming curiosity and a restless thirst for knowledge, and so he learned something new with each visit. He began to assimilate his knowledge. Foreign craftsmen taught him how to use their saws, planes, gimlets and hatchets. During this period of his life the young Peter also learned the two foreign languages which he was later to put to such good use—German and Dutch.

The superior knowledge of the inhabitants of the *Sloboda*, compared to that of even the highest classes of Russians, was soon abundantly clear to Peter. Prince Yakov Dologoruky had brought back an astrolabe from abroad. But neither the prince nor the Boyars nor the monks had any idea of how to use the instrument. So Peter asked a Dutch technician, Franz Timmermann. The latter informed him that the astrolabe was an instrument used in astronomy, for calculating the position of the stars, and thus for working out the positions of ships at sea according to those stars. The more detailed explanations of how to use it meant nothing to Peter, for he could not count. His tutor, Nikita Sotov, a clerk employed by the Duma of the Boyars, had taught the young Tsar nothing, except for a hazy knowledge of how to read and write. He was henceforth to learn from the foreigners.

Timmermann instructed the sixteen-year-old boy in mathematics and geometry, taught him how to read maps, and gave him lessons in geography, gunnery and the art of building fortifications. From Menesius (Menzies), a Scot, the Tsar learned European history, and from a Dutchman, Karsten Brant, the elements of shipbuilding and navigation. Foreign officers, of whom many had been living for years in the *Sloboda*, were ordered to set up a small body of troops for Peter to command in person: since his earliest days he had shown an interest in the art of war. Strict discipline was enforced on European lines; the soldiers were ceaselessly marched and drilled, first with wooden dummy weapons, later with real muskets and cannon. General Simon Sommer trained them in the handling of grenades. The Tsar was known as Bombardier Peter and proudly wore a blue German uniform. At Peter's request a miniature fortress was even built on the bank of the Yausa

Wooden houses along the Moscow streets in the 17th century. (Drawing by Olearius.)

Arrival of the Russian expedition headed by E. I. Ides at the Great Wall of China in 1693.

for what he called his 'martial' exercises. The first troop, which soon grew to two companies, later became the nucleus of the famous *Preobrazhensky* and *Semyonovsky* Guards Regiments—the latter named after a village in the neighbourhood.

During these years of close contact with the *Nyemetskaya Sloboda*, a seed was sown which was later to flower in the Tsar's ambitious plans to build a navy. Peter had found a dilapidated English sailing-boat, and Karsten Brant and his countryman, Kort, had made it seaworthy. On Lake Pleshtcheyev, one hundred miles north of Moscow, the excited young Tsar had his first sailing trip. He was so delighted by the experience that he ordered a group of Dutchmen to build a shipyard on the shores of this very lake.

Peter not only learned about craftsmanship and military matters in the Foreign Quarter, but also first heard about European trade. Over a thousand foreign merchants, buyers of furs and of caviar, came to the inns on the Yausa each year. It was Dutchmen who first drew his attention to the importance for Russia of East Asia. The Burgomaster of Amsterdam, Nikolaus Witsen, a geographer of high repute, had travelled through Russia at the request of Alexei Mikhailovich, Peter's father, and in 1672 he wrote a widely read work on northern and eastern Tartary (*Noord en Oost Tartarye*) which Peter studied assiduously. In a letter to the young Tsar dated 1691 Witsen described in detail the possibilities of trade with China and Persia, and offered his services for this purpose. Peter declined his offer. On the basis of Witsen's proposals he organized his own expedition to China, with a German merchant, E. I. Ides, as its leader.

In the *Sloboda* Peter got to know the Scottish General Patrick Gordon and Colonel François Lefort from Geneva, both of whom had been in the Russian service for many years. These two experienced soldiers from Western Europe became his most indispensable advisers. Gordon and Lefort showed Tsar Peter I how to escape from the narrow world of Old Russia, and gave him great understanding and an abundance of facts concerning the modern West. They also helped him to achieve his ambition, growing ever stronger, of importing the technical and cultural achievements of Europe into Russia. It was largely due to the influence exercised upon Peter by the clever Lefort that the Tsar later forced through radical changes in the Russian way of life. He ordered long beards and traditional Russian clothing to be abolished, and insisted that European manners and customs be adopted.

In 1689 Peter became Autocrat. Now was his chance to put into effect all his plans for the modernization of Russia, and to make use of what he had learnt from the foreigners in the *Nyemetskaya Sloboda*.

As always, what came first was his extraordinary passion for ships.

In the summer of 1693 the young Peter, consumed by curiosity, visited Archangel for the first time and saw the sea. Archangel was then a very different place from what it had been in 1584 when the English built the first stockade there and the Dutch the first docks. Out of what was once a gloomy, uninhabited post on the edge of the Polar Sea a thriving port had developed, the only one in Russia, built by the Dutch and the English and kept going by the enterprise of the Amsterdam merchants.

The Tsar sailed in a frigate for many miles through the Polar Sea. His excitement knew no bounds, and his resolve was reinforced. Russia, too, must possess a navy. Then and there he ordered the building of two ships.

A Dutch shipowner offered to build the first one. The keel was to be laid immediately in his yard in Archangel. Peter agreed, but he wanted something better. He was accurately informed about the most modern and largest ships afloat. But these were built in Amsterdam. The Burgomaster of Amsterdam, Mynheer Witsen, received an urgent order for an ultra-modern frigate, equipped with forty-eight guns.

In the spring of 1694 Peter was back in Archangel filled with joyful anticipation. He was accompanied by Gordon and Lefort, as well as by numerous Boyars, officers and many others, including all the Dutchmen from the *Sloboda*.

In the harbour a shiny new frigate lay at anchor, with twenty-four guns. The Dutch had built it as a 'rush job', in the course of the winter. It was named the *Apostle Paul*.

And the frigate from Amsterdam was due in port any day. Peter could not wait. He set sail to meet her in a small sailing-ship, day after day, until one day they were hit by a storm, and he only just escaped death by drowning. As a thanksgiving for his escape, he constructed a cross, which stands by the sea shore and bears the inscription, in Dutch: *Dat Kruys maken Kaptein Piter van a Cht. 1694.* At last the frigate arrived; Burgomaster Witsen had not let the Tsar down. Slowly, under full sail, the ship entered harbour, the muzzles of its forty-eight guns an ominous threat. Amidst the clamour of bells and the firing of the guns, the new flag was run up aboard the frigate from Amsterdam. One day her guns would be firing shot and in the direction whence she had come—against the West. Meanwhile a navy was born and Russia possessed the best and latest European warship.

The construction of the Russian fleet started by Peter the Great, employing naval architects from Holland and England.

The Tsar thanked the Burgomaster of Amsterdam in a letter written in clumsy Dutch, which ended with the words: *Schiper van schip santus profet*— Seaman on board the ship *The Holy Prophet*.

Peter had already appointed the commanders of the new Russian fleet. Prince Romodanovsky was to be Admiral, Buturlin Vice-Admiral, and Gordon, his adviser and friend from Scotland, Admiral-General. He himself remained an 'ordinary seaman', and wore Dutch sailor's clothes.

Up to this time none of the Russians appointed to the new Admiralty had ever set foot on board a ship. No matter, Peter would soon import the experienced sea captains from Europe that his brand-new navy needed.

In the autumn of this same year, 1694, Peter ordered something which had never before been attempted in Russia, large-scale manœuvres involving thirty thousand men. Two Western-trained, well-drilled Guards Regiments had been formed, under foreign command, using as cadres the Tsar's small training squad at Preobrazhenskoye. Among the Russian princes the ill-feeling against the 'beardless men' had increased, for none of them approved of Peter's reforms nor of the westernization of the army. The Tsar was determined to show them all what had been achieved.

Gordon and Lefort had been preparing these army manœuvres for many months. Plans were drafted by General Gordon for a fortress, bristling with guns, to be built on the banks of the Moskva River at Kosukov. When the day came, the troops were drawn up in two bodies, one consisting of the Streltsi—the regiment founded by Ivan the Terrible as his Life Guards— together with the levy of noblemen and of Kremlin servants, while drawn up against them were the numerically much smaller foreign-trained troops. It was East against West.

Old Russia held the fortress, which was to be besieged by the 'New Army'; such was the plan of the exercise. After a bitter struggle, which lasted for days, and cost twenty lives as well as uncounted casualties, both light and serious, the besiegers captured the fortress.

Troops trained according to the rules of modern Western warfare had defeated the numerically superior forces of Old Russia. This was precisely what the Tsar had wished to show his Russians.

Encouraged by the success of the manœuvres, Peter decided on a real test for his troops. He wished to drive the Turks out of the fortress of Azov, which controlled the south of the Don where it flows into the Sea of Azov. After ninety-six days of fruitless combat, the siege of Azov had to be lifted on 13th October 1695. The Turks were the technically superior soldiers. Russia lacked officers with a knowledge of saps and mines, and of how to blow up strong fortifications. Peter immediately dispatched dozens of letters abroad.

He wrote to the Emperor in Vienna and the Elector of Brandenburg, to England and to Holland: 'Send me specialists . . . engineers, experts on mines, pyrotechnists, gunners . . .!'

The Holy Roman Emperor sent a colonel of artillery, accompanied by experts on mines, explosives, and gunnery; army engineers came from the Elector of Brandenburg, and from Holland there arrived a major of artillery also with some gunners.

Most important of all, Peter also built a navy in the far south. He realized that the failure of 'Operation Azov' was due not only to his lack of sappers and of mine-laying units, but also to the fact that the Russians had been unable to blockade the port of Azov. In Voronezh, on the Don, a vast shipyard sprang up with twenty-six thousand workers, and Dutch and English shipbuilders in charge. A Dutch galley had been taken to pieces and transported here to act as the prototype for the mass production of twenty-nine identical galleys. One thousand transport boats were also built in haste. Now the harbour of Azov could be blockaded. In the summer of 1696 Azov fell.

But Peter had no illusions about his real strength. He fully realized that a superior opponent faced him in the north in the form of Sweden, should he decide to force his way into the Baltic—and this was his principal, long-range objective. He was no more capable of defeating Sweden than his predecessors had been, despite all his and their efforts to achieve great power status. He knew what he needed but it was all in Western Europe. Therefore what he must do was to import everything that was best and most up to date from Europe into Russia. It was not enough merely to bring specialists across. It was not enough merely to send the boyars' sons to Western Europe so that they could learn the languages of these superior countries, and anything else that Peter considered necessary such as ship-building and navigation, mathematics, gunnery and defence. Such methods would not suffice to satisfy Peter's ambitions; he decided to take matters into his own hands. He would go to Europe himself.

On 10th March 1697 two hundred and seventy people set off on the 'Great Embassy'. The Tsar travelled incognito as an NCO called Pyotr Mikhailov,

*The Boyars' dress before
Peter the Great made
European dress compulsory.
(After an engraving of 1656.)*

so that he might observe and study undisturbed. The young noblemen and soldiers were divided into groups of ten, and some of them had been instructed to remain in the West, in order to learn what they could there. The Generals Golovin and Vosnitsyn carried secret instructions to enlist certain specialists—sea captains, sailors and engineers—and to purchase certain items of machinery and equipment and weapons. Wild Cossack horsemen escorted the group, which was also accompanied, absurdly enough, by a troop of dwarfs.

Because of his knowledge of Western Europe Peter had appointed François Lefort head of the mission; he was rigged out in the most gorgeous Russian clothes for the part, and wore a long, fabulously rich *kaftan*, with a great high-crowned sable hat on his head. Though a Western European, a son of the city of Geneva, he had to act this part as head of the Russian mission.

The Europeans were, if anything, amused by this first appearance of Russians in their countries, much as they are today, when Lortzing's popular and harmlessly cheerful *Czar und Zimmermann* is done on the operatic stage. But the 'Great Embassy' was by no means a pleasure trip, nor even an *opera buffa*.

Tsar Peter's journey to the West reads like a list of instructions for all future Russian spies in the field of commerce and industry. The incognito member of the 'Embassy' had money and notebooks ready in his pocket at all times. Educated persons who talked to Pyotr Mikhailov noticed his superior intelligence, and the smiths and master carpenters in the Dutch shipyards were astounded at his great skill, his interest in their work, his thirst for learning and his knowledge of their crafts.

The first stop, and the first European city to be visited, was the port of Riga, the bulwark on Sweden's frontier. Peter's father, Alexei, had besieged it unsuccessfully. This was not the least of the reasons why the son showed interest in its mighty fortifications.

While most of his entourage set off to find lodgings, Peter went at once to examine the bastions, with their trenches, ramparts and curtain-walls.

Swedish sentries spotted the foreigner 'in shabby clothes' and with a yardstick in his hand, and stopped him. This was in the frontier zone, and espionage was frowned on. Quickly the other Russians dragged Peter away with them for otherwise he would have been held prisoner. Nobody in Riga could then have realized that a few years later Peter was to use this incident as a pretext to declare war on Sweden.

Pyotr Mikhailov was very seasick during the trip across the Baltic from Libau to Königsberg, where the Elector of Brandenburg, Frederick III, later to become King Frederick I of Prussia, received the foreigners with pomp and ceremony.

'Bombardier' Peter took advantage of his short stay in his usual manner: he arranged to be given gunnery instruction by Colonel Steitner von Sternfeld. Peter was proud to accept a testimonial at the end of the course which said that he had made a thorough study of artillery techniques, and conferred on him the title of 'Master of Artillery'.

Peter travelled to the fortress of Kolberg by sea, inspected the fortifications and moved on to further fortresses, Spandau on the Havel and Magdeburg. From there he went to Ilsenburg in the Harz to see the ironworks, an especially attractive place for a man as interested in armaments as was Peter. In Coppenbrugge Peter met Sophia of Hanover, the mother-in-law of the Elector Frederick III. This princess, a cultured woman and a devotee of Leibniz, introduced the Tsar to the works of the great philosopher, and offered to put them in touch. In one of the letters written by the philosopher to the Tsar we read: 'Because your Majesty's kingdom is for the most part a blank sheet of paper as regards cultural matters . . .' Thus did Leibniz write to the Tsar, and this began a comprehensive programme for the future remodelling of Russia according to the dictates of Western European culture. Of the many suggestions advanced by the German philosopher, the one that was to produce the most important results for the Eastern Empire was the founding of a Russian Academy of Sciences. Peter first met the philosopher in 1711 in his camp at Torgau.

Leaving most of his train behind him, Peter hurried to Holland and set to work in Zaandam, in one of the famous yards of the time. He found the perfect job, with a shipbuilder named Rogge. The amount that the energetic Russian prince got done in a day was well-nigh unbelievable. He went everywhere, in the shipyards and docks, examining the ships at anchor and studying minutely every detail of shipbuilding. After work he would visit the ropemakers, the cloth bleachers or the oil-presses, learn about the running of a paper-mill and even work in the pulp-vats himself. For hours on end he crouched over work benches or demanded explanations of how to operate sextants and telescopes. Late at night, in the dockside taverns, he would go on asking questions over drinks. His notebooks became filled with page after page of the information he had acquired and with his own first-hand observations.

After he had been in Zaandam for about a week, people began to wonder who this alleged carpenter, Pyotr Mikhailov, might really be. To preserve his incognito the Tsar moved to Amsterdam on 26th August 1696. Burgomaster Nikolaus Witsen, who had been responsible for sending Russia her first warship, and who had also sent to Russia nautical instruments, engineers, metal-workers and shipbuilders, saw to it that every door in that important city was open to his guest. He found Peter a job as carpenter in the shipyards of Holland's famous United East Indies Company. They laid a ship on the stocks one hundred to one hundred and thirty feet long for the 'royal prentice', which would later be the frigate *Peter and Paul*. Master shipbuilder Gerrit Claas Pool, who designed the big East-Indiamen for the company, was at Peter's disposal for information.

For four whole months and five days—apart from short holidays, which he utilized visiting Utrecht, The Hague and Delft—the Tsar worked and studied in the shipyards, the drawing offices and in the workshops where the ropes and anchors were made. As a tribute to their guest, and for his edification, the Dutch even mounted a naval exercise.

During this period, when he was working in the shipyards, Peter wrote a letter to the Patriarch of Moscow. In this he said: 'I am here . . . to learn seamanship, so that I can bring back the knowledge I shall have acquired and . . . conquer our enemies in the name of Jesus, and set the Christians free.' Reading between the lines, one of his many objectives is thus revealed. The knowledge he was acquiring would be used to conquer the Black Sea. For its shores were then held by the 'enemies of Christendom'—the Turks.

Holland, so small and yet so great and so modern, was the perfect place for Peter to study. Here medicine flourished as did the natural sciences of which even the names were then unknown in Russia. The Dutch builders of fortifications enjoyed a world-wide reputation, and nobody surpassed them in the digging of canals, the construction of sluices, and indeed in every branch of hydraulics.

Besides working extremely hard and studying under Gerrit Claas Pool, Peter arranged an incredibly varied schedule for himself, not least in the matter of purchases. He and his people bought equipment and enlisted specialists of every sort. Shiploads of goods and instruments, regiments of technicians and mechanics, set off by sea for Moscow. In Professor Friedrich Ruysch's famous anatomical laboratory Peter frequently observed the dissection of human cadavers, eventually carrying out autopsies himself;

he also spent much time in the laboratories of Doctor Hermann Boerhaave at Leyden. He watched glass being ground, and the world-famous lenses being made. For hours on end he sat huddled over a microscope in Delft; Antony van Leeuwenhoek, who had opened a hitherto invisible world to mankind, explained the microscope and its mysteries to Peter. He made the acquaintance of the architect, Simon Schynvoet, from whom he learnt about town planning and building. He sought out Van Heyden, the engineer, whose water-pump fire extinguisher had attracted his attention. Fires often raged unchecked through the wooden buildings of Moscow, for there was no machine in all Russia capable of putting them out. Among those who helped satisfy the Russian's thirst for knowledge was Menno van Coehoorn, after Vauban the greatest builder of fortifications of the age. Peter studied the plans and drawings of this engineer officer and listened to his explanations. He would have liked to take this outstanding soldier back to his own country. But Coehoorn declined the most attractive offers, for he wished to remain in Holland. He proposed, however, that Peter engage some of his best pupils. This was done, and thus Russia obtained for her service some of the most talented military engineers available. In years to come the Tsar frequently turned to Coehoorn for advice. The answers he received were of great use to him.

The Dutch shipbuilding industry was founded on many generations of practical experience, as Peter soon learned. His raw and inexperienced Russians could scarcely hope to emulate the Dutchmen. Therefore they needed perfect models. The English, however, had evolved certain simple mathematical formulae—this was the very latest development in the craft of universal application in the building of ships.

It was therefore with keen anticipation that Peter accepted an invitation from William III to visit London. He crossed the English Channel in January of 1698.

When he visited Kensington Palace, he immediately engaged the King in a long and detailed discussion about seamanship and sea power. Peter had no eyes for the beautiful furniture, nor the long gallery hung with paintings. On the other hand he found his way to the royal workroom at once, eager to see the latest model of a recently invented manometer-cum-tachometer.

Seated behind a window he watched one session of the English parliament, but only briefly, for democratic institutions were of no interest to him. He spent far more time with the clockmakers and in the workshops of skilled mechanics where he studied in detail the operation of ironworks and the principles of bridge-building.

Ever greedy for new knowledge, he hurried to Deptford—to the Royal Shipyards. An engineer was instructed to teach him all about ship construction, and to give him those formulae which made it possible to calculate accurately and in advance the dimensions of every type of ship. He visited the arsenal at Woolwich, where England's newest guns were housed. Here, however, his barrage of questions about the latest and most secret methods of gun-making were answered only briefly and evasively—much to his annoyance.

In England or in Holland Peter lost no opportunity of enlisting skilled workers from the foundries and the workshops. By chance the names of two sea captains whom he now engaged have survived: John Perry and Kreys. Here, too, he bought goods on a colossal scale. Whole shiploads of his purchases, weapons of every sort, scientific instruments and industrial tools left the Pool of London for Moscow.

In April 1698—after the English king had invited him to watch the great naval manœuvres off Spithead—the Tsar left England. He took with him a splendid yacht, a present from the King.

The 'Great Embassy' now moved across Germany, through Bielefeld, Halberstadt, Halle, Leipzig and Dresden, observing, ordering, buying, recruiting, stopping to examine and take note of every fresh object of interest. Finally they went to Vienna, which city greatly interested Peter. Thanks to Prince Eugene it had become a sort of military college for all Europe. On 19th July 1698 he hurried back to Moscow—for a mutiny had broken out among the Strelits Guards which brought his travels to a sudden end.

The 'Great Embassy' had been well worth while. Soon Russia was to reap the benefits, but the West was to bear the cost. For under the cloak of an embassy this journey had been nothing more nor less than a well-organized plundering expedition across the length and breadth of Europe. The object of the enormous retinue was 'to seize or buy men, equipment, and anything else which appeared interesting or valuable'. Thus does Arthur W. Just describe it, and he goes on: 'The nine hundred specialists were plunder picked *en route*, enlisted into the Russian service for every conceivable purpose, and obliged to work for Russia's benefit.'

In 1697 Prince Dimitri Mikhailovich Golitsyn had also gone abroad, in his case to Italy, and he too had systematically looted the West, though of a different sort of treasure. He bought a collection of books, six thousand volumes in all, which was to form the foundation of one of the finest private libraries in Russia, in his castle of Archangelskoye near Moscow. But from the days of Peter I until now Russia has sadly failed to make any use of the great treasures in this library which include the writings of the leading expert on natural law of the age, Samuel Baron v. Pufendorf's famous tract on *The Duties of Man and of the Citizen*, and the works of the great Hugo Grotius, the father of international law. Such *kultura* was no use in building a mighty nationalist state.

In 1846 an Englishman who had spent many years in Russia remarked: 'Russian policy is to acquire all those practices of civilized countries which lead to national aggrandizement. It is the usual story, to be seen in all uncivilized countries where the natives hasten to throw their bows and arrows away and quickly learn how to fire European rifles. In all spheres apart from the physical, and above all in intellectual matters, Russian policy has been to instil in her subjects maximum subservience, a superstitious terror of power and a mindless materialism.'

'In the German universities Peter's journey, and the future transformation of Russia along European lines as a result, were constant topics of discussion,' writes the historian, S. F. Platonov. 'The philosopher Leibniz planned the reorganization of Russia on lines in accordance with the principles of European culture. Europe realized clearly that after Peter's tour Russia could not remain as it had been before.'

Then, as now, discussions in the West concerning Russia's future contained much hope and many illusions; meanwhile no sooner had Peter returned to his own land than he issued confidential orders for a 'crash' programme. In the strictest secrecy he set about using his newly acquired knowledge of modern shipbuilding, and his Western specialists, to prepare a shock—what might be called a 'Sputnik shock'—for the Turks.

On the wide banks of the Don a navy was rapidly being built. Its finest vessel was a man-o'-war carrying fifty-eight guns, The Providence. The Tsar ordered that only Englishmen and Dutchmen were to work on this ship. By May of 1699 a fleet of eighty-six ships was being built in the yards at Voronezh by thousands of deportees working overtime under the skilled supervision of the 'Beardless Men'.

Russia possessed neither efficient sea captains, trained navigators, nor experienced seamen, so the fleet was ordered to sea with Westerners on board. All these brand-new ships set off together on their first voyage down the Don and anchored off Azov. Then they sailed across the Sea of Azov to Kerch.

On 18th August 1699 the Turkish commandant of Kerch was horrified by the noise of guns firing at sea. Foreign ships, Russians, were testing their guns in the Black Sea. An even greater shock was sustained at Constantinople on 7th September of the same year. The Russian man-o'-war Providence suddenly dropped anchor off the Golden Horn and all its guns fired a salute. The noise reached the Seraglio, up on the heights, and the Sultan. On board was Yemelyan Ukraintsev, who had been ordered by the Tsar to compel the Turks to sign a peace treaty. This appearance of the Russian warships in the Black Sea was not only completely unexpected, but was regarded as totally impossible, and the surprise achieved did not fail to have the desired effect. A year later the Sultan signed a peace treaty. Danger no longer threatened from the south, from Turkey: the way was now clear for

The Providence, *58-gun warship, on the Black Sea. Built by Dutch and English shipwrights.*

large-scale operations in the north. In this same year, 1700, Peter declared war on Sweden.

Three years earlier Peter had ordered six hundred cannon from Sweden, which was then the leading iron-export country. A further three hundred new guns had gone as a present from Charles XI to the Tsar. The Swedish king had protested over and over again his desire to be on good terms with his much-esteemed 'friend and neighbour'. When the young king, Charles XII, came to the throne (1697) Peter sent him, via the Swedish ambassador, a letter bearing the great official seal, in which he promised 'to work for eternal peace, true, secure, indestructible'.

Now the Tsar suddenly seized upon a grotesque excuse to open hostilities. The members of the 'Great Embassy' had been so ill-treated at Riga, in 1697, 'that even the Tsar was distressed thereby'. Swedish sentries had actually dared to prevent the Tsar, disguised in simple clothes, from spying in a Swedish frontier fortress!

The Western-trained Russian troops marched on the fortress of Narva. Under command of a Saxon engineer, Hallart, the first mines were being dug under the walls of the fortress, when Charles XII suddenly appeared at the head of his army, attacked the Russians, and routed them utterly. Peter's entire army was destroyed.

Nine years later, at Poltava, Russia dealt a decisive and annihilating blow to what was then Europe's mightiest military power. Hitherto, as the Soviet professors Biryukovich, Porshnev and Skaskin admit in their *History of Modern Times*, 'Russia, under Peter I, had learned much from the West.... She had learned the art of war from Sweden, and used that knowledge to defeat her eventually.'

'During his European journey of 1697–98,' remarks the Italian historian Lo Gatto, 'Peter was astounded by the material prosperity of Central Europe in contrast to the conditions prevailing in Russia, by the multitude of factories and workshops and by the abundance of trade.'

An immense increase in the tempo of construction took place after his return from the 'Great Embassy'—a striking parallel to the Bolshevik Five Year Plan in our century—with plans and production quotas laid down to the last detail, under the centralized control of the Tsar himself. 'Every industrial undertaking was tightly planned and controlled,' writes Lo Gatto. Peter introduced the system of a state-controlled economy. Countless plans and instructions were sent out, written in his own hand. Peter was, in fact as well as by analogy, the author of the first Five Year Plan. 'In 1712, he founded cloth factories and then leased them to a group of merchants, with orders that they take over the running of them (whether or not they wished to do so). They were simultaneously compelled to undertake this forced labour on a permanent basis and were ordered so to develop production that they could fulfil all the uniform requirements of the entire army *within five years*.' V. Gitermann refers to this Five Year Plan in his *History of Russia*, and adds laconically: 'The aforementioned target was not reached.'

Peter laid down the exact amount of canvas to be used in making sails, and ordered that rowboats should be built narrower in order to save wood. That nothing should be lost, corn was to be cut in the European manner, and the peasants were taught to mow with the scythe. He laid down where new industries and production centres were to be built, and was especially keen in promoting mining enterprises in the Urals and in Siberia. In 1700 Greek engineers sank silver mines on the Siberian-Mongolian border in the Nerchinsk area; peasants were drafted to work in these mines, for Peter made the provision of a labour force part of his royal prerogative.

'Peter's industrialization decrees meant the mass conscription of forced labour,' states M. Pravdin without ambiguity. 'There were massive shifts of population from one end of the country to the other, and whole villages were uprooted so that their serfs could be turned into slave labourers in the factories and mines.'

1702 was the year in which the most important measure for the planned development of Russia was drafted, and one without which the whole ambitious programme could never have been realized. Throughout this year the Tsar's couriers were scouring every country in the West. They issued countless appeals, translations of the Great Ukase, in their attempt to enlist the large skilled-labour force the country needed. The Tsar's Ukase contained handsome guarantees to all foreigners who would come to Russia, including special privileges, security of employment, good pay and religious freedom.

The great Narva triumphal arch in St Petersburg which was built by Giacomo Quarenghi of Bergamo.

Alexander Palace, Tsarskoye Selo, built by G. Quarenghi for Catherine II, showing the decorated pillars, a feature brought to Russia by the Italians and copied to this day.

The academy of Fine Arts (1765–68), St Petersburg, one of the most beautiful buildings in the classic style. Built by the French architects Vallin de la Mothe and Georges Felten.

Catherine II, born Princess of Anhalt-Zerbst. Painting by Pietro Rotari, about 1760.

The world-famous Hermitage, St Petersburg. Built by V. de la Mothe (1765), G. Felten (1773), G. Quarenghi (1779–85) and lastly (1840–52) Andreas Stakenschneider and Leon von Klenze of Munich.

The Tsarina with her family—her son Paul, with his German wife, the Princess Sophie Dorothea of Wurttemberg, and her grandsons Alexander and Constantine on the left.

Peter's Ukase of 1702 remained a permanent feature of Russia's development. It served as a model for successive Tsars and for the Bolshevists in our own age. On 23rd November 1920 Lenin issued similar regulations about foreign concessions, and thus, with his 'New Economic Policy' (NEP), launched 'aggressive Communism'. Appeals for help to the West and the promise of 'privileges'—such was the tried method. It opened wide the channels to and from foreign countries and helped Russia to ever greater strength and power. It proved equally successful during periods of expansion and in times of crisis. 'Privileges' under the Tsars, 'concessions' under the Bolshevists, were the bait at which the free world nibbled promptly and regularly whenever it was dangled before them by the Russians.

Tsar Peter's appeal for foreign capital, contractors and specialists did not go unheeded. They would help him make Russia 'self-supporting'. Thousands of men from all the nations of Europe, specialists in every conceivable profession, answered Peter's call and formed the backbone of Russia's vast development programme.

The creation of a textile industry in central Russia dates from the beginning of the eighteenth century. In 1720 Tamess, a foreigner, founded a cloth factory at Kochm, near Ivanovo-Vosnessensk, later known as 'the Manchester of Russia'. Its historian, J. Garelin, says of Tamess's factory: 'Here the textile industry was founded. Tamess's success influenced the local inhabitants, who soon began to build similar factories themselves.' Thus the contractors of what became the factory town of Ivanovo-Vosnessensk followed in Tamess's footsteps, and big factories soon appeared in Moscow and in Yaroslavl as well. 'Tamess had Russians working with him, but he remained in complete control.' At the same time Fiebig, Prank and Lichten were starting textile mills. In Moscow a Frenchman, Montbrion, opened a stocking factory, while his compatriots built linen mills and carpet factories in many parts of the country. The facts prove that 'even before the industrial revolution, it was foreigners who took the lead in the oldest branches of Russian manufacture, and provided the necessary guidance. Western European manufacturing techniques were introduced into the Tsar's empire by the English, the Germans, and, after 1812, by French prisoners-of-war' (B. Ischchanian). It was the same story in other fields. An Englishman, Humphrey, introduced improved methods for treating hides into the tanning industry.

To improve and modernize stock-breeding, bulls were brought from Western Europe, and these developed what became known as the Kholmogory strain. Shepherds arrived in the Ukraine, driving enormous herds from Silesia. This produced a sound and marketable breed of sheep, and made the wool trade and the manufacture of woollen goods possible in Russia.

But the main objective of this planned and forced development of industry was the production of armaments. Russia was to be made strong enough to defeat Sweden and to settle accounts with Turkey. A shortage of military supplies, and not the requirements of the people, was the reason behind all the factory-building. Thus the wool from the Silesian sheep went to the Dutch-run cloth factories, where it was used exclusively for the manufacture of uniforms. Peter later said how proud he was to wear a uniform made of Russian stuff, rough and coarse though it might be.

And above all there was tremendous development in the mining industry, of every kind. The leading figures in this field were Lübs, a Dutchman, and a number of Germans, men such as Johann Friedrich Blüer, Vinzent Kaiser and Johann Schlatter. Wilhelm von Hennin was put in charge of all the ironworks in the Government of Olonets, and the Tsar later extended his territory to include the Urals. Hennin also built the first munitions factory at St Petersburg, and also opened an architectural school at Ekaterinburg (the modern Sverdlovsk), of which town he is reported to have been the founder.

The iron-ore deposits discovered by German and English mining engineers and geologists were exploited, and the Tula foundries and ironworks, started and developed by the Dutch, could now be used for the making of munitions. Andrei Winius won especial fame as Inspector of Artillery. At Narva the entire Russian artillery had fallen into the hands of the Swedes. Within one year A. Winius had forged three hundred new cannon, the bronze for which came from church bells. This Andrei Andreievich Winius, who also played a big part in opening up of new iron-ore deposits in Siberia, was none other than the son of the Dutchman, Andreas Winius, who had founded the Tula ironworks in 1632.

Within twenty years Russia, with a population of some fourteen millions, possessed close on two hundred works and factories thanks to Peter's extreme measures. By 1718, Russian iron production was the largest in the entire world.

In order to establish an urgently needed communications network across this vast country, which had no proper roads, Peter—as the Bolsheviks were also to do—placed great emphasis on the building of canals and waterways. In the far south, Captain John Perry, with a large number of skilled English workmen, supervised the building of the Volga–Don canal. But, despite a colossal outlay in men and materials, this work was suddenly suspended and the canal remained half-finished.

Prince Dolgoruky managed to procure the services of another gifted specialist for Russia, the Engineer-General Burkhardt Christoph von Münnich. The completion of the Ladoga Lake canal in the far north, which had been started in 1719, was entrusted to this German. In the most trying circumstances Münnich finished this magnificent waterway. It is close on one hundred miles long, and was regarded at the time as a masterpiece of hydraulic engineering.

Construction of the Volga–Don Canal under the direction
of the Englishman Perry. (Contemporary map.)

Over one thousand foreigners were 'recruited' to develop a modern army and a modern fleet. Under a Dutch captain, Cruys, who was created a Russian Vice-Admiral, twenty-three foreign ships' captains and hundreds of the best-trained seamen were engaged.

In order that Russian specialists should also be available eventually in the shipbuilding trade, the same procedure was adopted as had been in use before the 'Great Embassy'. Russians were sent to Italy, Holland and England. In the introduction to his *Fleet Regulations*, Peter I himself explained his purpose to his subjects. 'So that the work in progress can continue in the centuries to come, the Sovereign has decided to instruct the entire population in the craft of shipbuilding. For this reason he has dispatched a large number of young noblemen to Holland and other countries. There they shall learn about shipbuilding and navigation. Furthermore, since the Monarch is determined not to lag behind his subjects, he has himself already undertaken such a journey to Holland.'

Peter deliberately continued the military policy of his predecessors, and employed foreign as well as native troops. Under Mikhail Feodorovich, the first Romanov and Peter's grandfather, there were already five regiments in existence, in which six thousand five hundred Russians served beside three thousand foreigners; the number was increased in 1700 to sixty-three 'mixed foreign regiments', with a total strength of ninety thousand. 'As Peter the Great advanced into Europe in his twenty-year war of aggression,' Dieter Friede tells us, 'Germans, Dutchmen, Scots and Scandinavians were working and fighting for Russia—against Europe.'

No man can say today exactly how many thousand Europeans worked in Russia and fought for Russia against Europe—as instructors and officers, experts and specialists, contractors and teachers. Yet the shortage of skilled labour remained enormous. So crowds of Russians were sent abroad for training in the English factories, or to learn seamanship in Venice, or to study medicine in Paris.

'Study, study!' This was the slogan of Peter's reign, as it has been of the Soviets in our time. Young men of the nobility who could neither read nor write nor speak foreign languages were deprived of their birthright. French and German tutors, therefore, taught in the houses of the nobility, while a Frenchman, Rambour, instructed the daughters of the Tsar.

In the first issue of the first Russian newspaper, *Vedomosti* ('News'), dated 2nd January 1703 (Peter edited it single-handed), the following item was proudly printed: 'On the orders of His Majesty, the number of educational establishments in Moscow is to be increased. Forty-five students are reading philosophy, after having finished the course in dialectics. In the faculty of mathematics, there are already three hundred students.'

The new education laws were of the same sort, and had the same objective, as the 'Socialist education' of today. Technical training received priority.

The first technical schools were set up under foreign teaching staffs. In the gloomy Sukharev Tower in Moscow, Englishmen taught mathematics and navigation. The College of Higher Mathematics and Navigation, founded in 1701, formed the nucleus of what later became the Naval Academy. The titular head of this was a Russian, Andrei Matveyev, but his Director of Studies was a Frenchman, Saint-Hilaire. James Bruce—in Russian, Yakov Bryus—founded a naval and artillery school; he was the real founder of Russian engineering. In recognition of his exceptional services, the Tsar conferred an earldom on this highly qualified Scotsman, and later appointed him president of the College of Mining and Manufacture.

This appointment was rather exceptional, in that foreign collaborators, S. F. Platonov tells us, 'were almost never given positions of authority by Peter, these being reserved exclusively for Russians'. A later Russian Vice-Chancellor, Heinrich Johann Friedrich (in Russian, Andrei Ivanovich) Ostermann (1686–1747) and Field-Marshal Burkhardt Christoph von Münnich, who built the Lake Ladoga canal and several important ports, were among the rare exceptions to this rule, which is still applied by the Soviets today.

In the Moscow Military Hospital Dr Bidloo established Russia's first college of surgery, and to Peter's especial joy a German pastor, Ernst Glück (from Marienburg in Livonia), founded a technical college in Moscow. The subjects included mathematics and geography, French and German, and the classical languages; there were also courses in dancing, fencing and riding.

Pastor Glück became, incidentally, a sort of 'father-in-law' to all modern Russia. For in his house in Marienburg there had lived a peasant's daughter by the name of Martha. When the Russians took Marienburg in 1702, she became the mistress of Prince Menshikov and later of the Tsar Peter. In 1712 Peter married her, and after his death she succeeded to his throne as Catherine I.

Scot, James Bruce, father of Russian engineering and director of a naval and artillery school.

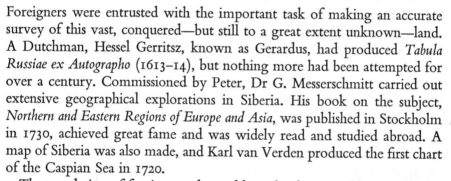

Foreigners were entrusted with the important task of making an accurate survey of this vast, conquered—but still to a great extent unknown—land. A Dutchman, Hessel Gerritsz, known as Gerardus, had produced *Tabula Russiae ex Autographo* (1613–14), but nothing more had been attempted for over a century. Commissioned by Peter, Dr G. Messerschmitt carried out extensive geographical explorations in Siberia. His book on the subject, *Northern and Eastern Regions of Europe and Asia*, was published in Stockholm in 1730, achieved great fame and was widely read and studied abroad. A map of Siberia was also made, and Karl van Verden produced the first chart of the Caspian Sea in 1720.

The translation of foreign works could not be done quickly enough, for Russia urgently needed the knowledge they contained. European technical books on warfare and seamanship, machinery, mill construction and natural history had first priority. Whole libraries of technical works were bought abroad and collections of minerals for the study of mining problems. During Peter I's reign alone, the Russian language acquired from Europe a vocabulary of foreign words running to over three thousand. The greater part of the technical vocabulary used in Western Europe in the fields of administration, military matters, handicrafts and general technology was taken over into the Russian language, in particular from the French, Swedish and German. A few examples were: *burgomistr* (burgomaster), *magistrat* (magistrate), *feld-marshal* (field marshal), *feldfebel* (sergeant), *feldsher* (army surgeon), *feldzoigmistr* (master of ordinance), *soldat* (soldier), *dragun* (dragoon), *reytar* (mounted trooper), *kapitan* (captain), *gubernator* (governor), *gildiya* (guild), *parikmakher* (wig-maker or hairdresser).

As the language changed so did the alphabet. The old ecclesiastical Slavonic letters, evolved almost a thousand years ago by the Slavonic apostles, Cyril and Methodius, were redrawn, simplified, and more closely assimilated to the Western alphabet. This was largely done by printing. Holland made the first letters in the new type. It then became possible to print translated works in 'modernized' Russian. The printer, Tessing, was given the concession to start a Russian printing works in Amsterdam; his first order was to supply Moscow with instructional manuals and school books. There were five printing works in Russia already —two in Moscow, one in Novgorod, one in Novgorod-Seversk and one in Tchernigov—but they were quite inadequate. The first training manual printed in Moscow was an arithmetic primer; it was followed by a book of etiquette, translated from the German.

The Amsterdam printing works 'for the glory of the Tsar and his empire' had a secondary, secret function. They were used as a camouflaged instrument for Russian propaganda, giving the lie to European publications which described the incredible backwardness and barbaric conditions prevailing in the East. For a German, Neugebauer, after a visit to Moscow, had described the 'contemptible treatment' meted out to foreigners by the Muscovites. And the news of Peter's unprovoked and unsuccessful attack on Narva had severely damaged the Tsar's prestige.

Yet Russia has never had any cause to complain of a shortage of Russophiles in Europe. European literature in Peter's time contained as many panegyrics of the Russian 'experiment' as it was to do in the period after the Bolshevik revolution, and often in identical terms. The Tsarevich Alexei's German tutor, Baron H. v. Huyssen, produced a series of propaganda publications for Peter. He wrote, for instance: *The Nation of Tomorrow* (1704), *The Present State of the Muscovite Empire* (1706), *The Life and Works of the Great Czar and Grand Duke of Muscovy, Petri Alexeivich* (1710). And there appeared in Amsterdam not only works justifying Russian aggression, but also publications commenting favourably on the murder of the Tsarevich Alexei by his father, Peter.

This hunting in foreign countries for anything that would be useful for the creation of a great Slav state meant that the Tsar needed ever more agents abroad. 'Peter,' writes Harry Schwartz, 'made the embassies throughout Europe virtual employment agencies.' Here is a contemporary report concerning one of the many Europeans, forerunners of Fuchs and Pontecorvo, whom the Russians then used for their own purposes.

'General Hennin has been sent to Germany, France and Italy, to make drawings, plans and models of every new type of useful machinery,' an English eye-witness report of 1723 informs us. 'The Tsar paid all his expenses for this journey, which lasted two years, and the General was ordered to make particularly accurate and detailed notes and plans of foreign mining and industrial installations, and to enlist as many craftsmen and workers as possible for the Tsar's service.'

Tsar Peter not only longed to possess the ability and the knowledge

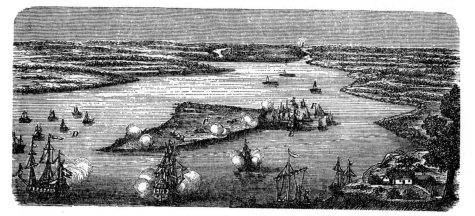

The site of what is now Leningrad (from an engraving of c. 1700). In the distance, the Dvina emerges from Lake Ladoga into the Delta. On the left (D) the Swedish fleet fires upon the Russians, who cluster under the guns of Kronstadt (E). On the right are the marshes that Peter the Great drained to build his 'Piterburch'.

available in Western Europe, in order to make Russia into a great power; he also wished to have a capital city on Western lines.

In the midst of war, when the Swedish warships were actually in sight, the Tsar issued his orders for building the future metropolis, the splendid capital of Tsars as yet unborn. The soil on which it was to rise is not Russian, for here, on the shores of the Gulf of Finland, Finns had lived for many years. The builders and designers of the city were not Russian, and the city itself bore a non-Russian name. Peter christened his new city 'Sankt Peterburg', 'Piterburch', as he pronounced it. In 1914 the German name was Russianized into Petrograd, in 1924 bolshevized into Leningrad.

The mouth of the Neva—the gateway to the Baltic—had been recently captured from Sweden by the Tsar. In October 1702 the Swedish fortress of Nöteborg (where the Neva flows out of Lake Ladoga) fell; the Tsar rechristened it Schlüsselburg. On 25th March 1703 the small Swedish fort of Nyenschanz, at the mouth of the Ochta, was taken after a short bombardment. This was the site that Peter chose for the building of his new capital, which was soon to lure a vast concourse of European wares and know-how into the Russian empire.

On 27th May 1703 Peter dug a spadeful of sticky mud from an island in the delta. On this marshy ground building was to begin.

From the very beginning foreign specialists worked on the bleak, deserted stretch of swamp that was the Neva Delta, with their plans, ideas and superior knowledge—dyke-builders, hydraulic engineers and forestry experts from the *Sloboda*. There was Gonts, a Dutchman, Pirchenstein from Germany, the Englishman Perry.

Foreign help was needed for the laying of the foundations. To make a firm base in such soft, wet ground, sufficient to take the weight of a vast city, was a task requiring years of experience and the highest technical qualifications such as no Russian then possessed. For this special job the ambassador Ismailov had already engaged the foremost expert of the age, an hydraulic engineer and architect named Domenico Trezzini, a native of Tessin, born in Azano, near Lake Lugano. Trezzini was familiar with such problems. He had already earned the gratitude of the people of Copenhagen by transforming the soft and dangerous marshlands on the Danish coast into solid ground.

Using Trezzini's plans and calculations—and with the help of engineers from Italy, Saxony and Holland—the great task was begun. This quaking, bottomless stretch of delta swamp would be turned into firm ground capable of

The fortress of Kronslot, later Kronstadt, built on an island off St Petersburg in 1703.

taking the weight of great buildings. Trezzini's work took him ten long years, ten icy winters and ten fly-infested summers.

Like the great Soviet industrial projects, St Petersburg was built by forced labour, and the work meant heavy sacrifices for the Russian people. 'Peter the Great used similar methods to those of the Bolsheviks in recruiting workers for his great enterprises,' an Englishman, L. E. Hubbard, has said. 'Peter's forced labour camps are reproduced almost exactly in the Bolshevik camps of Northern Russia.'

An English eye-witness, writing in London in 1733, says: 'It is a bottomless pit, in which countless Russians perish and disappear. I am assured by reliable persons that during the building of the Taganrog fortress on the Sea of Azov more than three hundred thousand peasants died from hunger, or from the pestilences bred by the swamps. An even larger number of people perished during the building of St Petersburg and Kronstadt.'

When whole forests had been felled and had vanished to form a firm base deep in the mud, the first buildings began to appear. They were in most cases utility edifices such as quays and dock installations, shipyards,

Peter the Great's first palace in St Petersburg, built by Domenico Trezzini.

warehouses and—in its first form made of wood—the Admiralty Building. The first colony, on the right bank of the Neva, consisted of Dutch and Germans. By 1705 Germans were also building on the left bank, near where the Hermitage now stands, and where the spire of the first Protestant church soon rose against the sky. It was here that Peter later had the beautiful Summer Gardens laid out—in pure Franco-Dutch style. His Summer Palace was also built here, and the Winter Palace in Great German Street. On the Vassily-Ostrov (Basil Island) a French colony came into being.

The architect from Tessin not only drew the plans for the city as a whole, but also designed the individual buildings in accordance with the Tsar's preference for the Dutch style of architecture. Among what little remains of Trezzini's work are the magnificent Summer Palace and the cathedral inside the old Peter and Paul Fortress, with the great bell that the Tsar had bought in Amsterdam for forty-five thousand roubles and which was hung to the famous belfry at a later date.

In 1713 two new men of genius appeared on the site by the Neva: Andreas Schlüter, who had made a great name for himself as a sculptor and architect in Berlin, and Johann Gottfried Schädel. Outside the city, towards the Baltic, the first country residence was taking shape, Prince Menshikov's Oranienbaum. It was built by Schädel. Its architectural style pleased the Tsar so much that he had it copied for the Peterhof, his own country seat near the city. In Moscow Schädel also built the Annenhof in the Kremlin; in Kiev

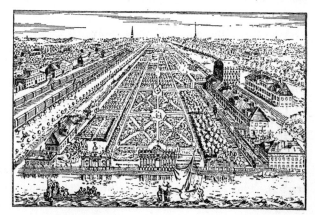

The Summer Garden in St Petersburg, one of the most beautiful creations of the Frenchman François Leblond, architect-in-chief of Peter the Great. He also designed the gardens of Peterhof and Strelna, modelled on Versailles. (Engraving, 1717.)

he was responsible for the belfry of the Pecherska Lavra, the famous monastery hewn out of the rock, and for the ornamental gates of the Cathedral of Saint Sophia.

After Schlüter's early death in 1714, the Tsar appointed François Leblond, a most brilliant man, Russia's Architect-in-Chief. Leblond came to St Petersburg in 1716. His great influence soon made itself felt. The homely and intimate character of the Dutch style of building gave way to ornate baroque. With Leblond the spirit of French architecture made its triumphal entry into the city on the Neva.

A whole group of palaces now sprang up in and about St Petersburg. Like some powerful magician, Leblond transformed the Summer Garden, inside the city, into a paradise in the style of Louis XIV, while outside he worked on the palaces of Peterhof and Strelna, with their monumental architecture, exotic parks and fountains. The great palace and pavilion of the Hermitage in the Peterhof were the work of this Frenchman, and he transformed Peter's original, primitive palace into the jewel called Mon Plaisir. Its hundreds of water-jets, its fabulously beautiful fountains and waterfalls, were beyond compare; they were Leblond's masterpiece, a brilliantly executed feat of artistic engineering.

But the Tsar soon lost this brilliant architect, for in 1719 he died of smallpox. An Italian, F. P. Michetti, succeeded him as Chief of the Building Commission. He was responsible for the Palace and Park of Strelna, modelled on Versailles. Michetti and his compatriots, Gaetano, Chiaveri and Cipriani, introduced the jubilant Italian baroque style to St Petersburg, with its magnificent brackets, garlands and pilasters. A German architect with the Italian name of Matarnovi was also at work there at this time, as was Stefan van Zwieten from Holland. Then there was Carlo Bartolomeo Rastrelli the Elder, from Venice, whose son, another Bartolomeo, later achieved fame as an architect, and who executed the bust of the Tsar which subsequently so pleased the French sculptor, Etienne Maurice Falconet, that he copied the head for his famous equestrian statue of Peter I, commissioned by Catherine.

Amidst all the names of these artists of every kind from Germany, Italy, Holland and France we only encounter one Russian, Mikhail Semzov. He was brought to the colony on the Neva in 1703 to learn Italian, Dutch and German, in order that he might act as interpreter. Later he was to act as assistant to Trezzini and Michetti. The best known of his works is the small pavilion where the little boat was kept, in which the young Peter had made his first sailing trip. It was called, amusingly enough, the 'Grandfather of the Russian Fleet'.

Marvellous parks and artistically laid out gardens are meaningless without statues. The sculptors for the Summer Gardens came chiefly from the studios of Venice, where the pupils of the great Bernini worked. Such

distinguished southern European masters as Pietro Baratta, Giovanni
Bonozza, Giovanni Svizoni and Antonio Tasia received commissions from
Russia. Whole shiploads of nymphs and muses arrived in the harbour at
the mouth of the Neva. Antique statuary was also represented, including a
Roman Venus of the second century—a particularly valuable piece—which
was placed between the flowerbeds in the Summer Gardens, beneath the
grey Baltic sky.

The long story of acquisition thus continues. Determined bargaining and
occasional trickery enabled the Tsar to obtain the splendid effects that he
desired above all else. Despite the strict law that forbade the expert of
antiques from Rome, Peter's Russians were ordered to smuggle the statue
of Venus on board a ship. Cardinal Ottoboni had already guessed at the
Tsar's intention and insisted that it be returned. The statue had to be
unloaded again. When the Tsar heard of this he was obstinately determined
to acquire it despite everyone and everything, and he did not rest until he
found a way of doing so.

The Russians had stolen the relics of St Bridget from Reval Cathedral
after the siege. Using this item of loot as bait, Peter intrigued long and
obstinately until he had the unhappy cardinal exactly where he wanted him.
In return for the restitution of the holy relics, the prelate was to give Peter
the antique statue of Venus. One can imagine the feelings of the cardinal
when, after faithfully carrying out his part of the agreement, he learned that
the Venus had not made the long journey to St Petersburg alone, for on
board the ship there were ten other pieces of antique sculpture, among them
valuable busts of Lucius Verus and Vitellius, of Marcus Aurelius and of Nero.
These carefully selected pieces had been secretly smuggled on board by the
Russians along with the Venus.

While the gardens were being decorated with foreign statues and
sculptures, the splendid rooms of the country residences, palaces and government buildings, and the houses of rich and aristocratic Russians were being
crammed with other European art treasures, Dutch tiles from Delft, French
Gobelins, musical boxes and ivory carvings, globes and telescopes, polished
mirrors and magnificent lustres and chandeliers, whole libraries and galleries
filled with the works of foreign masters. From its foundations deep in the
swamp to the gilded tips of its elegant spires, the new St Petersburg
represented the cultural triumph of the foreigners from the West, so hated
by the Old Russians. This magnificent product of imported culture was
raised to the status of a capital city by Peter I in 1712.

While the new capital was growing out of the swamps on Baltic land
captured from Sweden, the crisis of the Northern War occurred deep inside
Russia, on 8th July 1709. At Poltava, south-east of Kiev, Sweden's King
Charles XII suffered a crushing defeat. Out of 24,500 Swedes who, with
only four cannon, met 44,000 infantry, 10,000 cavalry and the fire of

72 cannon under the command of a Scot, James Bruce, 20,000 were taken prisoner. Only a handful of them ever left Russia again.

Peter ordered that the thousands of Swedes be marched through Moscow in a victory procession on New Year's Day, 1710. In the Tsar's eyes the captured soldiers were so many assistants to help develop Russia's potential, or to act as cultural 'fertilizer'. Just as Peter had ordered that the citizens of Narva and Dorpat and part of the population of the Baltic provinces of Esthonia, Livonia, and Ingermanland be transported, so the prisoners of war taken at Poltava were scattered throughout the country and finally absorbed into the Russian population. They had to establish themselves as craftsmen or teachers, if they were not ordered into the administration. The officers were compelled to instruct the Russian aristocracy in such subjects as dancing and formal etiquette. A use was found for all of them; in the Tsar's words— 'they either know how to do things, or they are able to teach.'

As in the time of the Goths, Russia now absorbed a flood of talent from Sweden. Towards the end of the nineteenth century a traveller in Siberia could still find traces of these men compelled, for years on end, to work for the Tsar. 'After the Battle of Poltava Peter had thousands of Swedish prisoners of war transported to Tobolsk, then the capital of Siberia,' writes Alfred Count Keyserling. 'The ground was levelled and a fortress and city built by Swedish engineers and builders. The Swedes taught the people of Siberia brickmaking and stonemasonry. The skilled work done by the Swedes at that time is still in existence.'

Poltava not only marked the end of Sweden as the greatest and most feared military power in Europe, but also suddenly and unexpectedly raised Russia to the rank of a great European power.

It was with astonishment and anxiety, reminiscent of the effect on the Western world of the Sputnik, that the courts of Europe learned the news of Poltava. This colossus in the East had emerged so suddenly! The effect must have been all the greater in that nobody then realized what forces and influences had enabled Russia to make this mighty leap forward. An inadequately informed Europe was puzzled, and incapable of forming any clear opinion concerning Russia's emergence as a great power.

Peter himself dropped a hint in his oration on the very night of the victory. On the battlefield at Poltava he toasted the assembled Swedish generals: 'To my great teachers in the art of war!' The Battle of Poltava was won thanks to the European training and arming of Russian troops.

Once more a seed from the West had grown and spread in the East. The 'great teachers' and advisers had worked for years, and this was the reward. But nobody in the West understood this as the Westerners pondered over the Russian enigma, the mystery of the sphinx of Eastern Europe, and its sudden leap to power. If one reads the news reports of the day, they might almost have been written this year.

The military as arbiters and enforcers of fashion. A model at the city gate shows the prescribed coat length as worn in Europe. Soldiers cut the Russians' coats shorter and collected the fines. (Contemporary print.)

Poltava effectively put an end to the sneers about the 'rough, drunken ship's carpenter', and nobody now laughed at the 'barbarous Muscovites'. A disconcerted Europe hastened to pay its tribute of 'co-existence' to the new power. Hanover, Prussia and Denmark courted the Tsar and attempted to form alliances with him. In Vienna 'His Muscovite Majesty' was henceforth regarded as a 'considerable'. 'If the Tsar complains that We have despised him,' it was stated in Paris, 'the answer would be that Muscovy first became known to Us only through her present ruler, whose great achievements and personal qualities have won him the esteem of other nations.'

The 'Muscovite Grand Duke' became, overnight, a great emperor, sovereign ruler of a mighty power. Hitherto the pettiest princelings of Europe had refused to marry their daughters to a Muscovite; only two years earlier a request from the Tsar to the House of Brunswick-Wolfenbüttel for a consort for the heir to the throne, Alexei, had been rejected. Now the hands and hearts of Western princes and of their princesses were for the taking. And Peter made full use of it. His nieces, Catharine and Anna, became the Duchesses of Mecklenburg and of Courland. His own daughters, Anna and Elizabeth, were married to the brothers Karl Friedrich and Karl August of Holstein-Gottorp, and thus the Tsars of Russia were soon almost pure Germans by blood. The courts of the German princes became, as Baron vom Stein sarcastically put it, 'breeding establishments for the Russian Imperial family'.

Added to the amazed chorus, as after 1917, were the voices of the 'great figures of culture'. Poltava was the only battle which was constructive rather than destructive, enthused Voltaire, for the continent of Europe had thereby more than doubled its population.

More even than before, Peter set out after Poltava to give Russia a European aspect, to dress the Russians in European clothes—if necessary, enforcing this by law—and to teach them those Western customs which were still so strange to them.

When, at the beginning of the eighteenth century, Russians had first appeared abroad clothed in the French manner and clean-shaven—on Peter's orders—instead of in *kaftans* and fur caps, it had caused a minor sensation. Lord Paget, the British Ambassador to the Sublime Porte, had reported back to London, in July, 1701: 'The Muscovite Ambassador and his retinue have appeared here so different from what they always formerly were that yᵉ Turks cannot tell what to make of them. They are all coutred in French habit, with an abundance of gold and silver lace, long peruques and, which the Turks most wonder at, without beards. Last Sunday being at mass in Adrianople, yᵉ Ambassador and all his company did not only keep all their hats off during yᵉ whole ceremony but at yᵉ elevation, himself all of them pulled off their periwigs. It was much taken notice of and thought an unusual act of devotion.'

These were initial teething troubles, tentative beginnings. Ten years after Poltava the compulsory transformation of the Russians into Europeans was in full swing.

After his travels in the West, Peter had fully accepted the truth of a memorandum which a Croat, Yury Krishanich, a Pan-Slav enthusiast, had sent to Moscow during the second half of the seventeenth century, recommending drastic reforms. 'Foreigners are astonished by our outward appearance. The King of Denmark has said: "If Russian ambassadors should come here again, I shall put them in a pig-sty, for wherever they have lived is always left in so filthy a condition that no one else can sleep there." In another country, the news-sheet reported of our embassy staff: "When the envoys enter a shop to make a purchase, no one will set foot in it for an hour because of the stink. In one town they left a trail of filth behind them at the Golden Ox Inn." '

This memorandum was no exaggeration, as we can learn from many similar contemporary reports. The Governor of Leghorn, Antonio Serriscori, wrote to the Grand Duke of Tuscany at Florence, concerning the sojourn

Beard receipt tokens of 1705 and 1725. Russians who kept their beards had to pay beard tax.

Contemporary cartoon of Peter I's order to cut off beards.

of the Russian ambassador Chomdanov and his entourage: 'They are filthy; they sleep in their clothes on the floor ... At table they do not hesitate to pluck bits of food from their mouths and replace them in the dish ... They use neither spoons nor forks, and eat everything with their fingers. It is quite amusing to notice that when one of our people is eating with them, they try to emulate him, and to use their forks. They take a piece of food out of the dish with their fingers, stick it on the fork, and then put the fork to their mouths ... The gentlemen are not clean enough for one to risk putting them in a coach.'

In Moscow and St Petersburg foreign master tailors, and dancing-masters from France now abounded, and were called *maîtres de plaisir*. Swedish officers, prisoners of war, had persuaded Peter to introduce Western-style dancing and etiquette at his court. The police were instructed to see to it that all officials took lessons in etiquette, and that their ladies appeared at all formal assemblies—disobedience being severely punished. Once a week noblemen and courtiers had to dress in foreign, fashionable clothes—the women's very *décolleté*—and were personally inspected by the Tsar. 'Anybody contravening the rules of etiquette was compelled to down a large quantity of strong spirits out of a goblet bearing the imperial eagle' (Gitermann).

Compulsory new fashions and the adoption of foreign manners could not change the people basically. However, the desired object had been achieved. Europe began slowly to lose its mistrust and aversion for those whom it had so long regarded as weird and barbaric Muscovites. Suddenly these people were wearing the latest fashions, with combed wigs—at any rate, the upper classes. On their backs were Hungarian, Saxon or French coats, their hats and shoes were German, and their powdered wigs came from Paris. Similarly, the Soviet Russians of today travel abroad in English shirts, silver-grey ties and 'Anthony Eden' hats.

The cultural historian, Victor Hehn, a native of Dorpat, chief librarian of the Imperial Library in St Petersburg and thus a Russian government official, says: 'He who knows St Petersburg realizes once and for all that Russian culture is a whitewash designed to hide a chaos of conflicting interests and is deliberately applied to impress European critics. All this bowing and scraping and smiling and posturing is done solely for the benefit of the European public. As soon as the official comedy is over, the Russians live their own lives and continue their own activities exactly as before. . . . The preconditions of a humanistic, European education are lacking, and because of this lack all local culture appears in this form of a masquerade put on in St Petersburg.'

But the masquerade succeeded to an astonishing degree, thanks to the phenomenal imitative talent inborn in the Russians and which shrewd foreigners have always observed. 'In every country in the world one finds a greater or lesser degree of original talent,' comments Edward Daniel Clarke in his *Journey through Russia and Tartary, 1800–1801*, 'but to find a talent for imitation one has to go to Russia. Imitation is the highest pinnacle of Russian culture and the foundation of all their achievements.' When unobserved, the European veneer is dropped—'for it is not merely the outward manifestations of civilization, but its very essence that are appropriated and exhibited solely when foreign observers are present or when the knout is to hand.'

During the erection of this façade, and the compulsory instruction of the Russians in European customs, etiquette and fashions, the Tsar never for a moment lost sight of the objective which for him was the most important of all—the expansion of his empire.

The great Leibniz, with whom he had been in correspondence since his first trip abroad, provided him with an abundance of guiding principles. In his letters Leibniz outlined a great project for the founding of educational institutions through which all Russia could benefit from European science and culture.

On the occasion of his first meeting with the Tsar, at Torgau in 1711, Leibniz persuaded him to found an academy. Leibniz was given a position at the Imperial court, and entrusted with this task.

Reading the Leibniz letters today, it is impossible not to feel depressed. For we can see how tragic have been the consequences of the great philosopher's excellent intentions. His general suggestions, all of which were quickly accepted by the Russians, only served to build that massive strength which threatens Europe today.

The town of Novgorod which was destroyed by Ivan IV, after its reconstruction in the 18th century.

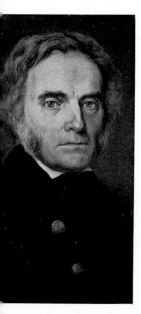

Novgorod flourished under Catherine II's governor Jacob Johann von Sievers.

Senate and Synod, built from the plans of Carlo Rossi, the great architect of St Petersburg in the 19th century.

Russian baggage waggons at the Leipzig Fair in 1835.

The Bolshoi Theatre, Moscow, erected by the "president of the reconstruction committee", Giuseppe Bove, under Alexander I.

Leibniz and the Tsar also planned an accurate geographical survey of the Russian empire, its people and its languages. In a memorandum dated 23rd September 1712, Leibniz advised that facts concerning the soil, flora and fauna of the vast empire be collected by organized 'Observatories', this research project to be tied in with the search for raw materials that could be mined and also with the encouragement of commerce and manufacture. His ideas leaped far into the future. Although many of his specific suggestions could not be put into practice, he showed the way, and Peter was enthusiastic. He sent Russians to Asia to learn oriental languages, and he appointed a Dane, Vitus Bering, to organize exploration and research in the Arctic and along the coast of Siberia.

For the people themselves, however, nothing was done. Peter was quite uninterested in raising their standard of living. The Russian masses remained —as they remain today—only a means to political ends. The peasants were robbed of their last rights to freedom. The so-called 'free' peasants were compelled, on penalty of death, to register either with a landowner or with a parish, who had to pay poll-tax for them. The lot of the serfs deteriorated, for Peter frequently ordered that they be sold or 'assigned' to his new factories and mines.

The upper classes, that is to say, the nobility and the negligibly small bourgeoisie, had to obey every decree of the Tsar, and thus the great mass of the population lost their last individual rights.

The Tsar was also busy in the field of entertainment. Among the amenities lifted from Europe was the theatre. Peter, like his father before him, brought drama teachers to the country. In 1701 he sent a Hungarian, Splavsky, to Western Europe to engage German actors. A company under Director Künst arrived. The Tsar built an enormous theatre in the Red Square. *Alexander and Darius* was often performed, a play that delighted Peter since it recalled his own struggle against Charles XII. Also in the repertoire were the folk drama, *Dr Faustus*, and *Le Malade Imaginaire* by Molière. The Muscovites were delighted, and Director Künst was ordered by the Tsar to start a dramatic school. Russians too must learn this Western art.

Since no students applied for training, the Tsar simply ordered that the students at the new College of Navigation and Higher Mathematics should be taught how to act.

The career of Director Künst came to a sudden end after only two years. Künst had invited the Tsar, the court and the people to a surprise performance, the title of the play being kept secret. When the curtain rose the expectant Muscovites faced an empty stage. A single notice replaced the backcloth: 'Today is April the 1st.' The Tsar was so annoyed that Künst had to flee for his life. His place was soon taken, however, by Otto Fürst and another German company.

Peter undertook a second journey to Western Europe. This time it was France which attracted him. Accompanied by an escort of fifty-seven persons, the Tsar landed at Dunkirk on 21st April 1717. He was more interested in the arsenal than in an exchange of courtesies, and insisted on visiting it, as well as the citadel, at once. His method of spying, for which he was now famous, had remained unchanged. On this occasion, too, he measured the sluices and harbour installations with his yard-stick.

Paris had sent splendid coaches for him, but Peter refused to use them. He wished to travel without any official escort—and thus to be free to study everything without let or hindrance. What no one in Russia was ever permitted to do the Tsar regarded as his unquestionable right.

The magnificent coaches evoked Peter's displeasure, among other reasons because they were difficult to see out of, and he was determined to have a good look at everybody and everything. The French officials finally put a phaeton at his disposal, a light, two-wheeled vehicle consisting of very little more than a coachman's box. It pleased the Tsar, and in order that he might see farther and even better, he had the driver's seat strapped on to the backs of the horses. Bumping along on this remarkable perch, an object of curiosity to all, he set off for Paris. Only when passing through a town or a village would Peter transfer to one of the official coaches.

Peter brusquely cancelled all the arrangements that the French had made. The Russian monarch was quite uninterested in ceremonial receptions. He wished to gain information for Russia.

After the arsenal, it was the magnificent Gobelins in the Royal Factory, founded by Colbert in 1667, which aroused the Tsar's greatest admiration while in Paris. He had drawings of the patterns made, and took two Gobelins home with him as a gift—as an example and an encouragement to his Russians. At the Mint he tested the machines, and he watched a surgeon perform an eye operation. But he spent most time in the factories. He sought out workers in the St Antoine district and questioned them about their working hours and wages. He rummaged about in shops, examining every-thing, cloth and hats and pocket-knives. Versailles impressed him deeply. He decided he must build a palace exactly like it in St Petersburg. He studied in detail the hydraulic engine at Marly with its fourteen water-wheels each thirty-five feet in diameter, and its two hundred and twenty-one pumps. André Lenôtre's wonderful landscape gardening also appealed to him.

The Tsar returned to St Petersburg after a visit abroad of twenty months, his luggage crammed with plans, drawings, models and books filled with rapidly scribbled notes, his head a-whirl with all the suggestions and ideas he had picked up in Europe which he planned to use in Russia. During this second journey it is astonishing how eager the West was to open all doors to the visitor. Factories and arsenals were shown to him, as indeed was every-thing that he wanted to see. He was allowed to pry and poke about as he wished. Meanwhile Russia denied free entry and transit to travellers, kept the Ural trade routes between the Far East and the West closed—and still does!

There was once a famous road—the Golden Road from the banks of the Hwang-Ho to Bactria and Samarkand—along which a flourishing exchange of trade took place between China in the east and Rome in the west. There were excellent roads in the Mongol empire under the successors of the mighty Genghis Khan. A very fast mail service, based on hundreds of relay stations, ran from Peking to the Volga and the Don. Merchants and priests, no matter what their nationality or faith, could then travel freely across the endless plains on the northern side of the Central Asian mountains. Embassies wended their way westwards and eastwards. Two trans-continental caravan routes, one through the empire of the Golden Horde, the other across Turkestan and Persia, served for the transportation of goods from China as far as the Venetian and Genoese ports on the Black Sea coast.

A book entitled *Mercantile Practice*, written about 1340 by Francesco Balducci Pegolotti, provided an excellent traveller's guide to China. Tana, then a Genoese port on the Sea of Azov located exactly where Azov which Peter I besieged in 1696 later stood, was the starting-point for a flourishing trade with Tartary, and Pegolotti assures us that 'the road from Tana to Cathay [i.e. China] is absolutely safe, both by night and by day, according to the merchants who use it'.

As soon as the Mongol empire collapsed and Russian Cossacks occupied the area, the iron curtain came down. From the onset of Russian rule the caravan routes across the Urals were cut and the thriving trade link between Europe and the Far East broken. On the rare occasions when Europeans were allowed into these parts at all it was solely to carry out geographical surveys, to study the flora and fauna, and above all to prospect for materials.

Even the modern Peter, who had travelled freely across Western Europe from Dorpat to Amsterdam, measuring fortress walls, and had been allowed to examine everything that interested him, refused to let Europeans travel across his country. His predecessors had done the same.

In 1635 a Russian ambassador visited Peking. This induced a Jesuit priest, Ferdinand Verbiest, a missionary in China, to try to reopen the Ural route linking Europe to China via Siberia. Fathers Louis Barnabé and Philippe Avril were chosen for the task.

They went from Rome through the Levant and Persia and as far as Astrakhan without incident; Astrakhan was then the 'Muscovite capital of Great Tartary'. As soon as they set foot on Russian soil endless difficulties began. After being held up for four months they at last received permission to travel to Moscow. Here they were delayed again on all sorts of pretexts and subjected to protracted interrogation. Month after month passed. Finally the two priests received notice from one of the Tsar's officials that they were to 'leave Russian territory immediately, and to go back to where they came from without further delay'.

Meanwhile Father Verbiest, in his reports from Peking, had referred repeatedly to the great advantages of the overland route from Europe to China. A further attempt to have it reopened was therefore made. Father Phillipe Maria Grimaldi, whom the Chinese Emperor Kang-hsi had appointed his personal envoy in Rome and Moscow, in 1686, was the next man to try to win the Tsar's permission to travel through Siberia to China. This Italian priest had formed a friendship with Leibniz in Europe, but even the recommendation of the German professor, to whom the Tsar owed so much, was of no avail. The Tsar refused to permit travel to China.

When Tsar Peter I died, on 28th January 1725, Russia's credit balance contained the following items:

1. 48 ships of the line, 787 galleys, 28,000 seamen, 25 shipyards.
2. 14 European and 17 Russian generals.
3. An army, trained and equipped on Western lines, of 210,000 men—not including 100,000 Cossacks—with an arsenal of 16,000 guns. (The army and navy swallowed up two-thirds of the national revenue.)
4. St Petersburg with 75,000 inhabitants, and a port visited by 240 ships per annum.
5. The number of factories and installations working metal had risen from 100 to 233.
6. Russia had become the leading iron-producing country in the world.

One item is missing from these statistics, an essential figure when dealing with Russian affairs, and that is an estimate of the number—running into thousands upon thousands—of foreign assistants, advisers, instructors and builders.

The great equestrian statue of Peter I, executed by the French sculptor Falconet, towers over its enormous stone base, brought from Finland. It stands in the Admiralty Square at St Petersburg, now called Leningrad. The Soviet Russians have not moved it. This Tsar, together with the third Ivan and Ivan IV, the Terrible, is recognized as one of the great builders of his country. And rightly so. He paved the road, as almost no other ruler has done, along which the Red Kremlin marches today.

According to Professors Ernest Lavisse and Alfred Rambaud, writing in 1895: 'The indomitable will of one man was sufficient to accelerate a trend which the Tsars Ivan, Boris Godunov, Demetrius, the men who ruled as regents for Alexei, and even the Tsarina Sophia, had initiated, and to revolutionize it. With his passion for work and his indomitable spirit, he

imported the West *en bloc* into ancient Muscovy. His creations all had a
Dutch, German, Swedish, or, briefly, a foreign look. Even when the im-
ported objects were "German", he still dreamed of a Russian version. . . .
Basically the old despotism had changed in form, but not in substance.
Russia remained as it had been before his reforms, with its customs and
ways of thinking inherited from the Byzantine and Mongol civilizations.
This Eastern State, with its "German façade", seemed to Europe a monstrous
and disturbing enigma.'

And at the same time Professor Otto Kaemmel wrote: 'What he achieved
has remained. Using the external aids of European culture he re-shaped his
semi-Asiatic people into a mighty power, but he was unable to change the
fundamentally oriental character of the Russians. The conflict between
European training and the nature of Old Russia has been the decisive factor
throughout Russian history, and this profound contrast between Western
culture and the traditional character of Russia still exists. While to the
south-east the Orient declined steadily after the fall of the Ottoman Empire,
in the north-east it was drawn inextricably into Europe's affairs and appeared
ever more of a menace, in that it combined the colossal material wealth
and unexploited potentialities of a young country with the achievement of
European technology. . . .

'Without the large numbers of foreigners, mostly Protestants, whom
Peter imported from Germany, France, Holland and England—among
them the Swedish prisoners-of-war from Poltava—the Tsar would not
have been able to carry out his plans. His new Russian state was not so much
Russian as Western, a German-Dutch creation, made by a colony of
Westerners working under a western-educated Russian ruler.'

6   An Academy of Foreigners

THE VIEW FROM the Strelka, an escarpment on the river bank, flanked by red-granite pillars, where the waters of the Great and Little Nevas divide, is one of the finest in all St Petersburg. Across the river on the left the Peter and Paul Fortress soars upwards, while on the right at the water's edge stands a row of palaces. Behind them are silhouetted the Admiralty's golden spire and the dome of the great Isaac Cathedral. Only a few yards away from this magnificent vantage point is a three-storied palace with a round tower, built for the Tsarina Praskovya Feodorovna, wife of Peter's half-brother, Ivan V.

Towards the end of 1725 an inscription *Imperatorskaya Akademiya Nauk* ('Imperial Academy of Sciences') was placed above the main entrance of that building. Nearly a year after the death of her husband Peter I, the recently crowned Tsarina, Catherine I, carried out one of his last orders. On 27th December the Imperial Russian Academy came into existence.

Peter did not live to open the Academy which he had planned as his crowning achievement, and through which he had hoped to catch up with Europe not only in the military and technical fields, but also in those of the sciences and the arts. After the death of Leibniz in 1716, another German philosopher, Christian Wolff, became adviser to the Tsar; since his visit to Paris, he had been even more enthusiastic about this project than before.

The Academy of Sciences, St Petersburg, founded in 1725 by European scientists under the stimulus of Leibniz. The old building on the right is the palace of the Tsarina Praskovya. The new building was built by the Italian architect Giacomo Quarenghi.

The invitation card to a public meeting of the Academy of Sciences, designed by the Director of the Art Department, Jacob von Stählin.

Peter's physician-in-ordinary, Dr Laurentius Blumentrost, who was later himself President of the Academy, had contacted Wolff and persuaded him to collaborate with the Tsar. In 1724 Peter had ordered that preparations for the establishment of the Academy be made at once. But at that time—over five hundred years after the founding of Europe's first universities—no native scholars were available, and once again foreigners had to be called in. Already a number of European scholars, whose co-operation was particularly valued, had received invitations. Then, early in 1725, Peter suddenly died.

All the members of the new Academy, whose work was to be of the greatest importance for the future of Russia, were foreigners. For apart from Mikhail Lomonossov, no eminent Russian scholar emerged until the beginning of the nineteenth century. 'The foundations of the ambitious Imperial Academy at St Petersburg,' wrote Jacob von Stählin of Memmingen, Director of its Arts Department after 1738, 'were laid almost entirely by the Swabians and the Swiss.'

Who now recalls the names of these Europeans, who almost monopolized the Imperial Academy throughout the eighteenth century, and whose principal language was German? Yet there were many famous scholars among them.

They included two Swiss members of the Bernoulli family of mathematicians, the brothers Daniel and Nikolaus Bernoulli, and their famous compatriot, the physician and mathematician Leonhard Euler, the French astronomer and cartographer, Joseph Nicolas Delisle, the physicist Georg Wilhelm Richmann, a Baltic German from Pernau, well known for his principles of physics, and the Dutch anatomist and physiologist A. Kaan-Boerhaave. Among the German members were the astronomer A. N. Grischow, who had gained fame by his lunar research, and his colleague, G. M. Lowitz, who made a series of important observations of the planet Venus from the Gurev fortress in the Urals; there were also the professor of mechanics and physics, L. E. Zeyher, and the mathematician and physicist Theodor Aepinus, whose theories of electricity and magnetism caused a sensation in their time. Other members of the Academy were Josef Gottlieb Kölreuter from Sulz, whose researches into the fertilization and cross-breeding of plants made him one of the great botanists, and the ethnologist and mineralogist, I. G. Georgi. It is to him that Russia owes an early work on the physical, geographical and botanical aspects of that country.

Gerhard Friedrich Müller, who later became the Russian 'Miller', published reports on the Academy's activities from 1727 (the *Commentarii Academiae Scientiarum Imperialis Petropolitanae*), and five years later he produced his *Comprehensive History of Russia*, published simultaneously in German and in Russian. This was followed by his *History of Siberia*, the fruit of ten years' research. On Müller's initiative the first Russian scientific and literary periodical was produced, in 1755. In 1761 he induced the Empress Elizabeth to invite the Göttingen professor, August Ludwig Schlözer, to St Petersburg. Schlözer was to become the pioneer of true historical writing in Russia.

There are famous botanical collections in St Petersburg. These also date from this period of fruitful activity on the part of foreign scholars. About fifty thousand plants, particularly Siberian species, were collected and classified, the result of years of research by the German naturalists, Johann Georg Gmelin, Georg Wilhelm Steller and Peter Simon Pallas.

To name only a few of their works, Pallas, a Berliner, who carried out extensive ethnological and natural history research all over Russia, Siberia and Mongolia, wrote: *Flora Rossica* (Russian Plants), *Zoographica Rossiae Asiaticae* and *Travels through the Various Provinces of the Russian Empire*. Georg Gmelin from Tübingen lived in the East from 1727 to 1747, and wrote his *Flora Sibirica*. His nephew, Samuel Gottlieb Gmelin, explorer and botanist, went to Russia in 1768, and died in 1774 as a prisoner of the Khan of Tartary down in the Caucasus. Georg Wilhelm Steller, from Windsheim in Franconia, also died early, worn out by hard work and primitive living conditions. He had gone to Russia in 1737, was a member of Bering's expedition to the north-west coast of America in 1741-2, discovered on Bering Island the giant Steller's sea-cow (*Hydrodamalis Stelleri*), named after him and soon to be exterminated. He died in 1746, at the early age of thirty-seven, in Siberia. After his death his books, *De bestiis marinis, Description of the Kamchatka District* and *The Diary of a Sea-Voyage . . . to the West Coast of America*, were published.

The learned works of Leonhard Euler, who worked in St Petersburg from 1727 to 1741 and from 1766 to 1783, constitute a small library on their own. He made contributions of great distinction to mathematics, physics and astronomy. His *Complete Guide to Algebra* is printed and read today. Euler's collected works are in the process of being reprinted by the Swiss Natural History Research Association; there will be eighty volumes containing over ten thousand essays.

The giant sea cow (A) and seals, discovered by G. W. Steller on Bering Island. Drawing by Sven Waxell made on Bering Island in 1741.

Title page of one of the works of the scientist Steller, who went to Alaska with Bering.

Furthermore, the Academy in its early days organized extensive exploration and research in the Arctic regions, a most important contribution so far as Russia was concerned. The Academy mounted, indeed, the greatest expedition of them all, and in 1725 a Dane, Vitus Bering, captain in the Russian Navy, set out on his exceptionally daring voyage of discovery. This had been ordered by Peter I, in accordance with a suggestion repeatedly made to him by Leibniz. It was to provide the answer to a question which had much preoccupied the Russians: was Asia joined to America? If an ancient tradition did not lie, there ought, somewhere in the distant north-east, to be a channel, the legendary Anian Straits.

With a hand-picked company, Vitus Bering set off on this dangerous voyage into the unknown, on sledges at first across all Siberia, a distance of some six thousand miles, until they reached Kamchatka on the Pacific coast. Then and there he put the craftsmen and shipbuilders whom he had brought with him to building a ship. It was the *St Gabriel*, and in her Bering circumnavigated the whole of the East Cape of Asia and thus discovered the straits which bear his name—the Bering Straits.

On his return from this enormous journey, Bering reported his fascinating discoveries to the members of the Academy. The intrepid Dane's expedition was followed by an organized research programme that took many years and led to the complete mapping of the whole Siberian coastline from the

North-East passage westwards. The learned members of the Academy of Science carefully prepared an itinerary for this 'Great Northern Expedition'.

In 1734 the expedition set off. The Academy had nominated Bering to command it. A staff of scientists and their assistants went with him, and these were to carry out subsidiary exploration. Long lines of sledges, loaded with enough essential supplies to last for years, and tools, and crates filled with the most up-to-date European survey equipment, set off from St Petersburg.

Bering set about his colossal task systematically. He divided the Siberian coast, over twenty-five thousand miles long and stretching from the White Sea to the Sea of Japan, into sectors. The mastering of this colossal stretch of unknown territory was done simultaneously from five different camps or headquarters.

Commodore Bering had learned by experience that in coastal exploration it is advisable to build the ships on the spot. At first the native *kotchas* were used as models—open boats forty feet long, with a twelve-foot beam and drawing eight feet of water. Only later did the expedition change to sixty-foot ships with covered decks. It is astonishing what unforeseen difficulties were overcome in such primitive vessels.

Bering decided that he would personally take charge in the most easterly sector, the Sea of Okhotsk and the Pacific. Accompanied by Steller, he set off from Kamchatka in the *Svyatoy Pyotr* (St Peter) into the unknown. He discovered the Aleutian Islands. In 1741 Bering and Steller set foot for the first time on another continent when they landed in Alaska. It was unfortunately not granted to the brave Dane himself to tell of this discovery in St Petersburg. On the return voyage from Alaska Vitus Bering died of scurvy. His companions buried him on a small island off Kamchatka, which still bears his name—Bering Island.

It was not until our own century that the world learned the details of the scope and importance of the work he did for Russia.

In 1935 an apology by the leader of the 'Great Northern Expedition' was discovered in the archives of the Petersburg Academy. Bering had written it on 18th April 1740, a year before his death. He had been blamed by the Russians for the fact that 'the expedition took far too long'. In fact, to use the contemporary phrase, he was being accused of sabotage.

Point by point the explorer refutes the accusation, which is itself unfortunately lost. In detail he describes the voyages and the tasks completed during his geographical survey. He gives exact accounts of the silver and iron-ore deposits in Siberia discovered by the expedition, refers to the building of an ironworks in remote Okhotsk, and speaks of the immigration of Russians and the transfer of the local population to Okhotsk with the object of cultivating the land and of breeding cattle. His report also mentioned that he had started the first regular postal service between St Petersburg and the remote villages lost in the wastes of Siberia.

Of the many sober facts contained in Bering's reply to the accusation of sabotage, perhaps the most striking is the incredible number and variety of the tasks undertaken by Bering and his associates on Russia's behalf. As a result of the nine years of determined exploration and research, involving many sacrifices, carried out by the 'Great Northern Expedition', the Petersburg Academy was able to establish for the first time the exact shape of the Siberian coastline. An overall map was drawn and nineteen sectional maps, covering the whole empire. The Russians insisted that this atlas should be classified 'secret', as were all the reports of the great scientific research done in surveying the equivalent of a continent. The maps only reached the West thanks to a Frenchman, Joseph Nicolas Delisle, who worked on the atlas in the Petersburg Academy and, strictly against orders, sent copies to Paris. Of the details behind this vast research project Europe knew nothing. A few superficial reports on the discoveries, and observations of animal and plant life, were published, but nothing more.

Why all this secrecy? All the Western Europeans involved, from Vitus Bering down to the most humble draftsman, were under oath to the Russians and were sworn to the strictest secrecy. A specimen of such conditions of employment reached the West quite early.

In the *Instructions* which an Englishman, Joseph Billings, received as leader of an expedition in 1785, under Catherine II, paragraph 1 reads: '. . . You must ensure that the promise you have made under oath to guard the secrets of the undertaking entrusted to you be not broken, and that you do not violate the Ukase of 1724, concerning secret matters. Under no circumstances will you give any information to anyone in any form concerning the plans and execution of your expedition.' Peter the Great had issued this Ukase 'concerning secret matters' the year before the founding of the Academy and Vitus Bering's first expedition.

Paragraph 25 of these same instructions issued by Catherine II reads:

'Before the end of your main expedition it is your duty to collect, under oath, all log-books or diaries or plans or drawings kept or drawn by members of the expedition during the voyage. These you will keep, under seal, until your return to St Petersburg, where you will hand them in, complete, together with any similar documents of your own. Such diaries etc. will only be returned, on the orders of Her Imperial Majesty, when they are no longer required. The officers, sailors, soldiers and Cossacks taking part in the expedition are forbidden to communicate, either verbally or in writing, any information of any kind concerning discoveries made or events which occurred during your enterprise.'

Such an order had also silenced the explorers and scientists who took part in the 'Great Northern Expedition'. A Russian curtain of silence was rung down upon the great scientific discoveries of these Europeans; even today the world does not know all their names.

An admission of this slipped past a Soviet censor in 1954, when it was written of the 'Great Northern Expedition': 'The information acquired in the course of this expedition was kept secret for many years.' Thus M. Chernenko of the Arctic Institute of the USSR: 'and was . . . not generally known until 1812.' This secrecy, incidentally, applied both inside and outside Russia.

The silence that concealed the results achieved by the 'Great Northern Expedition' inaugurated a policy that has been followed by the Russians ever since, a policy of secrecy in all scientific matters, 'an unwillingness on the part of the USSR to co-operate sincerely and honestly' with other nations—as Constantin Krypton, who worked in Soviet Russia for many years, wrote in his book *The Northern Sea Route* in 1953.

Just as large numbers of machines bought abroad bear a Russian trade-mark, so the Soviets have missed no opportunity of passing off the scientific achievements of Western Europeans as their own. They have produced long lists of hitherto unknown Russians as 'the great scientific heroes' of Russian expeditions.

'Geography and natural history,' an official textbook used in the High Schools of the USSR informs us, 'made great strides in Russia in the eighteenth century, and enriched immeasurably the store of knowledge throughout all the world. The expeditions of Bering and Chirikov, and the geographical researches of Chelyuskin, Pronchishchev, Chichagov, Krasheninnikov, of Laptev, Pallas, Gmelin, Lepyochin, Osertskovski, Rychkov and many others filled what had hitherto been large white spaces on the maps of Europe and Asia with concrete facts. They not only extended man's knowledge of places, people, beasts and the mineral treasures hidden beneath the earth's surface, but also exploded a vast number of superstitions, medieval myths and legends.'

Who are these nine Russians raised to an eminence equal to that of Bering, Gmelin and Pallas? Alexei Ilyich Chirikov commanded the second ship of the expedition, the *Svyatoy Pavel* (St Paul). After a voyage of several weeks' duration through snow, ice and sleet, in which contact was lost with Bering's ship *Svyatoy Pyotr* (St Peter), he had to return to Kamchatka without having set foot on American soil, and having lost most of his crew off the coast of Alaska.

On board Bering's ship, the *St Peter*, was a cadet with the typically Dutch name of Sind, who later—1764–68—led a secret Russian expedition to Alaskan waters in the galley *Svyataya Ekaterina*.

The important astronomical observations made during the Bering expedition were the work of a Frenchman, Louis Delisle de la Croyère. A Swedish naval lieutenant, Sven Waxell, who also gets no mention, took part in the voyage of the *St Paul*. His book, entitled *Vitus Bering's Second Kamchatka Expedition*, was not published, incidentally, until 1940.

The signature of Vitus Bering, the Danish leader of the 'Great Northern Expedition' and of the officers under his command of the vessels St Peter and St Paul, May 1741. The second signature is that of Chirikov, and the third of the Swede Sven Waxell.

There can be no objection to the mention of Captain Chirikov, who held an important command in the expedition. But why no mention of the other three ship's captains who happened to be Westerners, the Englishmen Walton and Shelting, and the German Captain Spanberg? In 1738 and 1739 they set sail with three ships from the expedition's base at Petropavlovsk, surveyed all the Kurile Islands, from Kamchatka as far as Japan in a great arc that encloses the Sea of Okhotsk, and plotted their exact position on new charts.

Of the other Russians mentioned, certain facts are now known. They were naval officers, and as the Russian, G. A. Zarychev, wrote in 1802: 'they carried out a partial survey of the Polar Sea at certain points'. Further, 'in 1735, Lieutenant Pronchishchev sailed westwards from the mouth of the Lena, while Lieutenant Dmitri Laptev sailed eastwards'. The navigator, Chelyuskin, after whom the northernmost point of Asia was named, because he was the first to set foot on it, was one of these 'naval officers who . . . surveyed part of the Polar Sea coast'. They contributed to the Academy's extensive research project as leaders of minor expeditions or as surveyors. The knowledge required for such work was taught to the Russians by Englishmen at the College of Navigation and Higher Mathematics in Moscow, where the principal was a Scotsman, James Bruce, or at the Naval Academy, directed by a Frenchman, St Hilaire. None of these naval officers, who acted as technical assistants, made any contribution to science worthy of mention, or if they did, their discoveries have been successfully concealed from the non-Russian world ever since.

A mania for secrecy, a ban on the publication of scientific papers, accusations of 'sabotage' against the great Vitus Bering—such was the typically Russian atmosphere into which science and research were born in Russia. The story was the same inside the Academy in St Petersburg as on the expeditions. One historically authenticated incident illustrates this best of all.

In the year 1741 Leonhard Euler, the famous mathematician, left the St Petersburg Academy, of which he had been a member for twelve years, and went to the Prussian Academy in Berlin, where the young King Frederick II was collecting the best brains in Europe. At a court reception, the Queen Mother, Sophia Dorothea, drew the great scholar into conversation, and commented on the fact that Euler's speech was very terse and monosyllabic. 'Madame,' replied Euler, 'do not forget that I have just come from a country where any man who speaks freely and openly is liable to be hanged.'

In the same year that Euler left Russia, a Russian scholar much in vogue in the Soviet Union today arrived at the St Petersburg Academy—Mikhail Vassilyevich Lomonossov. Lomonossov's name has been given to the mammoth building that is Moscow University—'the tallest in the world'— and students in the USSR are told of him: 'It can truthfully be said that among the more important representatives of European science in the eighteenth century . . . the encyclopaedic, learned and versatile innovator Lomonossov occupied an outstanding and honoured place,' and that 'for a true representative of Russian culture, such as the peasant's son Lomonossov, the overtaking of European progress was not a mere question of imitation, but a means of enriching and independently advancing science, literature and the arts, so that these might be raised to a level higher than that prevailing in the West.' According to the latest official textbook, compiled by a group of fourteen professors: 'At that time it is certain that both students and teachers in all our educational establishments' regarded 'Lomonossov as the defender of Russian science against the predominance of insignificant foreigners in the Petersburg Academy, and as a fighter for international science in its progressive aspects.'

A foreign reader, glancing through the pages of this Soviet textbook, would recall quite different names in connection with eighteenth-century science. He would think of Newton and Leibniz, Euler and Linné. Who was this Lomonossov, who fought so boldly 'against the predominance of insignificant foreigners'?

The alleged 'peasant's son', born in 1711, was in fact the talented offspring of an exceptionally able and wealthy wholesale merchant in a village near Archangel. His father, Vassily Lomonossov, as the English Professor C. L. Boltz has established (*Discovery*, August 1951, p. 251), cannot correctly be portrayed as a serf, worn down by poverty, living and dying in old, threadbare clothes, as the Soviets like to pretend. He was a shrewd merchant who traded in salt-water fish with the Scandinavian countries and with Moscow, the owner of a two-masted ship, in which he used to sail to the Arctic Circle, occasionally accompanied by his son. He was the leading citizen in his village on an island in the White Sea. Lomonossov's father not only dealt in fish, but also in timber and other raw materials. When there was a fire in his home town, he contributed a considerable sum of money towards the rebuilding, which included the construction of a new stone church.

Boltz says: 'This man was himself illiterate and apparently had no sympathy with education. But his son Michael was early able to consume all the books he could lay hands on. He took himself off defiantly when he was twenty, and proceeded to lie himself—he pretended that his father was a noble—into a school run by monks. He later planned to lie himself into the Church to gain further education, but this became unnecessary when the Academy of Science gave him his chance.'

So much for the true facts concerning the origins of the 'peasant's son'. They are unknown to the students at Lomonossov University.

In order to form a nucleus of Russian scientists, twenty Russian students were sent to study at the Academy. Among those chosen was Lomonossov. From 1734 he studied in St Petersburg at the government's expense, and as he proved himself to be extremely gifted, he was very soon sent to Germany —in 1736—with two other students, to 'learn all he could of science and technology'. He went first to Marburg, where he studied philosophy, mathematics, and the natural sciences. His name can still be seen in the yellowing pages of the university archives.

An inquiry has produced the following information:

'The Russian scholar Michael Lomonossov, with two other *Russi Petersburgenses*, Gustav Ulrich Raiser[!] and Demetrius Vinogradov, matriculated at Marburg in November 1736 (in the register his name appears as Michael Lomonosoff). According to a Senate record dated 15th October 1737, concerning the "quarrel of the Muscovite student Lomonosoff with Rosenthal", the former commuted a punishment of detention by paying a fine of three thalers on 24th October that year. At the Senate meeting, Professor Dr Wolf did not vote "because the Muscovite had been recommended to him". Unfortunately we have no further information concerning his time at Marburg.' We learn, however, from another source that he 'fled from Marburg because of his debts'.

Lomonossov then went to the Freiberg Academy in Saxony, where he studied mining and smelting. Lomonossov spent five years—ten full university terms—absorbing knowledge and technical training in German universities, and returned to St Petersburg in 1741. A year later he was the first Russian to be appointed to the teaching staff of the Academy. He lectured on rhetoric, poetry (he had written poems, both religious and secular on French classical lines, as well as a very important *Russian Grammar*), geography, physics, chemistry and mineralogy. Almost immediately he began to quarrel with, and jeer at, his former teachers, the German members of the Academy.

'For all his education and talents Lomonossov remained for some time a country lout, assertive and truculent on occasions, especially when he had taken too much vodka . . . There are reports of his indecent behaviour towards his superiors,' Professor Boltz tells us.

This situation remained unchanged until Lomonossov was restrained—not by detention as at Marburg, but by a severe reprimand.

However, he never got over his virulent dislike of the Germans, and he remained throughout his life an outspoken and aggressive nationalist. This accounts for his veneration by the Soviets.

Lomonossov, who had sworn 'to fight against the enemies of Russian science to the death', launched particularly vicious attacks upon the German academician Gottlieb Siegfried Baier, who had invented the 'Normannic' or 'Scandinavian' theory concerning the origins of the Russian state. Baier had first taught that Goths from Scandinavia gave the state of Kiev not only its dynasty, but also its name, 'Rus'. Lomonossov denied this and produced a 'Slavonic' theory; according to him the Kiev state was not a creation of Normannic foreigners but of the Polyani stock, who were also called 'Rus'.

Baier's theory, accepted by August Ludwig Schlözer and Gerhard Friedrich Müller, is acknowledged—with only slight modifications—by reputable Russian scholars today. Nikolai M. Karamzin, Mikhail P. Pogorodin, Sergei Mikhailovich Solovyov, Byelaev and Vassily O. Klyuchevsky have agreed with his 'Normannic' theory.

Lomonossov attacked the highly respected G. F. Müller. According to the Director of the Arts Department, Jacob von Stählin, who tried to have Lomonossov removed from the Academy, he 'passes decisive judgment on everything, even on subjects of which he knows nothing, such as history'.

Stählin also wrote in a letter:

'Do you wish this man to decry good work and praise to the skies things he scarcely understands? If so, well and good. If he were a decent man, he would not attack decent people. He is known for what he is and why should he be allowed to continue such foolishness? The only reason I can see is—fear.'

The account of a conversation at the funeral of Lomonossov, who died on the day after Easter 1765, shows the extent to which he must have terrorized his own countrymen. 'During the funeral the Russian poet (Alexander Vassilyevich) Sumarokov pointed to the body lying in its coffin and said: "There he lies, the blockhead. At least he can storm and rage no more." Stählin answered: "I shouldn't have advised you to say that while he was still alive!" Stählin had been reduced to such a state of terror during Lomonossov's lifetime that he had not dared open his mouth.'

In what did Lomonossov's great scientific achievements consist?

'I must do justice to Lomonossov, in that he had a great talent for elucidating physical and chemical phenomena,' commented the finest mind of the Academy, Leonhard Euler, who had returned to St Petersburg. His statement is valid today.

No one who has studied Lomonossov's writings can deny that he was a highly versatile scholar, and that his scientific theories were often very daring

Title page of 'Metallurgy' by
M. V. Lomonossov, published in
St Petersburg in 1763.

for his age. Even as a student in Germany, Lomonossov had once used the phrase 'physico-chemical', although 'physical chemistry', as an independent branch of science, first came into being towards the end of the nineteenth century. In 1747 he produced his *Remarks on the Causes of Heat and Cold* which contained a statement that caused his learned audience to shake their heads: 'Adequate cause for heat must be presumed to lie in movement, and as there is no movement without matter, it follows that the basic cause of heat must be found in the movement of certain matter.' This was only a theory, without foundation, without proof—at best, hypothetical. But he had clearly anticipated our modern concept—heat as a form of energy deriving from the movement of molecular particles. One year later, Lomonossov wrote in a letter to Euler, dated 5th July 1748: 'All natural changes happen in such a way that whatever is removed from one substance is added to another; therefore when matter diminishes in one place, it increases elsewhere.' This, surely, anticipates the law of the conservation of matter.

Lomonossov's was an advanced mind, full of daring concepts. Yet he remained unknown; his impact on the rest of the world was, and is, almost negligible, although the Petersburg Academy enjoyed a high reputation and took part in a lively interchange of ideas with the other academies and universities of Europe. Scientific progress in the West went on in ignorance of Lomonossov, and totally uninfluenced by him.

In 1947–48, when the Soviets suddenly began attributing all important inventions and discoveries to hitherto unknown Russians, and launching their hysterical propaganda on the theme 'Russia leads the world', Lomonossov's varied theses provided excellent source material. He became Russia's trump card. It has, however, been said that Western scientific progress owes him nothing whatsoever, and that his one major work was his *Russian Grammar* of 1755—a work which was evidently of great importance in Russia.

It is fitting that the new mammoth university on the Moscow River should bear his name, for Lomonossov was certainly Russia's prime scholar and university professor. But the first idea for such a university—contrary to the story put out by the Soviets—did not come from him. It was Voltaire who suggested the idea of creating a university to Count Ivan Ivanovich Shuvalov, with whom he was in correspondence. It was owing to the initiative of Shuvalov, who enthusiastically accepted Voltaire's suggestion, that Russia's first university opened its doors in 1755. A bust of Shuvalov now adorns the entrance hall of the old university.

In fact, Lomonossov's scientific achievements for Russia were nil. The Petersburg Academy, with its foreign professors, was and remained for many years the solid foundation on which modern Russian research was built. Another seventy-five years had to pass until, in 1800, a second Russian of scientific eminence appears there—the physicist, Vassily Vladimirovich Petrov, to whom the Russians attribute the discovery of electric light and its potentialities for industry and lighting.

The Academy remained a power-house of varied research in such fields as topography, ethnology, zoology and botany, in astronomy and geology, mineralogy and stratification.

There are few branches of the pure or applied sciences in which the West did not lay the first foundations. In the three-storied building opposite the great quay on the Neva was the workroom of the newly appointed court apothecary, a German by birth, Johann Tobias Lowitz. His duties consisted of expanding the herb gardens started by his compatriots and of producing medical drugs (the latest development in medicine) and he also made a number of improvements in chemical laboratory techniques.

A German forestry expert, Fokel, worked in Russia for over thirty years in the mid-eighteenth century. In fact, he devoted the work of a lifetime to that country of endless forests. Fokel even wrote his treatises on forestry in Russian.

Everywhere there were Westerners. Western Europeans were almost entirely responsible for the scientific and navigational calculations that permitted the later voyages of discovery undertaken in Catherine II's time.

In 1776–79 James Cook carried out his third journey around the world, which took him to the northern Pacific and the north-west coast of America. This also led to the charting of the southern part of the Bering Straits. Hearing of the Englishman's voyages of discovery, Russia hurriedly sent an

A crude copy (left) made by Lomonossov for his book 'Metallurgy' of the illustration of a water-driven 'chain pump' for draining galleries in the coal mines (right), from the classic work 'De re metallica' by Agricola (1556).

expedition to the area of 'the unknown American islands', lest she be left behind. The Russians knew who were the best experts for this. They engaged the services of an Englishman, Joseph Billings, who had accompanied his fellow-countryman, Cook, as cartographer, and thus knew at first hand the maritime regions in which the Russians were now so keenly interested.

Four years after Cook's tragic death in Hawaii (in 1779), Billings was resident in St Petersburg, in the service of Russia, and in 1785 he received the 'Admiralty Fleet Orders for Lieutenant Commander Joseph Billings, Leader of the Geographical and Astronomical Expedition to the north-eastern territory of Russia,' which included the security Ukase of the Tsarina Catherine already referred to. Billings's instructions were 'to survey the seas and coastal regions to the farthest easterly point of the Empire ... to plot the coast-line of the great Chukta Cape as far as the East Cape, and to chart the islands of the eastern Pacific as far as the American coast. Finally, and above all, to collate accurately all the information that has been acquired during our reign [Catherine II's] concerning the seas which lie between the mainland of Siberia and the coast of America.'

A German scientist, Dr Karl Merck, with his assistants, Karl Krebs, Daniel Hauss and John Main, accompanied Billings 'to observe and describe everything relating to the natural sciences'. The ships' doctors chosen for the expedition were the German staff surgeon Michael Robeck and the Italian Pietro Allegretti, with Anton Leiman as junior surgeon. Joseph Edwards, an Englishman, was ship's carpenter. We learn that another British member of the expedition, Captain Robert Hall, possessed an extensive knowledge of shipbuilding. Apart from these the list contains a Lieutenant Krestyan (Christian) Bering, whose date of birth was given as unknown—was he, perhaps, a grandson of Vitus Bering?—and a Russian naval officer, G. A. Zarychev. Another German, Martin Sauer, was Billings's secretary and assistant.

In 1785 Billings left St Petersburg, which he and his European research team were only to see again after nine long years of adventure and tragedy that had taken them across thousands of miles of icy wastes in eastern Siberia, and after dangerous voyages through the ice and snow between the Polar and the Bering Seas.

In the same year that the expedition set off, another foreign voyage of discovery was being organized. It had the same objective as the Russian one. The man responsible was an American, John Ledyard, well known to Billings, for he too had gone with Cook to the North Pacific, and had been imprisoned by the Russians in Siberia.

What had happened was that Thomas Jefferson had his eye on the west coast of North America. Jefferson was at that time the United States Ambassador in Paris. He there approached John Ledyard, because of his experience with Cook's third South Sea expedition, and spoke to him of his plan to open up trade between North America and East Asia across the Pacific. In order to do this it was essential that the United States should control the west coast of North America. Ledyard's immediate answer was that only an American should explore the American continent and its extremities. As he could not take the sea route, Ledyard decided to travel across Russia to Kamchatka and thence to the American Pacific with the ultimate intention of crossing the American continent from west to east. Jefferson was confident of obtaining permission for him to cross Siberia. The young American Republic had recently informed the Empress that they would be 'proud to number the wise and noble Princess among their friends, and to assign her a place among those great figures of the past and the present, who were interested in furthering the happiness of mankind and in opposing all tyrants in their mischievous ways.'

Catherine refused to grant Jefferson's request. When had any foreigner been permitted to travel through Russia in pursuit of his own interests? Ledyard, who had already set off filled with hope and confidence, was arrested in Siberia. In vain he protested that his expedition was undertaken 'in the interests of all humanity'. The Russians were incapable of grasping such a concept. A military escort brought Ledyard back to the Russo-Polish frontier, and the American plan came to naught.

Early in the year 1786 the Billings expedition arrived at the agreed point of embarkation in the Sea of Okhotsk. They were bitterly disappointed to discover that there was no sign either of the ships promised by the Russian Government or of the essential supplies. 'The five ships based in Okhotsk harbour . . . could not be used at all. . . . They were quite rotten. In the holds —if these piles of rotting wood can be so described—the ships' stores and other materials were also almost all in a state of decay and hardly any of them were fit for use.'

The base from which Russia was groping towards new continents, in order to acquire yet more 'Russian soil', was enjoying an extraordinary boom. It was not such an unknown and god-forsaken place as the government, six thousand miles away in St Petersburg, appeared to think. An entry in the expedition's log reads: 'Trade here is mostly in the hands of foreign merchants. They supply foodstuffs and all kinds of other goods to the Russians. . . . There are also "trading companies". . . . In Okhotsk or Kamchatka they build ships and send them to catch fish off the Aleutians and the coast of North America. The sailors come from all parts of the Russian empire.' Thus even in the most remote parts of the Russian-occupied continent there were already foreigners present.

In the summer of 1789 two new ships were ready to put to sea. Their gear, including the guns, the copper kettles for the galleys, anchors and the rest, had to be bought from Irkutsk on Lake Baikal—a distance of fifteen hundred miles as the crow flies. Captain Billings took command of the *Slava Rossii*—the other ship was dashed to pieces on the rocks at the mouth of the Okhotsk—and sailed across to Kamchatka. His plan was to set sail from the port of Petropavlovsk with destination America. This meant that he started from a point 20° of latitude further south than had the expedition which attempted to reach America from northern Siberia.

In order not to waste his time while waiting for the new ships to be completed, in 1787 Billings tried to sail from the Arctic Ocean, round the East Cape, to the coast of America. He set off in two ships built at the mouth of the Kolyma River. The attempt was abandoned, however, as completely hopeless. Was such a voyage round the East Cape, which the Cossack Semyon Deshnev was supposed to have made, really possible? The men taking part in the expedition were inclined to doubt it.

Their ideas are reflected in the comments of a Russian member, Zarychev: 'Experience has shown that this Polar Sea expedition cannot be undertaken by ship because of the enormous ice-floes from the mouth of the Kolyma onwards (Deshnev is supposed to have started from there). Although we learn from earlier expeditions that the sea is occasionally ice-free the fact remains that of the large numbers of seamen who have set out to discover a route across the Polar Sea to the Eastern Ocean [the Pacific], only the Cossack Deshnev was lucky enough to reach Kotchas. Many people here are very dubious and believe that this voyage of his is a myth, made up by himself in order to gain fame as a discoverer, and that what he said about that coast was in fact based on information concerning Cape Chukta. It is possible that extraordinary natural conditions, such as only occur once a

century, existed when he set off. The local Cossacks state quite definitely
that there is normally so much floating ice that it is not possible to leave the
estuary.'

In the summer months of 1790 and 1791, Billings, in the *Slava Rossii*, twice
set sail from Kamchatka and reached his objective without incident. On the
first occasion he sailed northwards through the Bering Sea and crossed the
Bering Straits between the East Cape and the North American coast; on
the second voyage he took a southerly course, past the Aleutians from the
Alaskan Peninsula as far as Kayak Island off the southern coast of Alaska.
This island Cook had named Kay Island. Captain Hall, on board the *Cherny
Orel*, carried out surveys in the Bering Sea.

The work of the two Englishmen led to excellent maps and charts; those
drawn by G. A. Zarychev, in particular, were so accurate that they are still
usable today. Billings's report was the first authentic information, and it put
Catherine II's mind at rest; Russians had unquestionably landed on the north-
west coast of America. This was important, for trappers and seal-hunters
from Kamchatka had already begun to hunt the Aleutians. On the advice
of a big Russian fur dealer, G. Shekhilov, as early as 1750 they had been
planting poles, with the Russian arms on them, in the islands off the coast
of Alaska. Billings had been specifically ordered by the Admiralty in
St Petersburg to carry such poles with him.

On Kodiak Billings visited one of the Russian trading settlements. He
described it in the expedition log: 'It consists of mud huts, as well as a shed
and two huts made of pinewood. In this Russian settlement live a group
of trappers and hunters led by a Greek sailor, Delarov.'

Delarov, who had the Russian Christian name and patronymic of Yevstrat
Ivanovich, was a Greek seaman from Macedonia. He had carried out a
number of successful hunting trips, and had been appointed head trapper
by Shekhilov, the merchant.

In Prince William Sound, close to Montague Island—which lies off the
Alaskan coast at latitude 60°—Billings learned that other foreigners 'had
been here before with their ships . . .' and that 'every year two- and three-
masted ships arrive, two vessels this year, which set their course for Kenai
Bay. I asked them about Commodore Bering. . . . One of the "Americans"
told me that he had heard of his ship from his father; she had sailed as far
as an island called Kayak, which lies about a day and a half's journey eastwards from here.'

Close on the heels of Billings's expedition came the usual Russian echo:
'If it had only been possible for foreign seamen to make such voyages of
discovery as the Russians did in the eighteenth century!' boasted the Russian
navigator, Vassily Mikhailovich Golovnin, in his book, *Journey around the
World in the Sloop 'Kamchatka', 1817–19*. The Russian naval officer, Sarychev,
who had certainly achieved a great deal, was lauded to the skies by the

Russian authorities while the achievements of the Englishman Billings were denigrated and he himself insulted. It was said that he had not bothered to make proper charts and surveys—yet this did not stop the Russians from assigning to him further important tasks of exactly the same sort. In 1795 Billings was chosen by the Russian Admiralty to 'survey the northern coastal waters of the Black Sea, from the Straits of Kerch to the Dniepr—Liman inclusive.'

The ethnological and natural researches and the collections of specimens made by the scientists who went on the Billings expedition were dismissed as almost valueless. Yet all their drawings and notes went to St Petersburg under a 'top secret' seal. Their variety is impressive. Staff-Surgeon Robeck had compiled a *Dictionary of the Twelve Dialects of the Primitive Inhabitants.* Dr Merck brought to St Petersburg detailed notes and diaries, as well as extensive scientific collections, the fruit of nine years' work by himself and his three assistants, Krebs, Hauss and Main; these alone filled long columns of ledgers. The rocks and minerals were put into the Imperial Russian Mineralogical Collection, as the most important of their kind, and the magnificent collection of birds, fish and animals of all sorts went to embellish the Museum of the Science Academy. What the Billings expedition brought to St Petersburg was studied by the great Berlin naturalist, Peter Simon Pallas. The outcome was his book on the fauna of Asiatic Russia, the first zoological work to appear on the subject (*Zoographia Rossiae Asiaticae*). Dr Merck wrote a *Description of the Chuktas, their manners and customs,* the first ethnological study of the people of the Chukta, and the only such book written at that time.

But whatever the contributions of the foreigners to Russian research and however much they wrote about and for Russia—the activities of the Academy evoked no response from the Russian people. It could only be kept going by renewed appeals for foreign scholars. For many years after its foundation there were no Russian academicians—with the exception of Lomonossov—and not a single major idea originated in the Slav empire.

'We shall need Europe for a few more decades, after which we can turn our backs on her.' This remark of Peter the Great's, often quoted with approval by the Soviets, was pure wishful thinking. Even today, more than half-way through the twentieth century, the West is and remains the inexhaustible source of new stimuli and new thought, of all developments and all discoveries—so inexhaustible that Russia has a hard time even keeping up.

The French astronomer and geographer, Jean Chappe d'Auteroche, who was a guest of the Academy in the year 1761 after a journey through Siberia—in Tobolsk he had made observations of the planet Venus passing in front of the sun—experienced the oppressive atmosphere of isolation known to all the foreign scientists who lived, as it were, on an island lost in a sea of Russians. He wrote: 'The Academy of Sciences, founded by Peter the Great, is famous. Bernoulli, Delisle, Hermann and Euler brought here the fame they had garnered in their own countries. The arts, too, add their lustre. But it all fades away at once when the great men from abroad leave Russia or die. The rulers take great trouble to replace them by importing new men from abroad, while they do their best to discover and promote talent at home. In 1761, when I visited it, the Academy had among its members a number of very distinguished foreigners. But after more than sixty years of effort it was impossible to name a single Russian who had made a reputation for himself either in the sciences or the arts. Such a state of affairs in science and the arts shows a deficiency which can only be ascribed to a lack of ability in the nation, to its system of government, or to the national climate.'

7　Art and Artists from the West

On the distant coasts of the Arctic and the Pacific Oceans highly skilled Europeans might strive to explore the vast continent conquered by the Russian people: in the Academy of Sciences foreign scholars might be laying the foundations of Russian science and research, tasks scarcely appreciated by the Russian government: but Peter I's basic enterprise was doomed to failure under his successors, Catherine, Anna and Elizabeth. A reaction against his over-hasty development of the country had set in.

Only a few of Peter's faithful collaborators remained. Heinrich Johann Friedrich Ostermann, from Bochum in Westphalia, had been living in Russia since 1704 and had been among Peter I's closest advisers. With Prince Alexander Danilovich Menshikov he continued to run the 'Supreme Privy Council' after its creation in 1726. It constituted a sort of government, responsible to Peter's widow, Catherine, and the senate was subordinate to it.

When the Tsarina ennobled him and appointed him one of the three ministers of her 'Cabinet', Ostermann really controlled Russia. Loyal to Peter I, he did his utmost to carry out his policy, but in this he failed, for Anna had quite other interests. Engrossed in the splendour and extravagance of her court, she neglected the administration and economy of her realm.

The versatile and gifted Count Burkhardt Christoph von Münnich also carried on Peter's work. He built the Lake Ladoga Canal, the Kronstadt naval base, fortified Riga and was responsible for the naval bases on the Gulf of Finland. In 1731 he was appointed Master General of the Ordnance and a year later (1732) Field Marshal. He reorganized the Russian Army. During the reign of Anna, Count Münnich was made head of the Army Council in recompense for his great services to Russia. In the war against Turkey that ended with the Treaty of Belgrade in 1739, he showed his brilliance as a soldier in the field. While the Irish-born General Lacy recaptured the fortress and port of Azov, Russian troops under Münnich's command first conquered the Crimea in 1736. A year later the important Turkish fortress of Otchakov, covering the mouths of the Bug and the Dniepr, was taken, and Russian troops even reached Moldavia.

Only in one respect did the three Tsarinas attempt to emulate the great Peter, for they even surpassed him in the building of luxurious palaces and vast country residences. The greatest artists of the Western world achieved real triumphs in the city on the Neva and in Moscow. St Petersburg became the largest building-site in Europe, one vast studio filled with Western European architecture. No one else in Europe could thus spend millions as though they were trifles. Hosts of famous architects, sculptors, painters, decorators and landscape gardeners transformed the already beautiful 'Pitersburch' of Peter the Great into the most splendidly homogeneous city in Europe, a gem of eighteenth-century European art.

This was in striking contrast to the rest of that unbelievably primitive and undeveloped country. The vast majority of its population of eighteen millions lived in a state of serfdom, and could be sold like cattle. But the St Petersburg façade was to deceive visitors in the years to come.

Russians of talent had now been going to Europe's most famous academies and studios for several decades. I. Koroboff had studied architecture in Holland, P. E. Ropkin had been trained in Italy and the painters Andrei Matveyev and Ivan Nikitin in Italy and Holland. Feodor Argunov was one of the many Russians who learned under foreign masters in Russia itself, for he was taught by the great Trezzini. But the outcome was paltry; not a single Russian attained the skill of a master, not one became an outstanding painter who created something specifically Russian. K. Golovin, in his memoirs, rightly quotes the author, Feodor Sologub: 'Architecture is the basic art. And architecture is the one subject that we Russians know nothing about. That is to say, we Russians lack creative ability. This is noticeable in our architecture, sculpture and painting, but is also perceptible in the other arts.'

How else explain the fact that since the reign of Ivan III and Ivan IV, foreign artists had always filled the coveted post of court architect and indeed been entrusted with all major artistic undertakings?

It was under the Tsarina Anna (1730–40) that Bartolomeo Rastrelli (1700–71) began his career. He was the son of the sculptor Carlo Rastrelli, who had worked in Russia in Peter's time. Bartolomeo Rastrelli was—as Tamara Talbot Rice puts it—'decisively to influence the architectonic future of Russia' by his beautiful work.

No better choice could have been made. As an architect Rastrelli surpassed all his contemporaries. Even the famous William Kent, creator of the English Garden, and his British colleagues lacked his imagination and intellectual richness. He excelled the French in splendour and the Germans and Austrians in grace.

The Annenhof, a wooden palace at Lefortovo near Moscow, was the first building constructed according to his plans. The Italian's next assignment brought him to St Petersburg. In the year 1732 he was building the second Winter Palace. Before it was finished, Rastrelli was ordered to construct another palace for the Tsarina's favourite, the Count Ernst Johann Bühren (in Russian, Biron), whom she made Duke of Courland. In this palace at Mitau, Rastrelli first showed the particular style that was to characterize all his later buildings. A suite of brilliant and glittering reception-rooms, opening the one into the other, was the first Russian example of such an interior design. The magnificent vistas thus obtained

Burkhardt von Münnich of Oldenburg, who constructed the Ladoga canal and the naval base of Kronstadt. He was commander-in-chief of the Russian forces in the 18th century.

through a series of saloons and galleries was to be the hallmark of future Russian palaces.

The St Petersburg Summer Palace, completed by Rastrelli in 1744, was a wooden building in the late baroque style, and was subsequently much imitated throughout Russia. Rastrelli was copied now just as the Italianate Kremlin fortress had been slavishly reconstructed in the old frontier towns. 'Which is why all Russian towns look exactly alike,' says the Baedeker of 1900. John Gunther also refers to this in his book *Inside Russia* (1955). Rastrelli's buildings started a passion for pillars, which culminated in the early nineteenth century in a veritable mania for colonnades. Owing to Rastrelli pillars are considered an essential part of architectural decoration even today in Soviet Russia and are to be seen on the skyscraper façade of Moscow University as well as on all public and private buildings. They are even to be seen on such strictly non-residential edifices as the quays and lock-gates of the Don-Volga Canal.

It was the same story with Rastrelli's treatment of windows and gables. Since the mid-eighteenth century Rastrelli-type windows and gables have been built everywhere in Russia and the Ukraine, on country houses as well as on official buildings. Similarly, all rooms, small or large, have been built *en suite* and the mirrors Rastrelli was so fond of are still very popular and are hung exactly where the great Italian used to hang them—between the windows. It would be interesting to study the far-reaching effect of this man's work and the amount of slavish imitation it has produced.

All the more so since his enormously high windows, often the height of two full storeys, were not at all suitable to a country with such long and severe winters. Yet they were much admired. Once Rastrelli had built them into a palace in Moscow, he had to repeat them everywhere. The only way of adequately heating such huge rooms containing so much glass, was the superb Dutch tiled stoves of corresponding dimensions. On the rooftops high above, Rastrelli placed balustrades with gilt figures, and from giddy heights they overlooked the gardens, the orangeries, the gazebos and the tea-pavilions. The manufacture of wrought-iron gates and railings, with beautiful, intricate patterns designed by Rastrelli himself, won St Petersburg a considerable reputation as a centre of metalwork.

Another star from Rastrelli's native land shone brightly beside the Neva: the Italian actress and prima ballerina, Signorina Giannina, mother of a man the whole world would talk about, Casanova. In Florence she had danced in the opera *Berenice*, composed and there conducted by the Neapolitan, Francesco Araja. As soon as the Tsarina heard of the great success of this opera, she sent a message inviting Francesco Araja to St Petersburg and offering him an enormous fee. The whole company arrived, together with the ballerina and the set designer, Girolamo Bono. They won the city's heart. 'The first Italian opera'—a member of the Academy, Jacob Baron von Stählin, writes in his memoirs—'was presented by an Italian company, and Signorina Giannina Casanova enjoyed a triumph.'

This event marked the beginning of the opera in Russia—and of the ballet.

The Russian audiences, used only to the uncouth dancing of Cossacks, were so impressed by the performance of Casanova's mother that she also became the mother of the dance in Russia, and thus the grandmother of the famous Russian Ballet. During her first visit a dancing school was founded in St Petersburg. Twelve girls and twelve boys were selected for training. The teacher of gymnastics at the exclusive Imperial Cadet School, Christian Wellmann, was ordered to instruct the children until such time as famous ballet-teachers from Italy and France could be sent for. The ballet-master Fusano came from Venice, Landet from Paris. Landet created the first *corps de ballet* in Russia.

The Araja company remained permanently in Russia. The Tsarina saw to it that they were all highly paid. A year later the official gazette announced: 'Director of Imperial Music Francesco Araja's Opera *The Power of Love and Hatred* will be performed for the first time on 2nd February 1736, at the Court. The text has been brought by the Chevalier F.P. from Rome. The music has been composed by the conductor, Signor Araja, himself and the scenery designed by the painter Hieronymus Bonus, Director of the Court Theatre. A ball has also been organized by the Master of Ceremonies, Signor Antonio Rinaldi.'

The Opera came to Russia with Araja, Bono and Rinaldi. Giuseppe Valeriani, a professor at the Academy of Fine Arts, instructed Russian set-designers in the art of the theatrical décor. The indefatigable, creative and much-gifted Valeriani has been called the father of the famous Russian 'School of Perspective'. Even today the opera *Cefalo e Procri* is often in-

The famous Smolny monastery, St Petersburg, which rates among the most beautiful baroque creations of Bartolomeo Rastrelli (1748).

correctly described as the first Russian opera. But though the libretto was written by a Russian, Sumarokov, Araja wrote the music. A book could be devoted to the influence of the Italians from the time of Elizabeth onwards. All court conductors were Italians.

In 1741 a basic change of policy took place when an unexpected *coup d'état* put the Tsarina Elizabeth Petrovna upon the throne. The last remaining supporters of Peter's policy trembled. The foreign, particularly the German, influence had grown so strong under Anna and her successor the regent Anna of Brunswick (mother of the baby Ivan VI), and hatred of the foreigners had increased to such an extent, that a violent reaction now set in. Many German, Dutch and English craftsmen fell victim to the fury of the mob. Ostermann and Münnich were arrested as soon as Elizabeth had come to the throne.

Field Marshal Münnich was condemned to be publicly whipped. Only vigorous intervention by the British Ambassador, whose feelings as a European were deeply outraged, prevented this disgusting spectacle. Ostermann and Münnich were both sentenced to death and led to a public place of execution. At the very last moment the Tsarina granted them a reprieve. Both men, who had done so much for Russia, were exiled to Siberia for life. Ostermann died in 1747 in Siberia, at the age of sixty-one. Münnich was reinstated with full honours by Peter III after Elizabeth's death in 1762.

This outburst of hatred, especially against Germans in high positions, did not however diminish Western influence in Russia. At court, men from other European nations, and particularly Frenchmen, now took the lime-light, such as the physician, J. H. Lestocq, and the ambassador, La Chétardié. With a new English trade agreement, trade expanded; St Petersburg profited from this and the British gained in popularity and prestige.

Not one of the countless foreign artists was expelled nor in any degree molested. They were all needed by Elizabeth, who lavishly and extravagantly continued her predecessors' work of beautifying Russia. Rastrelli worked on, and it is almost impossible to catalogue all that he built in the twenty years of Elizabeth's reign. His works included the Peterhof Palace, the famous castle at Tsarskoye Selo, the Great Palace, many palaces of the nobility on the Neva and Moskva Rivers, and the Smolny Monastery at St Petersburg, said to be one of the most beautiful examples of baroque in all Europe. The Church of St Andrew that Rastrelli built in Kiev may well be the most beautiful church of his time.

Rastrelli was still working under Catherine II. For her he built the Fourth Winter Palace, which to this day retains its place as Europe's most immense palace. No other royal residence equals it; not even Versailles has the splendour, the overwhelming decoration and baroque ornamentation of this vast palace that the Italian built. The Fourth Winter Palace covers an area of many acres, contains one thousand and fifty halls and rooms, nearly two thousand doors and portals, a similar number of gigantic windows and one hundred and seventeen staircases.

A host of imitators followed in Rastrelli's footsteps and his style remained dominant for many years. Most of his successors simply copied his architectural plans exactly. Only a few are worth mentioning: S. I. Chevakinsky (1713-83), A. V. Kvasov (died in 1772, year of birth unknown), A. F. Kokorinov (1726-72) and Prince D. V. Ukhtomski (1718-80). The architects who rebuilt Moscow after the devastating fire of 1737 were also influenced by Rastrelli.

What about painting? Almost all decorative painting done under Elizabeth was the work of Italians—especially of Valeriani, Perezinotti, Borozzi and Torelli. The Russians remained mere assistants while the enormous murals on walls and ceilings were being executed. As with Peter, Elizabeth ordered many of the designs for these murals from artists resident abroad, who sent them to Russia without ever having visited the country themselves. The ceilings in the Castle of Oranienbaum, painted after Tiepolo's designs, are the most beautiful example of such an importation. Carlo Bibiena Galli designed the lovely painted ceilings, using a special perspective to give the suites of connecting rooms an impression of even greater space.

All the prominent figures at the Russian court in those years were painted by the brothers Grooth, by Lagrenais the Elder and by Stefano Torelli.

In the year 1748 Pompeii was discovered, and hidden beneath the earth, the lava and the ashes lay an entire ancient city capable of reconstruction in detail. As a result a new style of architecture appeared. The classical—as interpreted by Winckelmann and Lessing—began to replace the current style of European architecture. From the West this new creative force travelled to the East. Vallin J. B. de la Mothe was the first to build in the

classical style in Russia. Georg Felten followed. Antonio Rinaldi, who came
to Russia in 1752, remained faithful to the baroque. The new style finally
triumphed in the year 1779 when Charles Cameron, the great Scot, was
summoned to Russia by Catherine. He had worked for Pope Clement XIII
in the excavation of the Baths of Caracalla. For nine years Cameron worked
on the interiors of Rastrelli's great Palace of Tsarskoye Selo for the Tsarina,
in purely classical style. He designed Greek rooms and Chinese rooms.
Catherine's study was completely in silver, her bedroom in the style of
Pompeii. The gardens were laid out in the English manner, as Kent had done
in England, with little temples and pavilions and Roman statues and
fragments of sculpture imported from Italy dotted among the trees and
shrubs. The Temple of Friendship, which he built in 1780, was the first
building to sport Doric pillars in Russia. At Pavlovsk, near St Petersburg,
he built colonnades, a temple of the Three Graces—a copy of the Erechtheion
—and the aviary in which Gonzago later painted his lovely frescoes. The
Greek Hall of the Palace of Pavlovsk was embellished with Corinthian
columns of porphyry on huge alabaster bases and classical statues. In 1800
Cameron was appointed architect of the Admiralty.

Four English painters worked in St Petersburg under Catherine: Richard
Brompton, John Augustus Atkinson, John Walker and Edward Miles, who
painted the Imperial family. Later, about 1800, five other English painters
joined the colony of foreign artists: Saxton, Allen, George Dawe, Christina
Robertson and Robert Porter, who painted General Suvorov crossing the
Alps. Russian artists studied in foreign studios. Feodor Roktov (1735–1808),
for instance, was taught by Claude Lorrain and Rotari: Dimitri Levitski
(1735–1822) was apprenticed to Lagrenais and Giuseppe Valeriani in St

*Partial view of the huge Fourth Winter Palace built by B. Rastrelli for
Catherine II.*

Petersburg. Levitski, who painted Diderot in Geneva, was judged by his compatriots to be the first Russian painter to compete with the foreigners. Ivan Firsov lived and studied in Paris for ten years before he became known.

Thus did Russia, with foreign help, construct its tremendous architectural façades, St Petersburg and Moscow. But for many years no visitors from abroad came to admire them. Catherine said in her memoirs of the reign of Elizabeth: 'Very few foreigners were then to be seen in St Petersburg.'

The vast palaces and many of the houses of the nobility remained empty shells. 'St Petersburg was a dead city,' Catherine wrote. 'Most of the people living there were obliged to do so, and no one lived there by choice. Whenever the Court returned to St Petersburg from Moscow, most of the court officials quickly applied for leave for a year, six months, or at least for a few weeks, so as to remain in Moscow. Civil servants and government officials did the same, and when nothing else availed they feigned sickness for their wives, husbands, children, brothers, sisters or parents. At least six months and sometimes more passed before the city and the court regained their former aspect; meanwhile grass grew in the streets of St Petersburg, because there was no traffic.'

The Russians did not like these palaces which were—to complete the resemblance to a façade—not even properly furnished. Catherine, in the year 1755, noted: 'At the end of September we moved into the Winter Palace. The Court at that time was so deficient in furniture, that we had to take our mirrors, beds, chairs, tables and chests of drawers from there to the Summer Palace then to Peterhof and even to Moscow. On the way many of the pieces were so badly damaged or broken that we could hardly use them . . . so I resolved to buy, bit by bit, cupboards and other essential pieces for the Summer Palace and for the Winter Palace too out of my own pocket. Then when I moved from one to the other, everything would be ready for use and the dangers of transportation avoided.'

Later, when Catherine became Empress, she saw to it that the thousands of rooms were properly furnished.

The furniture came from the West, the best that Europe could produce, brought by land and by sea. As soon as Rastrelli had finished the Fourth Winter Palace, which the Empress called 'her Hermitage', a long list of what was needed went off to Diderot in Paris. Catherine wanted paintings, sculptures and furniture, and in bulk. Voltaire helped choose the best for her regardless of price, and some of the world's most famous pictures moved across Europe: 'St George' by Raphael, 'Judith' by Giorgione, 'The Descent from the Cross' by Paolo Veronese, Titian's 'Danaë', the 'Holy Family' of Murillo, two paintings by Moretto da Brescia, several by Sebastiano del Piombo and Fra Bartolomeo. And many canvases of Van Dyck, Rubens, Rembrandt, Jan Steen and what were then the contemporary French masters, Poussin, Le Sueur, Watteau and Largillière. The prices were astronomical.

Wouwermans' 'Hunting of the Stag' cost 108,000 French livres, the 'Descent from the Cross' 220,000 livres, and Murillo's 'Holy Family' no less than one million.

Let us return to the Empress Elizabeth. In her passion for building, she neglected much: the government of her country, and the economic development which her father, Peter I, had inaugurated with such superhuman effort and at such immense cost. She even ordered that many of the new factories be closed down. When it was proposed to her that Russia should start mining coal, as in the West, she turned down the proposal. She would not even believe that 'stones can burn'. One day her attention was drawn to the use of petroleum: it could feed the lamps in the churches and also possessed medicinal properties. This interested Elizabeth and she ordered that the matter be gone into. The 'Mines Board' and a committee of physicians were to meet. But when the gentlemen could not agree, the Tsarina herself made the decision concerning this new discovery which could have been of immense value to Russia. Elizabeth ordered that the man who had discovered petroleum be imprisoned for life! Meanwhile she did not hesitate to grant special privileges to an Englishman, Bottler, who supplied such unnecessary luxuries as 'tapestries and linen'.

The story was the same in other departments of her government. The fleet decayed, the sailors were not paid or were discharged, and the Admiralty became a morgue. Nevertheless, as previously stated, the first Russian university was founded in 1755, in Moscow, on Voltaire's recommendation and under the direction of the far-sighted Count Ivan Ivanovich Shuvalov. Two years later an Academy of Fine Arts was formed on the French model. The painters Le Lorrain and Stefano Torelli, the sculptor N. Gillet and the engraver G. F. Schmidt were engaged as instructors. In the year 1763 the Academy had seventy pupils who were eventually intended to replace the many foreign artists. Russia had had enough, more than enough, of the hated foreigners. . . .

Catherine, the future Tsarina, witnessed an event which was typical of the age in Russia. She has described it in her diary. In the year 1752, 'the Empress [Elizabeth] commanded us to join her at Kronstadt from Oranien-baum, for she was to be present when water was let into the canal which Peter I had begun and which had just been completed. We stayed at Kronstadt for three days. During this time the canal was ceremoniously opened and the water was let into it for the first time. In the afternoon the event was celebrated with an inaugural ball. The Empress wished to remain in Kronstadt to see the canal emptied; but on the third day she left, because it had proved impossible to drain the canal, since its bottom was below sea-level. Nobody had taken this into account.'

A similar disaster occurred to the canal which had been begun by the Tsar's favourite, Menshikov. Menshikov was an ambitious man who wished to show Peter I that he was as good as the German expert, Burkhardt Christoph von Münnich. Münnich was told to construct an artificial water-way from Lake Ladoga to Schlüsselburg. Menshikov was officially in charge of the project and, envious of the more efficient German, he completely ignored the precise and detailed plans and drawings made by Münnich. Disaster was thus unavoidable. Menshikov knew nothing about technical hydraulics and ignored the most important point, the variation in the water level of the lake, which Münnich had quite correctly taken into account. When Peter heard of this he lost his temper and told Münnich to finish building the canal on his own. He did the job so well that when the Tsar inspected it, he kissed him, and praised him to the skies. Yet Münnich, to whom Russia owes its canal system, and who also built the naval base at Kronstadt, was exiled to Siberia by Elizabeth. As a result the Peter Canal at Kronstadt had to be built without the help of this superb expert. The sea-water poured in, but its locks could never be emptied, because nobody had calculated the water-levels.

Later, under Catherine, this was put right. After twenty years of exile in Siberia Münnich was reprieved by Peter III and put back to work. He drained the locks with an imported steam-pump!

8 Catherine Educates an Empire

WITH THE SUCCESSION in 1762 of Catherine II, born Princess Sophia Augusta of Anhalt-Zerbst, barely forty years after the death of Peter I, a new era began, and new influences poured into the land. Relying on help from the West the German princess began her task of rebuilding the new Russia, which had fallen into decay under her predecessors. During her reign Russia began once again to thrive. However, though her policy concerning the introduction of scientific and technical knowledge succeeded, Catherine II also tried to introduce Western ideas and ideals into her adopted country, and in this she failed. If ever anybody attempted to draw Russia into the world of Western culture, it was Catherine.

Her inheritance had been squandered long before she came to the throne; the national finances were in a hopeless state, the public debt enormous.

'When I came to the throne in 1762,' she wrote, 'two-thirds of the army had not been paid. In the Treasury I found imperial Ukases for payments totalling 17 million roubles, which had not been met. The currency was valueless . . .'

To avoid total bankruptcy, Catherine decided to assess the wealth of the empire through the municipal authorities. Yet when she had summoned the senate not one of the members could even tell her how many towns there were in Russia. The senate did not even possess a map of the country.

Catherine began to draft her economic plans and worked out an amazingly complex programme. To her horror she found that the country had never been surveyed, neither the private properties nor the land belonging to the monasteries or to the crown. With energy and sense she began to clear up the mess, and to give her empire a new firm backbone, on the Western model. And again she was helped in this by men from the West. She insisted that schools be built and the general level of education raised. In the autumn of 1763 the foundations for a foundlings' home were laid, a training-centre for midwives opened, and a school for young girls of noble family. Three hundred schools for the children of the aristocracy were eventually built, agriculture encouraged and new industries created.

The Empress set about the huge job with amazing thoroughness, energy and foresight. She accepted personal responsibility for the whole country. The Imperial Household and the people themselves were inspired by her example, for she often worked far into the night. Meanwhile the foreign ambassadors at her court have described how much opposition and lack of co-operation she encountered. Even her own councillors often opposed her orders.

The French Ambassador, Breteuil, wrote to Versailles: 'The Empress can rely on no one save Panin to understand her ideas of government.' (Count Nikita Ivanovich Panin was her Foreign Secretary.) 'Nevertheless she still has to listen to her aged Russian advisers who think of nothing save their own privileges. I can well imagine what a strain it all must be for her. She recently told me that she is most unhappy, having to rule a people whom it is almost impossible to control.' The British Ambassador, Lord Buckingham, wrote in similar terms to London: 'The Empress is far superior to everyone else here by virtue of her education, her talents and her ability.'

Soon after coming to the throne Catherine launched a major plan of resettlement and land cultivation. She received, as usual, assistance from abroad. She sent men to Germany in an attempt to recruit farmers. In a decree dated July 1763 she promised free travel and free land to any farmer who would settle in Russia and set the Russian people an example in cultivation and stock-breeding. For agricultural expansion had come to a halt in that vast country. Many Germans, particularly peasants from Swabia and the Palatinate, resolved to go East. Transport via Lübeck and Danzig was organized and during the next five years over thirty thousand Germans emigrated to Russia. Despite all the promises, they were only given poor steppe land in the Saratov region or on the lower reaches of the Volga. Nevertheless this was the beginning of the flourishing settlements of the so-called Volga Germans. At the beginning of the First World War over six hundred thousand of their descendants were living there.

Among the first-comers was a delegation representing Count Zinzendorf's Moravian United Brethren. They were allotted a huge stretch of barren land on the lower Volga, between Tsaritsyn (now Stalingrad) and Astrakhan, and in the Samara and Sarepta districts.

The settlements of the United Brethren were soon famous. Ten years after the arrival of the first settlers the Governor of Astrakhan reported on their amazing achievements as homesteaders. In the midst of formerly bleak and empty steppes model settlements had sprung up. In Sarepta and near Samara, in the Volga bend, their new factories were producing corduroy, previously unknown in Russia, and also a cotton material called *sarpinka* which was soon to be renowned as a Russian speciality. These fabrics were as good as the best cloth produced in other countries.

The colonists also built canals, thus diverting the water from the nearby hills to their settlements. They soon had a chandler's works, a pottery, and a stove factory in commission. There were mills and saw-mills. A dam was built to supply the water-power with which to drive the mill-wheels and the flax-flails. They constructed a tannery and a tobacco factory and a dye-works for dyeing the cloth they made. Hitherto all Russian fabrics had been sent to Holland to be dyed.

The German colonists' settlements—which also existed in the governments of Voronezh and Chernigov as well as to the north of St Petersburg—were set in a landscape of trim and well-tilled fields.

Ten years later a second wave of immigrants from the West responded to Catherine's appeal. Thousands of Swabian peasant families settled the recently (1774) conquered and still quite empty province of Ekaterinoslav. From 1789 on Mennonite families from West Prussia were trekking eastwards.

In Jakob Johann von Sievers, a German Balt, Catherine found the right man to carry out a gargantuan task. His father, Karl von Sievers, had been Court Chamberlain under the Tsarina Elizabeth. Against the opposition of her Russian councillors, Catherine appointed Sievers Governor-General of the province of Novgorod, where there was large-scale pioneer work to be done. This was in 1764. She chose Sievers because none of the Russian candidates was as conversant with modern political economy, nor as experienced as he in the techniques of road and canal building, irrigation and drainage. The decision aroused much ill-feeling, though it was proved right in the end. The province of Novgorod soon blossomed into new prosperity.

Novgorod's most prosperous age had been in the time of the Hanseatic League. When Moscow was only an unimportant earthworks fortress, Novgorod was already a flourishing Hanseatic port, and the most important trading centre in the East. It was from there that trade with the Urals, the Polar Sea and the southern stretches of the Volga was carried out.

Novgorod had been a city of free craftsmen's guilds and rich merchants, ruled according to the so-called Lübeck Laws, until it was destroyed by the Golden Horde. During the thirteenth and fourteenth centuries it had been once again extremely prosperous. Magnificent monasteries, churches and cathedrals, unequalled in Russia, bore witness to its greatness. The lovely icons of the Great Novgorod School were famous. Novgorod, an island of advanced Western culture and civilization, was besieged by Ivan III in 1478 and finally destroyed by Ivan the Terrible. He sacked the town, murdered its Russian citizens—tradition has it that they numbered sixty thousand—and expelled the foreigners.

Another proud republic and important trading centre was the former Pleskau (Pskov), where German merchants had done business. In the year 1510 Vassily III forced the town to accept Muscovite rule. Since then it had declined. Now Sievers was made governor of Pskov as well as of Tver. The capital city of this government, also called Tver, had been destroyed by fire in 1763.

His was a formidable task. In the past two centuries the towns of Novgorod and Tver had declined until they consisted only of a handful of wooden buildings. Pskov had a mere four hundred and fifty inhabitants.

There were no police and only one postal service in the whole vast area, from Novgorod to St Petersburg. When Sievers assembled the nobles and asked them why the orders issued by Peter I—such as the afforestation of the land—had not been carried out, he was surprised to find that not one of these senior officials could read or write.

For the second time the Novgorod district was again made prosperous, thanks to Western help. The peasants were shown how to grow flax and how to treat it, and they were subsidized to plant potatoes—the first in Russian soil. Catherine supported Sievers in all his endeavours. 'Try to induce these people to build on stone foundations,' she wrote to him. 'Any man who builds his house entirely of stone will be exempt from taxes for ten years.'

With the help of foreign engineers Sievers built the first modern transportation system. A new canal system connected the lakes and rivers and thus the raw materials, mainly timber and hemp, which the government produced could be brought to St Petersburg for export in bulk.

Russia's needs and Catherine's wishes were insatiable. With Voltaire's help the Empress organized the importation of Swiss clocks. She was determined to employ Swiss dairymen and cheese-makers. They were to show the peasants of southern Russia how to breed healthy cattle and to make first-class cheeses. Catherine's wishes went far beyond this, however. On one occasion she asked Sievers how the Russian population could be taught the ideals of honesty, personal freedom, respect for the law and democratic thought. Sievers advised her to transplant the whole of a Swiss canton to Russia as a living example to her people.

The Swiss were promised exact replicas of their own chalets, to be built in the Crimea. Many Swiss farmers settled there and began dairy farming.

Catherine was not solely interested in colonization; she also wanted to build schools and other educational establishments. A German professor, August Ludwig Schlözer of Göttingen, came to Russia in 1761 and drafted a school programme. 'The boys will be taught in three classes, from the age of five to that of fifteen. The first class will include boys from five to nine. Elocution, religion, drawing, arithmetic, reading and writing will be taught. In the second class, for the ages nine to twelve, the following subjects will be added: geometry, history and ethics. The pupils in the third class—up to the age of fifteen—will study higher mathematics, physics, the natural sciences and the principles of architecture.'

A fine programme, but there were no teachers. So Professor Schlözer was told to import them from abroad. Hundreds of scholars and teachers were required, not only for Schlözer's proposed establishments, but also for the three hundred schools reserved for children of the aristocracy. In the next few years many teachers came to Russia, thanks to Schlözer's efforts. Schlözer himself proved indispensable and helped Catherine in many ways.

Following the German example he introduced parish registers, which became the basis for a complete registrar system. The German professor systematically collected Russian historical research material in the libraries of the monasteries, which were now being opened for the first time as a result of his request to the Empress.

Schlözer did not stay in Russia for long. In 1769 he returned to Göttingen to continue his scientific work. He could not tolerate the depressing atmosphere of the country.

Catherine was far in advance of her time. She founded a Public Health and Hygiene Institute. For this she relied on a Russian who had studied at Cambridge, and who could therefore safely be entrusted with the task, Baron Alexander Cherkassov. In 1764 there was a severe smallpox epidemic. Catherine was in favour of immediate inoculation, but Cherkassov hesitated. He agreed that Doctor Dimsdale come over from England. Dimsdale gave Catherine herself an inoculation, and when she saw that it was harmless she ordered that her subjects be inoculated as well.

Although the Academy had now existed for almost forty years, its members were still almost entirely foreigners. Therefore Catherine, who wanted Russians to join the Academy, offered exceptional opportunities to all those willing to study. In 1764 she issued a decree: 'Anyone reaching the required standard may become a member of the Academy, even if he has hitherto been a serf. The members of the Academy, their children and descendants are to be free citizens for all time. Nobody may ever make them serfs again.'

But even such promises as these were not enough. Catherine had to rely on foreign scholars, among whom were the research scientists, Anton Johann von Güldenstädt and Samuel Gottlieb Gmelin—the nephew of Johann Georg Gmelin—and Kaspar Friedrich Wolff from Berlin, who came to St Petersburg in 1766. It was there that he completed his work *Theoria Generationis*, begun in 1759, with which he inaugurated a new epoch in the field of embryology.

A violent quarrel between two well-known professors in Berlin gained Catherine another famous member for her Academy in St Petersburg. At the Berlin Academy differences of opinion between the famous Swiss mathematician, Leonhard Euler, and the philosopher, Johann Georg Sulzer, also from Switzerland, had reached such a pitch that Euler resolved to leave Berlin. He had been to Russia before and had left for sound reasons, but he now accepted Catherine's offer to join her Academy in St Petersburg. Frederick of Prussia was so annoyed by this *coup* of Catherine's that it became a diplomatic incident. Although Euler remained in Russia, Catherine had to pay a sort of 'compensation' for the privilege of retaining him— something that had never happened before and is unlikely happen to again. Catherine agreed to an increase in the Prussian postage tariff for letters to

Russia from 38 to 44 silver groschen, because Prussia had lost its most famous mathematician.

The St Petersburg Academy, supervised by Russian officials, did not run smoothly. The following incident is characteristic. In the year 1783 Catherine appointed a woman to administer the Academy. This was the Princess Katherina Romanovna Dashkova, a highly-gifted and educated lady, who had lived in Paris for several years, and knew Voltaire and the other leading personalities of the Age of Enlightenment. She was a member of several learned societies abroad and had founded a Russian Language Academy which in 1841 was amalgamated with the other Academy.

When the Princess set about reorganizing the administration of the Academy, she was surprised at the amount of alcohol being used each year. When she investigated the matter she was shown an order of Peter I's to the effect that two human heads were to be preserved, as he wanted to 'look at them from time to time'. And she found the severed head of a Swedish girl who had once run away from Peter, as well as the head of her lover, both preserved in the cellars of the Academy, in the year 1783! This is reminiscent of a rather more agreeable story Bismarck loved to tell. In the year 1859 the Tsar Alexander II noticed that one guardsman always stood in the middle of the lawn in the Summer Garden of the Paul Palace. When asked why he stood there, the soldier replied: 'Those are my orders!' The Tsar's aide-de-camp was told to look into the matter and received the same answer: a sentry was posted there all the year round, but nobody knew why. The answer was eventually provided by a very old servant. The Empress Catherine had once seen the first snowdrop on this lawn, and had ordered that a guard be posted there to prevent anyone picking it. And the sentry had remained on guard for close on one hundred years.

In the year 1770 Europe was shocked and astonished by an amazing event. A Russian fleet had destroyed the entire Turkish Navy, consisting of twenty-four ships with eight thousand men on board, in the Bay of Chesme, near the island of Chios.

Frederick of Prussia and the Emperor Joseph II met. The Austrian Emperor described Russia as a stream that was overflowing its banks and threatened to submerge Europe. Sweden was alarmed, France angry, and England worried by this new naval power that threatened her supremacy.

A fleet of Russian ships built in the distant shipyards at Kronstadt and St Petersburg had annihilated the much-feared Turkish fleet in the Mediterranean. This news plunged Europe into alarm. Nobody inquired how this had happened, nor why such an achievement was possible. Nobody mentioned that two Scotsmen, Elphinstone and Greig, had commanded the Russian fleet. They had sailed the ships from the Neva through the Kattegat, the English Channel, around the coasts of Europe, to victory. The

The three-hundred-and-thirty-foot dome of the Isaac Cathedral, the most ornate church in St Petersburg, built from plans by the French architect Augustin Ricard de Monferrand and with the co-operation of a number of foreign artists.

The extraction of mineral oil in Baku, developed by the Swedish Nobel brothers. Above: drilling plant. Below: refinery.

Russian Admiral of the Fleet, Alexei G. Orlov, theoretically in command of the Russian force, had watched the entire battle from the comfort and safety of his cabin—as reliable witnesses testified.

Catherine had a special medal struck to commemorate this battle—the Chesme medal—bearing a portrait of the Russian Count who had been officially in command of her fleet and who was described as the 'conqueror and destroyer of the Turkish Navy'. He was given the honorary title of 'Chesmenskoy' although he had been one of the murderers of Peter III.

After the Battle of Chesme, as after Poltava, many Europeans were delighted by the Russian victory. Voltaire wrote a letter to Catherine, expressing his jubilation: 'Your Imperial Majesty has given me a new lease of life by your annihilation of the Turk. . . . Your victorious sailors must have heard my song: *Te Catharinam laudamus—Te dominam confitemur.* . . . Madame, my joy could not be more heartfelt. I am delighted! I thank you!' For the great Voltaire seriously believed that if the Russians could only liberate Greece from Turkish oppression, ancient Athens, city of poets and philosophers, would rise again.

In the hope that he might even live to see this resurrection himself, Voltaire invented a new weapon. He designed a sort of armoured car like the war-chariots of antiquity, and assured Catherine: 'My invention differs completely from the old type of chariot. I am no warrior myself but yesterday I was with two outstanding German soldiers who assured me that if this "war-chariot" were employed at the beginning of a battle, no military unit could withstand its effect, when the flames spurt from it. For it would take them completely by surprise.'

Catherine and Voltaire wrote to one another frequently. She read Rousseau's *Contrat Social* and his educational novel *Emile*. She sent Ivan Betskoi to Paris, the 'metropolis of progress' as she called it, to keep himself posted about all that was new in the world of culture.

The Empress was determined that Russia should catch up with the West, and not only in science, economics and technology. She wished to introduce Europe's liberal ideas into Russia. She herself was an enthusiastic member of the Age of Enlightenment. She had studied Montesquieu, had read his *Esprit des Lois*, and one sentence in his chapter on *The Despotic State* had made a deep impression on her: 'Just as a Republic needs virtue and a Monarchy honour and glory—so a Despotism must be ruled by fear.' These words were directed at Russia. And it was Catherine's wish that the sun of enlightenment should also rise over her country.

The leading personalities of this new age were two Frenchmen, Diderot and Jean Lerond d'Alembert. Since 1751 they had been publishing their *Encyclopédie ou Dictionnaire Raisonné des Sciences, des Arts et des Métiers,* a work in which all knowledge and all learning were to be classified. When Diderot ran into trouble with the French censorship, Catherine invited him to come to St Petersburg to finish his work. But in Diderot's opinion Russia was a sinister place, and he declined the offer. D'Alembert, who was asked to take charge of the education of Catherine's son Paul, also declined. Diderot, however, did persuade many other people to go to Russia. Young engineers and scientists, artists and architects joined the Academy in St Petersburg, or were given important appointments. Among them were Etienne Maurice Falconet, who later executed the famous memorial to Peter I, and the astronomer and geographer, Jean Chappe d'Auteroche. Finally Catherine had her way. Diderot came to St Petersburg, although only for a few months, from the autumn of 1773 to the spring of 1774. He drafted a memorandum for the education of her son and heir, in which he suggested that after becoming acquainted with the administration of his realm, the young prince should travel through Russia, accompanied by a group of scholars and scientists, and then through Europe. '. . . He should visit Germany to learn thoroughness, England to learn wisdom and the ideals of freedom, Italy to acquire its exquisite taste, and France to appreciate elegance and pleasure.'

Whatever Catherine undertook, she required the help of non-Russians. A Swiss professor at the St Petersburg Academy found her a tutor for her grandson, later the Tsar Alexander I. He was Frédéric César Laharpe from the town of Rolle on Lake Geneva. Considerable persuasion was required before the freedom-loving Swiss would agree to come to this land of despotism and serfdom. In 1782 he agreed to educate the future Tsar and to make 'a human being of him'. He remained in Russia for twelve years (until 1794) tutoring Alexander and his brother Constantine, teaching them the ideals of Rousseau, liberty and human dignity. Alexander, when Emperor, once said: 'All that I am, I owe to a Swiss.'

Montesquieu, Diderot, d'Alembert, Rousseau and Laharpe, these are the men from whom Russia was to absorb the spirit of Europe. Diderot had begged the Empress to give freedom to Russia. But Catherine had long ago realized, bitterly, that Russia was not yet ready to receive this precious gift. At the very time that Diderot was visiting her, she had received shattering proof of this. The entire country was brought to the brink of disaster by a violent rebellion led by Emelyan Ivanovich Pugachev, whose hordes advanced from the south, devastating the countryside, destroying and burning. Democratic freedom, self-government on the Greek model, a parliament of the English sort, what use would these be to Russia?

During those weeks, as Pugachev's rebels advanced closer and closer to Moscow, Catherine wrote Sievers a bitter letter: 'Two years ago the plague raged in the heart of the empire. Now We face another plague, a political one, at the borders of Our realm, which is causing Us great anxiety. . . . With the help of the Almighty We will prevail . . . but it will end in hangings. What a prospect for me, my dear Governor, for I hate hangings.

In Europe's opinion we shall have retrogressed to the times of Ivan Vassilyevich.'

In 1787 Catherine, with her entire court and the foreign diplomats, visited New Russia, the southern provinces which had been placed under the authority of Grigor Alexandrovich Potemkin, Catherine's favourite, with instructions that he develop them. As the Italian historian Lo Gatto observes: 'The famous saying about "Potemkin Villages" dates from this journey, when failure was very skilfully and effectively concealed, while all examples of successful development were well displayed.' And he goes on to say: 'With the help of the foreigners Potemkin had really achieved a great deal, especially where the Germans had built their fruitful settlements.'

A quarter of a century before, Catherine had moved these German settlers to the south. Now she could reap the fruits of this enterprise and proudly show it to her foreign guests—exactly as, one and a half centuries later, the Soviets were to show their tourists the huge industrial plants, erected by the Americans, as typical examples of 'socialist progress'.

It was during the reign of Catherine that Russia was first visited by Americans. In 1783 a ship flying the American flag entered the harbour of Riga. One year later the *Light Horse*, a ship of three hundred tons, dropped anchor in St Petersburg. But within a year the first difficulties arose. John Ledyard, who wanted to reconnoitre a possible trade route between Russia and the United States, was arrested in Siberia and deported (see page 128).

In December 1787, the first American commodore, John Paul Jones, entered the Russian service as a naval officer. Catherine appointed him Rear-Admiral, in command of the Black Sea Fleet. Competent officers were needed down there because the Second Russo-Turkish War had broken out a few months before.

In May 1788 the fourteen ships under the command of Jones played the decisive part in annihilating the Turkish fleet. The ambitious Potemkin, however, in his capacity as Supreme Commander, intercepted and retained the American's report of the battle. Angry at the Russians' ingratitude, Jones left Russia in September 1789 for America.

Catherine showed little interest in the United States. She did not attach much importance to this new country with its mere three million inhabitants; her own empire contained more than twenty-seven million subjects, as estimated by the British Ambassador. But already the United States was exporting knowledge to Russia. At Catherine's own request the great George Washington sent her a dictionary of the Indian languages.

This modest dictionary was the first item in the long list of imports from America which are today beyond calculation. At the time of writing the latest items were the newest computers for Sputnik III.

9 The Nineteenth Century

THE CHIMES of the Kremlin bells on 24th March 1801, as Alexander I ascended the throne of his murdered father, marked the beginning of a century in which the process, begun under the two Ivans, Peter I, now called 'the Great', and Catherine II, was vastly accelerated. In the nineteenth century Europeans, and now for the first time Americans as well, contributed towards laying the technical, scientific and economic foundations for a great modern Slav power.

A Swiss tutor, Frédéric César Laharpe, had striven to make the young Grand Duke Alexander into a progressive, free-thinking man. 'Be a human being, even on the throne,' Laharpe had written to the Tsar from his home in Switzerland. And back in his own country Laharpe preserved a letter in which Alexander promised:

'My country is in a disastrous and unhappy state. The peasants are oppressed, trade is paralysed, the ideal of freedom and the welfare of the people have been destroyed. That is how I see Russia today, and you can well imagine how it saddens me. When my chance comes, it is necessary that I grant my subjects the right to choose their representatives, whose duty it will be to work enthusiastically towards the creation of a liberal constitution. Such, my friend, are my plans. May God help me to give Russia its freedom and to save it for ever from the abuses of tyranny. That is my dearest wish, and I am determined to devote my life to the fulfilment of this task.'

The letter is dated September 1797. Four years later the succession of Alexander provided the great chance to liberate Russia from oppression and bondage.

And, in fact, the young Tsar took various steps in the right direction. He summoned Laharpe back to Russia, selected the youthful Paul Stroganov, who is known to have belonged to a Jacobite club, to work with him, and appointed a liberal Pole, Prince Adam Georg Czartoryski, as his adviser. To another gifted liberal, Michael Speranski, Alexander entrusted the mighty task of planning a modern constitution for Russia.

Alexander cancelled a Ukase of his father Paul's, forbidding Russians to travel abroad. The importation of books and sheet music was again permitted; people who had been incarcerated in the ill-famed Peter and Paul Fortress were released and many exiles in Siberia were set at liberty by Alexander.

But all too soon these high hopes were dashed. Only the good intentions survived. It was to happen again, under Alexander II, the 'Tsar-liberator', and also after Stalin's death in our own century; each time the 'thaw' was of very short duration. Alexander seems to have shrunk from the enormous task which he had set himself to perform. There was also the threat of war, as Napoleon, after having occupied all Europe, cast his eye on Russia. Alexander's ambitious plans broke down. With surprising speed those forces hostile to every kind of free development again prevailed.

Meanwhile the stream of imported goods, of machinery and industrial plant, of technicians and scientists, increased steadily, at Russian instigation, until by the end of the century it had swelled into a mighty flood. This, however, was cleverly concealed by the Russians, and the nations of Europe, occupied with their own wars and struggles, were unaware of their co-operative efforts in the East. Concealment was therefore made easier, and to this day few of the facts are known.

More than seventy-five years had elapsed since the founding of the Imperial Academy of Sciences. The number of Russian members had increased since 1800, but only one of these had shown himself to be above the average. Vassily Vladimirovich Petrov displayed considerable ability as an experimental physicist. He was the first to make systematic barometric observations. His greatest contributions, however, were in the field of electricity. Petrov's studies anticipated, without Europe being aware of this, the later work of Sir Humphry Davy on the electric voltaic arc. Certainly Petrov contributed much to our knowledge of electricity. More than a dozen of his works were published by the Imperial Russian Academy.

The majority of the members remained foreigners, mostly German scientists as in the time of Peter. From their ranks were recruited the leading teachers of the universities of St Petersburg and Moscow.

The botanist K. A. Trinius was assisted by Franz J. Ruprecht, a native of Prague, who studied the plant life of the Urals and the Caucasus. Isaac Jacob Schmidt from Mecklenburg specialized in the languages, history and literature of the people of Central Asia, Mongolia and Tibet. The Leipzig philologian and archaeologist, L. E. Stephani, was considered in those days one of the greatest experts on classical Greece.

A German from the Baltic provinces, Baron Paul von Schilling, carried out some important original research. In 1832 he invented an electro-magnetic telegraph, which was later installed in England in accordance with his specifications. During his time at the university of St Petersburg, Professor Emil Lenz of Dorpat succeeded in clarifying for the first time the phenomenon of electro-magnetic induction. The Lenz theory, named after him, is to be found in every textbook on electricity. Moritz Hermann von Jacobi of Potsdam was his pupil. He was the inventor of galvano-plastic, and also invented one of the first electric motors which he used for propelling a boat on the Neva in 1838. This 'Nyemets', however, has now been deprived of his nationality, for the Soviets invariably refer to him as 'Boris Semyonovich Yakobi, the Russian inventor of the electric motor'.

The German university of Dorpat played an important but long-forgotten role as the link between West and East. In order to train Russian scholars for a university career, the 'Institute of Professors' had been founded at Dorpat in 1802; a staff of teachers had been engaged to instruct Russian scientific students who were needed for the universities of Kazan and Kharkov, founded in 1804.

There were several famous scientists at Dorpat: Karl Ernst von Baer, the father of modern embryology; the pioneers of research into the Russian geography, its flora and fauna, such as the Germans Alexander von Middendorf, Karl Friedrich von Ledebour from Mecklenburg, the Baltic German, Alexander von Bunge; the physicist Hermann Hess from Geneva; Wilhelm von Struve and his son Otto von Struve who then taught at Dorpat, and who helped to train whole generations of Russian astronomers and who built a chain of observatories, starting at Dorpat and extending from the Baltic, from Reval, to Moscow and on to Nikolauev, Kiev and Kazan.

Wilhelm von Struve, whom J. Delisle calls the greatest Russian astronomer, achieved international fame with his discovery of double stars and of a way of measuring the distance of fixed stars. This great scholar's crowning achievement was the building, at Pulkovo near St Petersburg, of the finest observatory in the world, which he equipped with European instruments and telescopes. Important astronomical observations initiated by Struve in Pulkovo are still valid today.

Scores of young Russians were sent to Europe during the first years of Alexander's reign. They were to be seen in the lecture rooms of every faculty in the universities of Marburg, Göttingen, Jena and Heidelberg as well as at the Sorbonne in Paris. As Tolstoy's Anna Karenina was later to say: 'First go to Europe and learn everything.'

The astronomer Wilhelm von Struve of Altona.

*The observatory in Pulkovo, established by von Struve in 1834,
was the most famous of its time.*

Under the aegis of the Academy in St Petersburg, scientific and ethnological expeditions set out once again. They continued what Bering, the
famous Dane, had begun a century before, the exploration of this vast
territory which in the intervening hundred years had been steadily enlarged
by conquest. To one of these expeditions Russia owes the first sensational
scientific discovery which she was able to offer to the rest of the world. In
1806 Adams excavated a mammoth from the perpetually frozen ground
near the Lena estuary. It had been found seven years before by a Tungus
named Ossip Shumakhov. He collected the 'mutilated' remains of this ice-age
elephant, with pieces of its skin to which the long hair still adhered, and
brought them to St Petersburg. When, after a long and difficult journey, the
perfectly preserved skeleton was exhibited, scientists from all over the world
flocked to inspect this amazing discovery. The first scientific report on the
mammoth had, however, been produced by a man from the West, Dr D. G.
Messerschmidt; in 1724 he had described the carcass of a mammoth found,
thawed out, on the banks of the Indegirka.

Three hundred years after the discovery of America and Magellan's first
journey round the world, Russia belatedly entered the picture. In 1803,
under command of a Baltic German, Adam Johann von Krusenstern, the
Neva sailed from the port of Kronstadt. In a three-year voyage touching at
Japan and Sakhalin, round the Cape of Good Hope, and down the north-
western coast of America, Krusenstern circumnavigated the globe; he thus
satisfied, even if belatedly, Russia's urge to 'catch up and overtake'.

In the most southern part of the Russian empire, the Crimea, the land began
to flourish. Here a gifted Frenchman, the Duc de Richelieu, had set to work,
a man of 'great integrity, unexceptionable morals and devoid of self-interest'.

The Crimea, annexed by the Russians in 1783, was in a pitiable state
when Armand Emmanuel Duplessis, Duc de Richelieu, accepted the post of
Governor-General of his Majesty's Empire in the three provinces of Kherson,

Ekaterinoslav and Tauris. 'The Crimean conquest was an event on which the attention of all Europe was focused,' wrote the Englishman, Edward Daniel Clarke, in his *Journey through Russia and Tartary in 1800–1801*. 'If one were to ask what the Russians did in the Crimea, there is only one answer: they spoilt the land, felled the trees, destroyed the public buildings and churches and the magnificent canals, and looted the people. Today the once magnificent city of Kaffa (in Russian: Feodosia) consists of no more then fifty families. During our stay there the Russian soldiers were allowed to overthrow the beautiful mosques, or to convert them into magazines, to pull down the minarets, tear up the public fountains, and to destroy all the public aqueducts, for the sake of a small quantity of lead, which they were thereby enabled to obtain.

'The German scholar, Pallas, who had performed innumerable services for the Russians, prevented them by his mere presence from destroying Akt-Metschet (renamed Simferopol) as totally as the other cities.

'None of these incidents has been generally known about until now, because it has always been the policy of the Russian empire to conceal the true history of their own people and the real state of their empire by all the means in their power,' Clarke's report concludes.

Under Governor Richelieu new life arose from the ruins. The Duke, assisted by Count Alexander de Langeron, collected a large French colony for his work of reconstruction.

An educational system was developed by the Abbé Nichol, and schools were opened. French wine-growers, invited there by Richelieu, laid out vineyards, cultivated the native grapes and imported new strains from their own country. They gave the Russians their first Crimean wines, and the 'Shampanskoye', or Crimean champagne, which soon became famous, was solely due to them.

Other wine-makers from the Rhine and the Moselle followed, and founded viticultural training establishments in the Crimea. German gardeners competed with their French colleagues in laying out those lovely gardens which transformed the Crimea into a wonderful landscape of parks and flowers, famous throughout the world. Gardeners and landscape-gardeners of the well-known Schmidt family from Erfurt worked for generations in the Crimea.

Richelieu himself founded Odessa in 1802. The French architect, Thomas de Thomon, drew the plans for the city and its more important buildings. A modern seaport arose from nothing to become the great commercial port for the Ukraine. By 1813 there were already 35,000 inhabitants in Odessa; its trade centre was founded by a German, Count Saint-Priest.

Meanwhile an appeal had once again gone out from St Petersburg: 'Come to our country!' Following the policy of his grandmother, Catherine, the Tsar Alexander sent recruiting officers to Germany. Without foreign help the Russian peasants could achieve little, despite the fertility of the Russian soil and the density of the population.

Colonists from all parts of Germany, particularly from Swabia, emigrated eastwards in great treks through Bessarabia as far as the Caucasus. All along the northern coast of the Black Sea, villages were built in the Ukraine, and the pioneer work of the Black Sea Germans began. These pioneers produced a hard-working race; owing to their industry and skill, their excellent standard of farming and modern methods of stock-breeding, these colonies flourished.

A new project of prime importance was introduced from Austria—the cultivation of the sugar-beet. On the Don a huge model farm was built and the sugar-beet harvest was sent to a sugar-beet factory operated by steam-driven machinery and organized on German lines. The cultivation of the sugar-beet was as important in the nineteenth century as the cultivation of Indian corn is today. The Soviet Union has learned about this latter crop from the United States, whence it has imported the seeds of hybrid maize, the modern methods of growing the crop, and the newest machinery for maize cultivation.

Towards the end of the nineteenth century more than 600,000 Germans were living and working around the Black Sea in widely dispersed model villages. Together with the settlers at Saratov on the Volga, and the Germans of Volhynia, they formed the third great island of Western civilization within the Slav empire. Thanks to them the southern districts and the Ukraine became the granary of all Russia.

After twenty-six years in Russia the Duc de Richelieu was suddenly summoned back to his native land, where another great task awaited him. On 14th September 1815, King Louis XVIII appointed the Duke as head of the French Ministry in succession to Talleyrand.

But the foundation was laid. A new impetus had been introduced into the country, and under Prince Mikhail Vorontsov, whom Alexander had chosen as Richelieu's successor, Count Alexander de Langeron's son continued the great work.

Vorontsov added to the development of the Crimea—he brought in the architects. His favourite residence was Alupka, where he built a magnificent castle in the late Gothic style of Henry VIII and Elizabeth. He had acquired his predilection for Tudor architecture during his time in London as Russian Ambassador.

The Crimea was soon filled with every style of architecture. At Yalta, some miles to the east of Alupka, a palace for Grand Duke Constantine Nikolayevich was built according to plans by Schinkel, the famous Berlin architect. Italian craftsmen built classical mansions and villas surrounded by colonnades and pergolas with Greek columns. The sanatoria and hospitals of the Crimea acquired a considerable reputation after 1850; the most famous was at Sudak, belonging to Dr Erhardt. Soviet workers in striped pyjamas nowadays spend their holidays in the lovely parks and palaces.

Industrialization was still insignificant in the Slav empire. In 1804, statistics show that there were only 2,423 factories in the whole of Russia, employing 95,202 workers. Production was on the increase, however, and the curve was rising. But even so it was minute compared with the other countries of Western Europe where rapid industrialization was already under way, and particularly with England.

Hence the importance of an event which took place at this time. In the autumn of 1810 Leipzig was preparing for its great annual fair—without much enthusiasm, as the goods offered for sale were expected to be rather poor that year, being limited to local products owing to Napoleon's continental blockade which cut Europe off from her overseas imports.

In the course of these preparations strange figures appeared in the city's inns and taverns. They demanded extensive stabling accommodation, rented storehouses, and reserved an astonishingly large number of stalls at the Fair. Rumour spread through the town like wildfire. This would be a sensational Leipzig Fair—and would astonish all Europe. A few days later the people crowded round the city gates, craning their necks to see an endless column enveloped in a cloud of dust, which was approaching the town. Seven hundred carts came rumbling and lurching over the cobbled streets to the fairground, and there was no end to the unloading and storing which went on. There were groceries of a sort which nobody had seen for years, farming equipment and above all cotton, bale after bale of cotton, all from Russia.

Where did all these goods come from all of a sudden? Not, surely, from the backward Slav empire. . . .

Once again Russia had cleverly exploited the quarrels of the Western powers to further her own interest.

At the turn of the century the United States began to compete with Europe, which till then had been the sole supplier and preceptor of the Russians. In 1803 President Thomas Jefferson sent Levett Harris as Consul-General to St Petersburg, and the Tsar Alexander received him in the Imperial Palace. 'I should be happy,' the Tsar wrote to Jefferson, 'if our two countries could be eternal friends. We are both equally interested in the freedom of the seas, as the wise policy of my illustrious grandmother, the Empress Catherine, showed.'

This new source of supply was officially recognized in 1809. James Madison, who had just been elected President of the United States in succession to Jefferson, sent John Quincy Adams to St Petersburg as his ambassador. The corresponding Russian envoy to the United States was not Russian-born but was a German Balt, Count Friedrich von Pahlen. Throughout the nineteenth century almost all the Russian ministers in Washington were from the German or Baltic German aristocracy, e.g. Baron von Stoeckl, Baron von Rosen, Baron von Thyl.

When John Quincy Adams presented his credentials at St Petersburg, the Baltic was closed to American ships by Napoleon's continental blockade. Denmark, allied to Napoleon, had recently seized several freighters, but the Tsar arranged that they be released, and from then on Russia's ports were open to ships from the United States.

Imports from America rose in six years, 1806 to 1811, from a mere $12,000 to more than $6,000,000 a year. Of cotton alone, more than 9·22 million pounds went to Russia in 1811, whereas in 1808 only 0·5 million pounds had been supplied.

In July 1811, Alexander achieved a major triumph. Some two hundred American ships entered Russian ports, during the warm ice-free season. America had a near monopoly of the Baltic trade; trade with Archangel was on the increase; and in 1810 an American cargo ship entered the port of Odessa for the first time.

The young America had given a proof of its ability to produce the goods. Russia was to benefit from this in every sphere of economic activity until the present day.

These imports soon produced a surplus of goods which the internal Russian market could not absorb. So Russia began to re-export the wares it had imported from the United States, just as today the USSR supplies the Far East with valuable medicinal supplies imported from Europe.

Via Brody, in Galicia, American goods went to Vienna and South Germany, even to Paris, Napoleon's own capital. The goods exhibited, as such a surprise, at the Leipzig Fair of 1810 were only a small percentage of the supplies from America that the Russians were exporting.

Napoleon knew quite well that the American ships were also carrying English goods to St Petersburg, for British traders were using the American flag. He realized that his plan for blockading England was therefore likely to fail. He tried in vain to persuade the Tsar that he seize these American ships. Alexander rejected his request and even issued a Ukase on 31st December 1810 permitting neutral ships to enter Russian ports.

This Ukase marked the end of the Russo-French alliance. Three years before, Napoleon and Alexander had met on a raft at Tilsit, and Napoleon's proposal that Europe be divided into French and Russian spheres of influence had been welcomed by the Tsar, and the Treaty of Tilsit concluded. Now that the Ukase interfered with Napoleon's plans, the French tyrant, unable to tolerate an eastern empire that threatened his ambition to rule the world, began arming on a vast scale.

Russia also started to prepare her army and to organize munitions and supplies for the great conflict which was imminent. The Tsar could rely on considerable help from the West in the carrying out of his rearmament programme.

American freighters brought British machinery and munitions to Kronstadt and Archangel, while an enormous number of Europeans hurried to join the Tsar's army—mostly Prussians, but also Frenchmen. Russian troops were once again being trained by experienced foreign officers, as in the time of Peter and the Ivans.

Lieutenant-Colonel Friedrich Karl Baron von Tettenborn, an Austrian officer from Baden, took over the training of the Cossack troops. A French general, Count Langeron, a German general, Count von Bennigsen from Hanover, General Barclay de Tolly, member of a Scottish noble family settled in Mecklenburg and Livonia, who became Minister of War in 1810 and Commander-in-Chief of the Western Armies in 1812; a Prussian, Colonel von Boyen, who had helped Scharnhorst reform the Prussian army—they all served in Russia. General Count zu Wittgenstein and his Chief of Staff, Count von Diebitsch, were also Germans, whose fathers had previously served as generals in the Russian Army. It was Diebitsch who in 1812 signed the Convention of Tauroggen with General Yorck, and thus began the War of Independence against Napoleon.

Karl Reichsfreiherr vom und zum Stein, the great Prussian statesman and reformer, had been exiled by Napoleon. He now went to Russia as adviser to the Tsar Alexander, and summoned the ardent patriot, Ernst Moritz Arndt, to work with him.

The beginning of 1812 was decisive. Prussia joined France in the preparations for the attack on Russia and was compelled to contribute an auxiliary corps of 20,500 men to the *Grande Armée*. In consequence three hundred Prussian officers left the service and hastened to Russia, among them Major von Clausewitz.

When Clausewitz arrived at Vilna, the headquarters of the Tsar and General Barclay de Tolly, in April 1812, he found a number of Prussian officers already there.

'The Tsar wished to exercise the supreme command,' says Clausewitz. 'He had been instructed in strategy for several years by Lieutenant-General von Phull. Phull had worked out a plan of campaign in St Petersburg. This plan was now being implemented at Vilna.'

Karl Ludwig August von Phull, once a member of Frederick the Great's general staff and later Chief of Staff to Frederick William III, had been in the Russian service since 1806. 'He had the idea,' says Clausewitz, 'of retreating voluntarily into the Russian interior, thereby drawing nearer to his reinforcements, gaining time, weakening the enemy—who would be forced to split up his forces—and achieving opportunities for strategic attacks upon the enemy's rear and flanks. This idea appealed to the Emperor; it reminded him of Wellington's campaign in Portugal in 1811.'

The basis of the 'Phull Plan', as it was later called, was to make the most of Russia's natural advantages—its severe climate and its great distances—in order to defeat the *Grande Armée*. The Russians had no wish to fight a decisive battle. They planned to sidestep Napoleon's attacks and thus lure him into the interior of their country. There he would find himself fighting against a vacuum, while his lines of supply and his communications grew longer, thinner and more vulnerable.

When the *Grande Armée* crossed the Memel on 24th June 1812, the soldiers found nothing on the far bank save an empty countryside, a veritable desert. All the villages had been burnt. There was no resistance anywhere. Napoleon failed to understand how the Russian Army could abandon Lithuania and Poland without a struggle.

On June 28th the French reached Vilna, but the Russians had retreated to the Dvina and the Dniepr and the two main Russian armies joined forces at Smolensk.

There a violent bloody battle was fought on 17th August, but when darkness fell the Russians once again retreated most skilfully, having first set fire to Smolensk.

However, there was a growing feeling of anger and disgust in Russia at these retreating tactics, particularly in Moscow and St Petersburg. Alexander gave in to public opinion and was compelled to sacrifice a foreigner; Field Marshal Barclay de Tolly was dismissed and a Russian, Mikhail Ilarionovich Kutuzov, was appointed to succeed him.

It made no difference. Only once, at Borodino on 7th September, did Kutuzov fight the *Grande Armée*. Then he continued to retreat, in accordance with the 'Phull Plan', although he met violent opposition at a Council of War.

On 14th September, leading units of the French van, advancing in open order, climbed the Sparrow hills outside Moscow, where Lomonossov University now stands. The next day Napoleon, from the windows of the Kremlin, watched the blazing fires lit by the Russians. This foreshadowed the approaching end of the *Grande Armée*.

Napoleon had over-reached himself, and must inevitably retreat, just as Phull had foreseen.

'Napoleon waits in vain,' Pushkin says in his *Eugene Onegin*. The year 1812 became a heroic legend, extolled by the greatest Russian poets and composers. All Russians rejoiced, though they had hated the idea of the retreat. The world admired the brilliance of the 'Russian' tactics and strategy, and Tolstoy's *War and Peace* is still read by millions. Certainly this novel is brilliantly written, and in general historically accurate, yet it overlooks one contemporary document of great interest. Tolstoy does not mention the letter which Alexander I wrote on 13th December 1813, when he was in Frankfurt on his way to Paris, to his old friend and adviser, Karl Ludwig

August von Phull. The Tsar, who usually spoke of 1812 as the year of the intervention of the 'hand of God', gives considerable credit to Phull:

'I have just come from the banks of the Moskva River to the banks of the Rhine, and I feel that I must write and thank you. If I now have any knowledge of strategy, I owe this to you, who initiated me into its first principles. But I owe you much more. It is you who planned the campaign which, with the help of Providence, saved Russia, and has finally saved Europe too.'

In 1812 the Slav empire once again had the opportunity of using suitable prisoners of war for its own purposes. 'The Russian Government,' Holzhausen tells us, 'wishes to take advantage of this opportunity and to persuade some of the prisoners that they settle in the country and work; it is a unique chance of raising the Russian standard of living.'

The Tsar Alexander's delegation to the Congress at Vienna in 1814 included the ambassador, Count Stackelberg; the Minister for Foreign Affairs, Count Karl Robert von Nesselrode; a diplomatic plenipotentiary, Johann Protasius Baron von Anstett; a Corsican, Carlo Andrea Count Pozzo di Borgo, later Russian Ambassador in Paris; a Greek, Joannes Anton Count Capo d'Istria; and an expert on Polish questions, himself a Pole, Prince Adam Czartoryski. This impressive group contained only one Russian-born diplomatist, Count André Razumovski.

At the end of the Congress of Vienna, on 9th June 1815, Russia put the question to her ally, Prussia: 'How shall we build our peace?' The answer, also supplied by Russia, was that in return for past help in the War of Independence against Napoleon, Prussia should cede Silesia, Further East Prussia and South Prussia—to Russia!

By the continuous acquisition of new lands in the north, east and west, Russia had become the largest country in the world; yet even the four million square miles of Siberia, a district larger by one-third than the entire United States, did not satisfy her lust for land. She looked towards Europe, to the Near and Middle East, and ceaselessly 'acquired more Russian soil', without however bothering to cultivate these vast new territories.

After 1917 the Soviets continued the tradition of annexation begun by the Tsars and nowadays the world is informed that 'Russian Columbuses' will claim the planets for Moscow. 'Our trouble is that we are incapable of moderation,' Dostoevsky once remarked.

It was not enough that after the Congress of Vienna Alexander I had increased Russian territory, in comparison with the empire of his grandmother, Catherine II, by over a quarter of a million square miles. Russia was now preparing to expand to the Pacific coast and to America.

In 1806 Nikolai Rezanov sailed into San Francisco. He planned to populate California with Russian settlers, and to annex this coast for Russia. That he might learn to know the people, he became engaged to the daughter of the

*From Fort Ross: built
in 1812 to the north
of San Francisco,
California was to have
been gradually taken
over by the Russian–
American Company.*

Spanish Governor of San Francisco, Doña Concepción. When Rezanov
died on the return journey to Siberia, a fur merchant named Baranov, from
Alaska, continued with the project. A Russian vessel appeared off the
Californian coast in 1808, under the command of Ivan Kusskov. Kusskov
found a suitable landing-place north of San Francisco, in Bodega Bay, and
began the 'collection of Russian soil'. All along the coast of California, they
put up large standards bearing the Russian coat of arms and, in Cyrillic,
the inscription: 'This is Russian territory.' In 1812 Kusskov built a powerful
fortress covering the estuary of the river which is still called the Russian
River. And the fort is still called 'Fort Ross'. The port in Bodega Bay was
named, after the Russian Prime Minister, 'Rumyantsev', and on the
Farallone Islands off San Francisco a Russian 'hunting-base' was built.

Minister Count Nikolai Petrovich Rumyantsev, who retired from public
life in 1812, equipped a ship at his own expense, the brig *Rurik*, named after
Russia's Swedish creator, which was to sail round the world. There was no
Russian research scientist on board, but only Adelbert von Chamisso of
Berlin, a Frenchman by birth and the author of *Peter Schlemihl*. In 1816 the
Rurik cast anchor in San Francisco. The Commander, Otto von Kotzebue—
the son of the Weimar poet, August von Kotzebue—stayed there for two
months and, by his overbearing manner, made it plain that Russia, after
having annexed Alaska, now considered herself the ruler of California.

When the Russians landed on the west coast of America, they immediately
came face to face with the Americans, for the Star-Spangled Banner had been
hoisted much earlier—in 1784, one year after the end of the War of
Independence—on the Pacific Coast. American ships regularly traded with
the west coast. Now these traders began to ship furs to China which had
closed the port of Canton to all Russian ships, and thus came into direct
opposition with the Russian traders. In 1805 President Jefferson sent the
first expedition under Lewis and Clark across the Rocky Mountains to the
Pacific. In 1808 Johann Jacob Astor, a German from Waldorf near Heidelberg, drafted plans for a fur trading company with trading-posts extending

to the Pacific. In 1811, two expeditions equipped by Astor entered the area which is now the state of Oregon, one by land, the other by sea, and founded the settlement called Astoria, at the mouth of the Columbia River.

As soon as the Russians heard of the presence of Americans on the Columbia River, the 'Russian-American Company' took drastic counter-action. They requested that the Tsar should send Russian men-of-war on regular patrol in the Pacific. The Russians were already complaining that the Americans sold firearms to the Indians.

But in 1811 and 1812 American exports were of great value owing to Napoleon's continental blockade, and the Tsar could not accede to the requests of his subjects in America. The Russian invasion of the west coast had already alarmed the Americans; there were rumours that all California was soon to be annexed by the Russians. Looking far into the future, the journal *Nile's Weekly Register* prophesied: 'We shall soon see this nation— with its vast resources and its energetic government—active in every corner of the world.'

Besides this 'acquisition of land' in the west of North America, the Russians attempted to occupy certain islands in the Pacific. Adam Johann von Krusenstern, dropping anchor off the Hawaiian Islands during the first Russian voyage round the world, intended to use them as bases and supply stations for the fur trade between Alaska and Eastern Asia. In 1809 Captain Hagemeister, another German in the service of Russia, landed on the northern island of Kauai and persuaded the native chief, Kaumualii, to ask for Russian protection. Kaumualii, King of the two islands of Kauai and Niihau, was fighting against King Kamehameha, King of the principal island of Hawaii. The government at St Petersburg, involved in European events, could not then accept his offer and waited for a more favourable opportunity. This opportunity came when yet another German, Dr Georg Anton Scheffer, at the instigation of the fur merchant, Baranov, took the matter up. Scheffer, a ship's doctor employed by the 'Russian-American Company', was a clever man. To conceal his real intention he travelled to Hawaii on board an American ship. On Oahu he acquired property with the consent of King Kamehameha. However, two Russian ships had to rescue Scheffer from the other white settlers who had guessed what his real intentions were. He was still unwilling to abandon his plan, and revived the old relationship which Hagemeister had established with the rival King Kaumualii, who placed himself and his two islands under the protection of the Tsar, and granted a trading and colonization monopoly to the Russians.

On the island of Kauai, Scheffer ordered the building of a Russian stone fortress. This project had to be abandoned before it was completed. American settlers intervened and the Russians were driven out. This marked the end of Russian hopes in the Pacific. Nesselrode gives us the true reasons. The Russian government was afraid of political entanglements, for Russia was not yet strong enough to do without American imports and could not afford to jeopardize friendly relations with the United States for the sake of a few South Sea islands. 'What is curious about these enterprises,' the historian, Erwin Hölze remarks, 'is that the more successful ones were planned by Germans, and not by Russians.'

The sign of the Russian-American Company

After the burning of Moscow in 1812, there was a great deal of rebuilding to be done by Alexander I. Whole quarters of the city lay gutted and in ruins, and the fires had badly damaged the turrets and walls of the Italian-built Kremlin.

The Tsar created a 'Committee for the Reconstruction of Moscow'—with the Italian architect, Giuseppe Bove, as its president. At the same time plans were made for the embellishment of the capital on the Neva. A contemporary writes: 'Having successfully concluded his military campaigns, the Tsar wished to make St Petersburg more beautiful than any of the other European capitals he had visited. With this end in view, he decided to appoint an architectural committee, with Bétancourt as President.'

There were still many foreign artists living in Russia, such as the Italian, Giacomo Quarenghi, whom Catherine II had employed as court architect, and Vincenzo Brenna. Other highly talented architects included the Scot, Charles Cameron, and the Frenchman, Thomas de Thomon.

Now that St Petersburg was to be 'the most beautiful capital in Europe', and Alexander had given the word to 'catch up and overtake' the West in architecture, European artists and craftsmen were sent for. Once again they poured into the Slav empire. Painters, cabinet-makers, stucco-workers and sculptors came from Italy and from Swiss Ticino, followed by others from France. Despite their hatred of the French, inspired by Napoleon, most of the tutors in the rich and aristocratic Russian families were in fact French, though there were many Germans as well.

In 1813 the foreign colony suffered a heavy loss when Thomas de Thomon died in an accident. He was the French genius who gave St Petersburg its Exchange Building and in 1784 rebuilt the Grand Theatre (originally by

Tischbein). De Thomon's great Fountain of Neptune is world-famous, and it was he who planned the town of Odessa. He died as the result of a fall from a scaffold while inspecting the damage caused by a fire in the Grand Theatre. Tamara Talbot Rice comments on his death: 'Russia was thus deprived of a great master but she was so rich in architectural genius at the time that the loss was not as deeply felt as it would have been in any less prolific age.' Besides, a new star was in the ascendant. This was the incomparable Carlo Rossi, from Lugano.

Carlo had come to Russia as an eight-year-old boy with his mother, the prima ballerina, Gertrude Rossi, in 1787. The boy was very gifted and he was brought up in the house of Vincenzo Brenna, who was a father to him as well as a teacher. He learned to draw in his master's studio and accompanied Brenna to his building sites. At the age of eighteen he helped with building projects in Pavlovsk, in Gachina and at the castle of St Michael in St Petersburg. In 1802 Brenna took young Rossi on a trip to Florence. In 1809 he began work with a group of architects in Moscow, who were given the task of restoring old houses in danger of collapsing. Then he was engaged as architect by the new Governor-General, brother-in-law to the Tsar, and moved to Tver on the Volga. This was the real beginning of his career. His work in rebuilding the old palace of Tver was so much appreciated that he was made 'commissar' for all building in the province. It was owing to Rossi's talent and steady work over the years that Tver became one of the most charming and attractive provincial towns. Its 'Millionaya', running beside the Volga, has long been considered one of the loveliest streets in the world.

Back in St Petersburg in 1817 he started on the work of replanning that city which was to bring him world-wide fame. 'Rossi', says the Italian historian Lo Gatto, 'created a new and magnificent St Petersburg, with fine parks and gardens. He built the square before the Winter Palace, with its superb Triumphal Arch, the square of St Michael's, the Alexander Theatre and the adjoining Imperial Library, the Chernyshev Square, with the Ministries of the Interior and of Education, and finally the area between the Isaac Cathedral and the Neva, with the Senate House and the buildings of the Ecclesiastical Council.'

It is incredible what Rossi accomplished in only forty years in St Petersburg. At this period many other Europeans were at work there. In the office of the French Engineer-in-Chief Bétancourt—officially in charge of all building—the plans for palaces, mansions, churches, country houses and bridges multiplied.

With a total disregard for expense, hardly justifiable in a completely undeveloped country with millions of poverty-stricken serfs, Alexander approved of more and more new buildings, obsessed as he was by his determination that St Petersburg should surpass all other cities. Russia was to possess everything that the finest European architecture could produce, everything that the Tsar had seen and admired during his trips abroad, only bigger, better and, of course, more beautiful. He would often order whole rows of houses to be demolished and better, larger and more modern ones put up in their place.

When Lord Cathcart visited Russia in 1819, he wrote home:

'Since his visit to England the Emperor has had foot-pavements of excellent granite made all over the town, which was effected by a single order, that such a thing was to be done and requiring each individual to finish the part in front of his house, in default of which the police would finish it at his expense.'

In his history of St Petersburg, Lo Gatto wrote, without exaggeration:

'St Petersburg, originally planned by an Italian, Domenico Trezzini, would never have become what it was—a truly European capital—without the work of the three Italian architects, Rastrelli, Quarenghi and Rossi, whose names are for ever linked with the city's architectural history.'

In 1849 Rossi died of cholera, his splendid work uncompleted. Large parts of the town on the Neva still resembled a building site. Thirty years had passed since Alexander I laid the foundation stone for the Isaac Cathedral, intended to be the most magnificent church in all St Petersburg, but the building, begun according to the plans of the French architect Ricard de Monferrand, was less than half finished. For forty years thousands of serfs were engaged in draining the marshy ground where it was to stand. Even when the foundations seemed firm enough, work had to be interrupted more than once in order to reinforce them, as the ground began to subside.

When in 1858 the cathedral was at last officially consecrated in the presence of Alexander II, it possessed a magnificent tower, over three hundred feet high, built of granite, marble and bronze and filled with European treasures.

Above the magnificent portico, copied from the Pantheon in Rome, were huge bronze reliefs which had taken I. Vitali, Peter Clodt von Jürgensburg and Lemaire many years to make.

The seven huge bronze doors were embossed by Vitali, who also cast the enormous bronze gate, some twenty-five feet tall and half as wide.

The paintings on the ceiling were executed by Karl Pavlovich Brüllo and the Frenchman, P. V. Bassin. Brüllo—the Russians write it Bryulov and pretend that he was a Russian—was descended from a Huguenot family in Lüneburg named Brulleau. The beautiful stained-glass window in the sanctuary, depicting Christ's resurrection, was ordered in Munich and made by Bavarian craftsmen. The firm of Nicholls and Plincke in St Petersburg supplied the sacred vessels and ornaments, which were made of eighty pounds of gold and approximately one ton of silver. In the square before the cathedral stood the equestrian statue of Tsar Nicholas I, designed by Ricard de Monferrand and executed by the sculptor, Clodt von Jürgensburg.

For many years the Italian architect Domenico Adamini, from Bigogno, was in charge of building the cathedral. He was also responsible for the Catholic church in Tsarskoye Selo, and a number of palaces, villas and barracks.

Russia spent twenty-three million roubles on this one building, the Isaac Cathedral, and the ambition of the East was fulfilled. Western Europeans watched and wondered—just as they do today when the Soviets dazzle them with some 'product of concentrated effort' which is, in fact, a mere copy.

Meanwhile in Moscow, too, the damage had been repaired and the town beside the Moskva River was splendid once again in the new classical style which the Russians liked so much. It was by now traditional that such building was left to Italians, and to a group of builders from Ticino in Switzerland.

Giuseppe Bove, whom Alexander I had made president of the Recon-struction Committee, drew the plans for the large Bolshoi Theatre which was now rebuilt, and reopened in 1824. He also built the first municipal hospital and numerous private houses for the Russian aristocracy. Giovanni Battista Gilardi, from Montagnola near Lugano, and his gifted son, Domenico, created a technical school for the training of master builders, engineers and building contractors. Many French architects collaborated with the men from Ticino. In those years Gilardi built the University, the Defence Ministry, the National Bank and some lovely palaces in the country-side outside the city. Moscow owes to the German architect, Konstantin von Thon, the Cathedral of the Redeemer and the large Imperial Palace within the Kremlin, which cost twelve million roubles.

The Italians, Gonzago, Bibiena, Ferrari and Scotti, as well as Luigi Rusca, from Serocca d'Agno in Ticino, were masters of stucco work and of interior decoration. They ornamented the new buildings with flower designs, cherubs and arabesques.

The uncrowned kings of sculpture were Vitali and Triscorni, who ran a big studio in Moscow. Vitali's best works are the two fountains at Lubyanka and on the theatre square, and his Venus now in the Russian Museum at St Petersburg. Peter Clodt was primarily a sculptor of equestrian statues; the four horses of the quadriga on the Victory Gate, erected in 1838, are his work, as is the Triumphalnaya Vorota, huge equestrian figures on the bridge of the Nevsky Prospekt over the Fontanka. There used to be reproductions of those figures in the Berlin Lustgarten.

A new genius of the so-called 'Russian' school of painting was the Italian, S. Tonci (1756-1844) of Rome, 'a typical representative of that large number of foreigners who, after a long stay in Russia, and having got themselves Russian wives and families, ended by becoming Russians'.

Nobody realizes nowadays that the Russian romantic painter, Feodor A. Bruni, was an Italian!

It was not only St Petersburg and Moscow which felt the influence of this huge colony of artists, architects and craftsmen. There were many, whose names have been forgotten, at work in the provincial towns and in the Crimea. In the Caucasus, Giuseppe Bernardinazzi, from Pambio in Ticino, built the town of Pyatigorsk, and the work of his countryman, Luigi Rusca from Serocca d'Agno, can still be seen from the north of Russia right down to the Black Sea.

The old commercial city of Nijni Novgorod (now called Gorki) at the confluence of the Oka and the Volga had flourished in the sixteenth century. But for many years it had suffered from floods, which each spring submerged the ground reserved for the booths and stalls of the great annual fair. Within sight of the eleven turrets of the Novgorod Kremlin, erected by the Italian architect, Pietro Frasiano, in the years 1508 to 1511, Bétancourt, the architect-engineer, had the whole ground surface of the fairground raised artificially. He laid out a whole network of subterranean canals through which all the refuse and dirt could be sucked away by means of a steam-pump. Water for extinguishing fires was also laid on. Sixty stone warehouses and over two and a half thousand booths and stands were erected on this vast fairground, the most modern then in existence.

The mania for enormous cathedrals and vast palaces, and for the acquisition of valuable art collections, was in sharp contrast to the unbelievably old-fashioned cultural and economic conditions prevalent in the country. Russia preened herself in borrowed plumes; but this was simultaneously the country of Gogol's *Dead Souls*, the country of which Pushkin said: 'O God, how sad our Russia is!'

Suspicion and distrust of Europe did not prevent Nicholas I (1825-55), the younger brother and reactionary successor of Alexander I, from employing all the talents of the West—in art, science or technology—in so far as these were available to, and exploitable by, Russia. Thus one day the Tsar called upon Alexander von Humboldt, the famous geographer and explorer of South and Central America. The Tsar wished him to lead an expedition across Russia, and was prepared to put all available means at his disposal.

On 29th April 1829, after a magnificent gala dinner given by the Tsar, the German guest was honoured with a reception at the Academy of Sciences in St Petersburg. Here, as at the university in Moscow, Humboldt met many old friends and acquaintances from Germany. He talked to Professor Gotthelf Fischer, a former fellow-student from the College of Mining Engineering at Freiberg, who because of his services as Curator of the Natural History Museum in Moscow had been ennobled and had acquired the name of 'von

Waldheim'. He also met his old teacher from Jena, Justus Christian Loder, under whom he and Goethe had once learnt to dissect human bodies.

From Moscow they set out on a most unusual expedition. Humboldt covered over fifteen thousand versts in twenty-three weeks—that is to say, some sixty miles a day—and went right across the whole vast country to the distant Fort Krasnye Tsarkie on the Chinese border. Couriers on horse-back rode in advance of the German scientists, and for the whole journey every detail was prepared in advance, so that nothing should go wrong. More than twelve thousand horses were held ready at five hundred stages, and it was the same story with the ferry-boats and ships. For five hundred miles were covered by water and they had to cross rivers fifty-three times—the Volga alone ten times, the Kama twice, the Irtysh three times and the Ob twice.

The inexhaustible Humboldt and his companions travelled by day and by night, through the northern and central Urals, measuring the altitude above sea-level, taking compass bearings and collecting specimens of minerals.

From the Urals he wrote a few lines to the Russian Minister of Finance, Kankrin: 'The Ural district is a veritable El Dorado and I predict—for similar experiences in Brazil make it seem likely—that during your term of office diamonds will be found there.'

'Kankrin', incidentally, was another name for the German lawyer, Georg Franz Krebs, from Hanau on the Main. The name had been latinized, as was the fashion of the time: the Latin *cancrinus* ('Krebs' or 'crab') became Kankrin. The father of Finance Minister Kankrin had already been employed in Russia. From 1784 onwards he had set up and run the great salt-mines of Staraya Russa in the province of Novgorod, having been appointed to this job by Catherine's Governor, Sievers.

The truth of Humboldt's prediction was soon established. The Russians followed the advice of the German scientist, and found diamonds in the district he had indicated in the Urals.

In Kazan Humboldt met the mathematician, Nikolai Ivanovich Lobachev-sky, and the astronomer, Simonov, and together they made observations of the sky and of the magnetic field. In the mathematician Lobachevsky, Hum-boldt found a congenial partner as he was a truly great Russian scientist. He had invented—in collaboration with Bolyai, the Hungarian—non-Euclidean geometry which was to be so important in modern physics. However, he owed the inspiration for his mathematical discoveries to the 'Prince of Mathematicians', Karl Friedrich Gauss, from Göttingen, who dared not publish his research work because he feared the usual violent outcry of the philistines against anything that their minds cannot grasp. Lobachevsky wrote in German and French.

When Humboldt returned to Germany in December 1829 he immediately wrote down the results of his spectacular journey across an entire continent.

Three works were published: *Fragments de Géologie et de Climatologie Asiatiques* in two volumes (1832), *Asie Centrale* in three volumes (1843) and *Journey to the Urals, Altai and the Caspian Sea* in two volumes (1837–1842). They were made full use of in Russia the moment they appeared.

Russia was generous to Humboldt, and his expedition more than repaid that generosity. For the rest the spiritual horizon had darkened since Nicholas I succeeded to the throne. Fearing liberal ideas from the West, Nicholas tried to resist Western influence whenever and wherever he could.

One of his first acts was to forbid young Russians from studying abroad. A special Imperial permit was only granted in exceptional cases. The principal subjects taught in Russia were Russian language and literature, history and folklore, Russian geography—and statistics. The police were empowered to investigate the education being given to children in the private houses of the nobility and rich bourgeois families, as well as the curriculum in all private schools, and thus to ensure that the Imperial decree was carried out.

This was a step backwards. The importation of culture from the West, however, continued even under this Tsar. The cultural forces active in Europe were too powerful to be resisted and their pressure against the cultural vacuum in the East was overpowering.

It is one of the ironies of fate that nineteenth-century Europe furnished Russia with a number of ideas which were enthusiastically accepted at the time, were developed and distorted, and finally misused in the fanatical attack of East upon West.

The seed of German romanticism, planted by Herder at the end of the previous century, became aggressive pan-Slavism. Every nation, Herder had taught in Germany, is one instrument in the symphonic orchestra that is entrusted with the fugue of human history. This led to an enthusiastic nationalism in Germany, where the romantic poets collected the stories and fairy tales, legends and folklore, and traditional beliefs of the multiform German race. But they did not merely delve into their own past; they also investigated that of Russia.

Herder uttered these prophetic words, addressing the people of Russia 'who have suffered so much'. 'The wheel of time keeps turning, and your people, who are now so oppressed, and who were yet once hard-working and happy, will be awakened again from their long sleep and freed from the chains of slavery. . . . They will delight in their fair countryside, celebrate their traditional festivals, and enjoy once again the fruits of their peaceful labour.'

Despite the censorship, the ideas of Herder and of the romantic school, their discovery of the 'Slav soul', found their way to the East. With what result? As soon as Russia had grasped its significance it transformed the romantic notion of Slav individualism into a weapon for use against the countries where this idea had originated. Pan-Slavism, a creed of hatred, was born; it became the mainspring of a Russian nationalism whose principal feature was to be xenophobia.

In the reign of Nicholas I the slogan about the 'corrupt west' became current. It is still being used in Soviet propaganda today.

Nevertheless the number of factories equipped with foreign machinery and run by foreign engineers increased very considerably. There were 4,578 factories in 1820, whereas in 1850 the total was 9,843, or more than double.

Western European manufacturing techniques were introduced into the Empire of the Tsar by the English, the Germans, and—after the so-called 'Patriotic War' of 1812—by French prisoners. B. Ischchanian has stated in an economic treatise: 'During the period of mechanization they were the forerunners of the technical revolution in manufacturing methods.'

Two Germans, Emil Zündel and Albert Hübner, introduced the first machines for printing cotton goods in Russia. They founded factories in Moscow. There a French subject, Steinbach, from Alsace, started a cotton factory in 1825. In St Petersburg three Englishmen, Hubbard and the brothers John and Joseph Shaw, built spinning and weaving mills, while James Thornton created a cloth factory.

A Russian saying proves the importance of one major foreign innovator in the textile industry better than any statistics. It runs: 'Where there is a church there is a priest, and where there is a factory there is a Knoop.' (*Gde tserkov—tam pop, a gde fabrika—tam Knop.*)

Ludwig Knoop from Bremen came to Moscow as a representative of the firm of Jersey, and immediately started to import spinning machines from England. But as nobody in Russia could operate them, he engaged 'a whole colony of English masters and craftsmen, especially from Lancashire, the centre of the textile industry at that time'. In the 1840's and '50's he built a chain of spinning mills which he operated 'with English personnel, mechanics, foremen and experienced artisans'. He did the same for weaving. Several such English-run factories were soon under Knoop's control. He ordered all his spinning machines from the well-known firm of Platt Brothers, the steam engines from Hick Hargreaves, and later from John Musgrave and Sons. His factory on the island of Kränholm near St Petersburg became famous, and his mechanized spinning works on an island at Narva were 'one of the biggest enterprises not only in Russia, but in the whole of Europe' (B. Ischchanian). Ludwig Knoop built one hundred and twenty-two spinning mills in Russia.

Imports from America—primarily cotton—had been arriving for some thirty years, when the first wave of technicians from the New World followed the cargo ships across the Atlantic. The year 1842 marked the

Programme of the opening of the first Russian railway, St Petersburg–Tsarskoye Selo–Pavlovsk. The railway was built by the German von Gerstner.

beginning of the enormous technical development work which the United States later carried out in Russia. In that year the American, Major George Washington Whistler, the father of the famous painter, arrived at St Petersburg. He was to build Russia's first big railway, with the help of a large number of his countrymen. The plans had been drafted ten years before by an Austrian.

At the beginning of the 1830's, Franz Anton von Gerstner, Professor of Applied Geometry at the Polytechnic Institute in Vienna, came to Russia. During his visits to the mines and factories, he realized how incredibly backward Russian communications were. He therefore drafted a very far-sighted plan. At an audience which he contrived to secure with Nicholas I, he showed the Tsar his project for a widespread rail network covering the whole of Western Russia, connecting Moscow, St Petersburg, Odessa, and Taganrog, and linking the Baltic with the Volga and the Black Sea. This would not only serve the interests of trade but also ensure the rapid movement of troops.

The Tsar was enthusiastic about the project, but the Minister of Finance, Kankrin, objected strongly to the enormous expense involved. Nicholas I finally consented to a 'specimen railway'—fifteen miles of line from St Petersburg to Tsarskoye Selo and Pavlovsk.

Gerstner could not begin his work until the end of 1835, when British capital was made available for the project. On 7th October, the first train on Russian soil steamed out of St Petersburg to the favourite residence of the Imperial court at Tsarskoye Selo, over tracks laid by Gerstner. He had meanwhile solved the problem of snowdrifts by digging ditches on either

The Alexandrovsk works near St Petersburg, run by the American engineers
Harrison and Weyness for the manufacture of railway equipment for the route St
Petersburg–Moscow. They also built the first Russian locomotives, one of which is
shown opposite.

side of the track. This track was extended to Pavlovsk. The engines, trucks
and rolling-stock came from England.

Soon after this Gerstner visited the United States on Russia's behalf and
a few months after his death—he died there on 12th April 1840—a Russian
commission arrived in America, as a result of his enthusiastic reports. Kraft
and Melnikov looked at the new double tracks of the Baltimore and Ohio
Railway and followed Gerstner's advice. They engaged Major George
Washington Whistler, one of the men who had built the American railway
system from the Atlantic to the interior of the continent. It was Whistler
who then built the first important railway in Russia, the line between St
Petersburg and Moscow. His chief assistant was Thomas Winans, the son
of the famous American railroad engineer, Ross Winans.

The American engineer carried out his task with masterly skill. He rode
a horse along the proposed line of the track for 405 miles and drew up
detailed plans for the Tsar based on Gerstner's original ideas. In order to save
money he suggested that all the materials needed for laying the track be
made in Russia itself.

All attempts, however, to produce sufficient materials on their own
account failed, and the government was obliged to accept another suggestion
of Whistler's. The 'Alexandrovsk' factory, founded in St Petersburg in 1844,
was entrusted to two American engineers, Harrison and Weyness, for the
production of the materials for the new railway. A second factory, which
was to be of vital importance to Russian industry, was established in
Kolpino, also by Whistler's people. Americans were detailed to instruct
Russian railway personnel in technical and administrative duties.

The 'Russian broad gauge' is due to the American, Whistler. It differs
from the European in that the width of the Russian track is 1·5 metres,

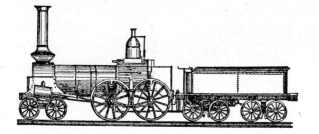

while the European (Spain and Portugal excepted) is 1·435 metres. When Whistler first explained his idea of a broad gauge to the Russians they were so enthusiastic that it was difficult to restrain them. His employers immediately decided they must have an even broader gauge, 'because', they said, 'such a broad country needs a broad gauge.'

Part of the line from St Petersburg to Kolpino, some seventeen miles, was finished in 1847. In that year Whistler was awarded the order of St Anne by the Tsar himself. For this indefatigable engineer had also built new docks in Kronstadt, had put up stone and iron bridges over the Neva, had drafted a plan for canalizing the Dvina, and had constructed the huge iron roof of the National Riding Academy. In 1851 the rails reached Moscow. Some four hundred miles were now ready for use, with 2,000 carriages and trucks built in Russia by American engineers, and 164 locomotives. On 31st March 1851 the line was officially opened. It now took only twenty-two hours to cover a distance that previously took four days and four nights.

The line was called the 'Nicholas Railway'. Whistler did not live to see this day, for Asiatic cholera had carried him off in 1849. With the 'Nicholas Railway'—built by the United States—a new and vital element came into existence, the economic importance of which was soon apparent. For the first time great quantities of the agricultural goods exported by Russia, such as cereals and hemp, could be transported quickly and cheaply from the interior to a seaport.

Russian illustration of the opening of the first long-distance railway route, St Petersburg–Moscow, built by Americans in 1851 under the direction of George W. Whistler.

This commission given to Whistler was not the only one the United States received. 'The success of Major Whistler created an atmosphere very favourable to an extension of commerce between the United States and Tsarist Russia,' said Vice-President Henry A. Wallace, describing his special mission to Soviet Asia and China in 1943. 'American steam excavators and pile-drivers were imported for use on public works. Tsar Nicholas I later sent to America for bridge builders and millwrights, much as Peter the Great had sent to Holland for blacksmiths and carpenters. Almost every steamer brought some enterprising son of New England, and one Yankee was even elected an honorary member of the Imperial Society for his work in improving Russian agriculture.'

New freighters, steamers and corvettes were ordered in the United States. The American Minister, Charles S. Todd, reported that of fourteen liners sailing the Black Sea almost all were built in the Eckford and Rhoades yards in New York.

During the years 1840 to 1860 American inventors, engineers, contractors and speculators bombarded the American Embassy at St Petersburg and the Imperial Government offices with letters and specimen implements, particularly ploughs and other farming tools, despite the fact that the Tsar had issued a Ukase forbidding 'unknown persons to send presents to members of the Imperial Government'.

But Nicholas himself could not resist the tempting American products. When he heard that the yacht *America* had won the prize in a regatta against the whole English Royal Yacht Squadron, he immediately ordered a model of the *America* built for himself. And when Cornelius Vanderbilt visited St Petersburg in his yacht *North Star*, Nicholas I ordered his naval engineers to make drawings of the yacht in secret. An American dentist, Dr Edward Maynard, the inventor of gold fillings, was awarded a medal for treating the Tsar's teeth and giving him gold inlays.

Bétancourt, the 'Engineer in charge of Reconstruction' in St Petersburg, built his much-admired suspension bridge on the Champs de Mars and the so-called Egyptian suspension bridge over the Fontanka near the Trinity Church. The senior engineer, Kerbeds, built the Nicholas Bridge, of granite and iron, with a movable opening to allow the passage of ships. The iron for the construction work was supplied by Kolpino, the huge ironworks built by Whistler on the left bank of the Neva, which was managed by two Englishmen after the Americans left. Fine metal and iron products, railings for gates, chains for bridges or candelabra—not to mention the heavy iron grilles for the Nicholas Bridge—all bore the name of 'Baird', after the owner of an ironworks which is still mentioned in the *Baedeker* of 1900 as worthy of notice. A contemporary report of the time of Nicholas I says of Baird that this Englishman 'produced nine-tenths of all the work which the government commissioned'.

During this period of very heavy 'foreign production' the attempts made under Catherine II by General Baier to supply the Old Palace on the Moskva River with fresh drinking water were at last realized thanks to the magnificent new Moscow Waterworks. With the help of two steam engines imported from England, '550,000 buckets of water' were pumped into the Moscow water-tower for distribution to the city.

Under the supervision of the great Munich master builder, Leo von Klenze, assisted by the Russian court architect, Andreas Stakenschneider, a complete rebuilding of the vast Hermitage at St Petersburg began in 1840. The Winter Palace, heavily damaged by fire in 1837, was also rebuilt.

And how did the Russian populace react to all this?

A Russian nobleman named Yuri Samarin visited the Baltic provinces and then wrote a book which was distributed illegally. In this *Letter from Riga* he demanded that the German builders be dismissed. Tsar Nicholas, who read the pamphlet and was afraid it might lead to trouble, had Samarin arrested on 5th March 1849 and imprisoned him in the Peter and Paul Fortress. Twelve days later he ordered that he be brought to the Winter Palace. During the interrogation to which the Tsar now subjected Samarin, Nicholas said to him: 'You exaggerate when you say that from the time of Peter I to my own we have all been surrounded by Germans and have thus become Germans ourselves. You have openly incited hatred of the Germans by pointing out the difference between Russians and Germans instead of promoting friendly relations. You damn whole classes who have loyally served Russia. Starting with Count Pahlen, I could name some one hundred and fifty devoted German generals. I have sent you to the fortress that you may reflect on what you have done.'

Although Russia was not yet in a position fully to exploit the latest achievements of foreign countries, she had her spies everywhere. 'We should be on our guard against Russian agents, who are at work among us, for purposes of their own,' wrote Frédéric Lacroix in 1845, in Paris. 'They have orders to observe all new discoveries in the arts and in industry and to obtain the secrets behind such discoveries in the interest of Russia. Their leader styles himself "Representative of the Imperial Ministry of Finance". These agents appear to patronize the arts and industry, so as to make the manufacturers believe that the Russians appreciate merit and genius more than any other people, that they encourage progress, that they reward useful service, and that they cherish all men of talent who trust the Russians.

'The real object behind all this is that Russia wants to compete with our industry. She is therefore interested in stealing our newest patents. Their agents lavish promises on our manufacturers and flatter them, tempting them with high-sounding but meaningless titles. They seek their confidence and sometimes manage to wheedle their secrets out of them, thus depriving them of their best source of income. Quite a number of our countrymen personally known to me have fallen victim to these scandalous tricks. They have given away the most detailed explanations of their projects, and have thus thrown away the basis of their prosperity. They have only realized later that Russia has exploited their indiscretions for her own purposes.'

Such warnings remained unheeded, then as now. Russia put out feelers in every direction, seeking contacts. The apparatus worked very skilfully, and an inclination to conceal nothing from Russia was apparent long before the activities of Klaus Fuchs.

On the night of 11th October 1843, the Munich historian, Professor Jakob Phillipp Fallmerayer, invited the Russian poet, Feodor Ivanovich Tyuchev, an enthusiastic pan-Slavist, to his house. The two had been acquainted for many years, but now there was a definite purpose behind the Russian's visit. Tyuchev, who had been a member of the Russian Embassy at the court of the King of Bavaria from 1822 to 1837, had returned on a political mission. In 'a lengthy secret discussion' he let the cat out of the bag. He asked the Bavarian scholar whether he would be willing to propagate Russian interests in Europe in return for a 'regular income from the Tsar'. Fallmerayer firmly rejected the offer. A similar proposal had been previously made to the Munich philosopher, Franz von Baader, who had accepted it. 'It seems as though whole generations have been stricken by blindness,' wrote Leopold von Ranke from Berlin at this time. 'They are paving the way for the common enemy.' And Friedrich List repeatedly pointed out in the Augsburg *Allgemeine Zeitung* from 1827 to 1846 that Russia was a menace, particularly in economic matters, because of the gigantic potential of the Russian empire. Who heeded him?

Russia's attitude, once she believed herself to be sufficiently powerful, became apparent after the middle of the century. Russian ambition was directed at Constantinople, which had been coveted by the Russians ever since the days of the Kiev State a thousand years before. Aware of his influence and power, Nicholas I was determined to solve the 'Eastern question', as it was called in diplomatic circles. He made up his mind to give the 'sick man of the Bosphorus' his death-blow.

With no declaration of war a Russian army suddenly crossed the Pruth on 2nd July 1853, and occupied Moldavia and Wallachia. The pretext was that Russia was holding this territory as a pledge for her just demands— namely to ensure the protection of the orthodox Christians in Turkey. The Turks requested that the Russians retire, and when no notice was taken of this they too mobilized. On 1st November Nicholas declared war on Turkey.

England and France attempted to intervene. They proposed a cease-fire and urged the Tsar to evacuate the Danubian principalities and the Black Sea. The Russians refused. An alliance was made between the Western powers and Turkey, and on 25th March 1854 war was declared, 'to protect Europe from the dominance of a power which violates treaties and defies the civilized world'. The conflict thus became a European one—the Crimean War.

Under the command of the French General Canrobert and the British General Lord Raglan, Allied troops, reinforced by a contingent of Sardinians, captured the Crimean fortress of Sevastopol, which had been bravely defended by the Russian general Edward von Totleben, a Baltic German by birth.

A few months before the fall of Sevastopol, Nicholas I died. His son and successor, Alexander II, was obliged to accept the conditions laid down in the Treaty of Paris of 1856. Russia ceded the estuary of the Danube to the principality of Moldavia. She also abandoned her claim to be the sole protector of the Christians in Turkey, and the Black Sea was neutralized.

For the rebuilding of Sevastopol the Russians managed to engage a foreign expert who carried out a technically brilliant job. To block the passage to enemy vessels during the siege, the Russians had sunk eighty ships in the harbour entrance, among them the *Vladimir* and the *Turk*. There appeared to be no other way of removing these obstacles save blowing them up. Nobody in Russia was capable of refloating the sunken vessels. It was again shown how well the Russian Embassies functioned as sources of information. The finest expert on the salvaging of ships at that time was soon found. The Imperial Ambassador in Washington, Baron von Stoeckl, engaged an American engineer, Colonel John E. Gowen, who, as von Stoeckl knew, had managed to refloat the American man-of-war *Missouri*, sunk at Gibraltar.

Gowen had huge caissons built at Sevastopol, ordered 700 h.p. steam engines and began with the raising of the smaller ships of 1,000 tons. While working on the 5,000-tonners, the chains broke again and again, but Gowen solved the problem. He ordered from the British firm of Brown, Lennox and Co. the strongest chains which had ever been made, each single link weighing a hundred pounds. Thus he managed to refloat even the largest ships.

A whole fleet of eighty ships was once more operational and a vast fortune had been recovered. But the Russians treated the American very badly. He fought in vain to get his well-earned pay.

'I have been waiting for years, hoping that the Russian government would pay me, and show some fairness in this matter. I have sacrificed six years of my life and my whole fortune,' Gowen wrote in a letter dated 14th March 1876, from New York. Apart from a small sum on account Gowen was never paid.

The Russian defeat as a result of the rapid and unexpected Western counter-attack had shown the true weakness of the vast state. The saying that Russia was a colossus with feet of clay became a European common-place. It may have been true in the last century but it is now a dangerous illusion. Since the beginning of the twentieth century, Russia has become a very great power, due largely to the enormous industrial and scientific assistance received from the West. The 'colossus with feet of clay' delusion had fatal results for Germany in the Second World War.

The Crimean War opened Russian eyes. The rapid defeat was a lesson. They realized how backward their enormous country still was, for they had seen how the well-equipped and properly trained divisions of Western Europe could check their plans of further conquest. But a modern army, as they also realized, requires modern industry.

While the Tsar had been having magnificent palaces built by foreign architects, Russian production lagged far behind that of other countries. In 1800 Russia had produced about the same quantity of pig iron as England. In 1850 twice as much was produced in Russia as at the earlier date, but English production had meanwhile increased tenfold. Russia had dropped to eighth place among the iron-producing countries of the world and by 1860 was lagging behind Austria and even the comparatively small state of Prussia.

Now that the reactionary Tsar Nicholas was dead, the Russians realized the true reasons for their defeat. The country was still backward technically, economically, and above all in the education of its vast population. It was impossible to create modern industries with illiterates and serfs in the factories, for such men were only capable of unskilled labour. As early as 1837, the owners of factories in the Moscow district had complained to the Minister of Finance that the serfs were almost useless for any sort of work which required brains and judgment. Under the new Tsar, Alexander II, the Slav empire therefore adopted a new policy. Reforms were introduced according to the old principle, 'Copy the West, and catch up!'

In 1861 serfdom was abolished. Numerous new colleges and schools were opened and the universities were granted their autonomy. Henceforth students and teachers were once again allowed to travel in foreign countries and thousands availed themselves of this.

The gates to the 'corrupt West' were opened wide. Tempting offers were made with a view to enticing foreign capital, foreign engineers and foreign manufacturers. The Eastern State was determined to make up for lost time.

Prince Kropotkin, in his recollections of his youth, describes how decent organization now led for progress in every field, and how the best instructors in Europe were brought to Russia. In his *Memoirs of a Revolutionary*, which he published as an émigré in London in 1906, he gives us a very instructive account of that period of history.

His country was just awakening 'from her deep slumbers and the nightmare of the reign of Nicholas I', when the fifteen-year-old Kropotkin and his two brothers joined the Corps of Pages at St Petersburg. This was in the year 1857. The first college for girls had also just been opened in the city on the Neva.

The government had engaged a Frenchman to take charge of the Corps of Pages, housed in a magnificent building designed by Rastrelli, and the director of studies was a highly qualified colonel of artillery, Winkler, whom Kropotkin describes as a 'brilliant mathematician and a liberal-minded man'. Instruction in science was given by Professor Roulier, who taught zoology for a time at Moscow University. Before Darwin's famous *Origin of Species* was published, the pupils of the St Petersburg Corps of Pages were told about the theory of evolution, or 'transformations' to use Kropotkin's word, by the French professor, Roulier. The teaching was extraordinarily up-to-date.

The latest theories from the West were included in the curriculum. The pupils were familiar with the ideas of the chemist, Karl Friedrich Gerhardt, and the physicist, Amedeo Avogadro. They learned about molecules and atoms. Kropotkin also mentions the great discovery which was to excite all scientists ten years later: the Periodic Law of chemical elements, a theory which was advanced simultaneously but independently by the Russian, Mendeleyev, and the German, Lothar Meyer. Kropotkin names these two scientists as the discoverers of the new Law, based on early work by the British scientist, Newlands. Today, however, Russian censorship has removed the name of Meyer, but they acknowledge the fact that Mendeleyev owed his skill in research to his years of study under two Heidelberg professors—Kirchhoff the physicist and Bunsen the chemist. Since the Soviet 'wave of inventors' set out to transform all the more important European discoveries into Russian ones, Russian textbooks and the lectures given by Soviet academicians mention only the name of Mendeleyev.

In the Corps of Pages, not only were there very efficient foreign teachers but the latest school-books from abroad were also used. 'Large numbers of books on special subjects were published at that time, in Russian translations,' Kropotkin tells us. He describes with enthusiasm how they 'stocked the laboratory with the instruments recommended by the excellent textbook for beginners written by Stöckhardt: *Lessons in Chemistry*, published in Chemnitz in 1846. With the help of this book we systematically carried out all our experiments . . .' Obviously an institution like the Corps of Pages in St Petersburg, which was reserved exclusively for four hundred high-ranking officers' sons, was far ahead of its time. Not until Sergei Yulievich, Count Witte (also of German origin, as his name suggests) was appointed Minister at the end of the century under the last Tsar, were technical schools built in large numbers.

Under the 'Reformer Tsar', Alexander II, Russia absorbed the technical and scientific progress of the West. Slowly at first, then more rapidly, the seeds grew which European teachers and scholars had sown throughout a century and more. By 1900 a few Russians had already achieved international renown.

'By 1890, or thereabouts, Russian scientists were nearly on the same footing as those in countries like Great Britain and Germany. Nearly but not quite—for Russia was technically and industrially a long way behind the Western nations,' writes Professor C. L. Boltz. And he adds: '. . . it is only in her contact with the West that Russia has ever produced scientists of note and scientific work that is read outside her borders.'

Indeed, not one of the great scientists of the Slav empire could achieve anything without first studying at the famous European universities. There was not one who did not work, at least for a time, with one of the great Europeans.

The gifted mathematician, Sophia W. Kovalevskaya, the first woman professor of mathematics in the world, studied at Heidelberg, Berlin and Göttingen, and later lectured in Paris, Berlin and Stockholm. Her husband, Vladimir Kovalevsky, a very competent palaeontologist and popular lecturer, studied in London, Heidelberg, Jena and Munich. Her brother-in-law, Alexander, well known for his work on the natural history of fishes, studied at Heidelberg and Tübingen.

The chemist, Alexander M. Butlerov—a great favourite with the Soviets—worked in 1857 with Karl Adolf Wurtz in Paris, before producing his theory of organic compounds. The biologist, Kliment A. Timiryasev, whose mother was English, and who is now cited by the Soviets as a brilliant example of Russian scholarship, lived for many years in Western Europe. It was there that he finished his education, which had begun in St Petersburg and was continued from 1866 to 1870 under French and English scholars—Boussingault and Berthelot in Paris and, like Mendeleyev, under Kirchhoff and Bunsen in Heidelberg. There he laid the foundation for his later work in spectral analysis, biophysics and biochemistry. Pyotr N. Lebedev, Russia's experimental physicist, worked in the West for nearly fifteen years. In 1886, at the age of twenty, he emigrated to Strasbourg, where he worked with the physicist, August Kundt. With his teacher, who had discovered a way of measuring aerial waves with 'dust particles', Lebedev went to Berlin University, where he attended Helmholtz's lectures on theoretical physics. When he returned to Russia in 1900 he published the result of his researches, which ranks among the classical works on physics, experiments which established a theory already advanced by Maxwell—that radiation pressure is exercised by light (and other) rays upon matter.

Nor would the achievements of the 'Father of Russian Physiology', Ivan M. Sechenov (1829–1905), have been possible without intellectual stimulus from the West and years of study in Europe. He had no sooner passed his examinations as a medical student at Moscow University than he went abroad. Johannes Müller, du Bois-Reymond, Helmholtz and Bunsen were his teachers. For two years after the completion of his studies in Europe, Sechenov lectured in Moscow. Then he returned to Paris. In the course of his research work there, while dissecting the brain of a frog, he discovered the nerve centre which controls the reflexes of the nervous system. These are named, after him, 'Sechenov cells'.

Sechenov's successor, Russia's greatest physiologist, Ivan Petrovich Pavlov (1849–1936) also worked in Western Europe. From 1884 to 1886 he studied blood circulation at German universities, first in the laboratory of Karl Ludwig in Leipzig, later on with Rudolf Heidenhain in Breslau. His work on the physiology of the digestive system made Pavlov the first Russian to win the Nobel Prize for medicine and physiology. His great achievement was his theory of 'conditioned reflexes'. This theory was intended to explain not only nervous reactions but also the conscious behaviour of human beings. Four years after Pavlov, the name of a Russian again appeared on the list of candidates for the Nobel Prize. This time the supreme scientific accolade was conferred upon a biologist, Ilya Mechnikov, who had then been working in the West for twenty years. Mechnikov had left Russia in 1888, at the age of forty-three, and had joined the Pasteur Institute in Paris where he had been co-director since 1904.

'Scratch a distinguished Russian'—to misquote Mme de Staël's famous epigram—'and you will find a product of the European universities.'

Yet there were ample facilities for research inside Russia. In the institutes and laboratories all the European technical literature as well as all the latest scientific apparatus were available to the students. True, 'the old Russia had practically no precision instrument industry, so essential for research work, and therefore had to import foreign apparatus,' as Dr Alexander Papkov, who worked at the Max Planck Institute of Physics in Heidelberg, has said. 'Therefore many German instruments were in use in the physics laboratories of the universities, made by Max Kohl and Leybold, electrical measuring apparatus from Siemens-Halske, von Hartmann and von Braun, scales from Sartorius and Bunge, barometers from Fuess, microscopes from Zeiss, Leitz and Reichert, monochrometers from Hilger, etc.'

With Western-made instruments on their laboratory benches and Western technical books in their libraries, the Russians achieved a great deal, often after long years of study under foreign teachers. Some surpassed the average in their contribution to the vast accretion of scientific knowledge. But no Russian has as yet risen to those solitary heights where all new ideas and truly revolutionary concepts have their origin.

While the Russians, in close contact with the West and particularly with Germany and France, were producing a certain amount of high-class scientific work, it was left to the Europeans and Americans to pioneer a different field, and one which was to be of vital importance to the future of Russia, namely the exploration of the Arctic regions.

The fact that the Russian empire failed to produce those 'Columbuses' which Lomonossov had prophesied, and thus could not even explore the regions 'on their own doorstep', is a fact unknown to the Soviet people of today. As usual in this field, as in that of scientific invention, the achievements and discoveries of other nations are misrepresented as being Russian in origin. The true facts about this perilous geographical enterprise are shrouded in mystery or simply falsified.

The official records in the USSR state that the 'first and most honoured place in the geographical exploration of the Arctic regions is held by Russian explorers'. Thus is it presented to the millions by Spirin in his book, *The Conquest of the North Pole*. 'For more than three hundred years men had been fascinated by the mysterious "top of the world". The foreign expeditions, however, were not interested in carrying out scientific exploration of the central Polar region. Such explorers were motivated by personal ambition and the hope of financial gain. The northern sea route was discovered and opened to navigation through the efforts of Soviet patriots.'

The exact opposite is true. Western Europeans and Americans found the northern passage, and 'Russian' contributions to the exploration of the high latitudes were made without exception by non-Russians, chiefly by Baltic Germans who provided the Eastern Empire with so many of its scholars, officers and officials.

In the nineteenth century, Baron von Wrangel, a lieutenant in the Russian Navy, initiated the exploration of the Siberian coast of the Arctic Ocean. Between 1820 and 1824 he made three expeditions, with sledges drawn by huskies, across the ice-packs of the Polar Sea as far as latitude 72°N, accompanied by a Frenchman, P. T. Anjou. They were looking for the mythical North Polar continent. On one occasion he sighted for the first time the island which bears his name. On these dangerous expeditions he covered some three and a half thousand miles, once travelling fifteen hundred miles in seventy-eight days. He got as far east as the Gulf of Kolyuchin. Wrangel was later promoted Admiral and Governor-General of 'Russian-America', i.e. Alaska, which was sold to the United States in 1876 against Wrangel's own bitter opposition.

In addition to Wrangel there were other 'Russian' explorers in the first half of the nineteenth century, such as Otto von Kotzebue, Feodor Count Lütke, Adam Johann von Krusenstern, G. von Maydell and Alexander Theodor von Middendorf.

In August 1849 a further expedition was made to the most distant part
of the Arctic Ocean, where Wrangel had had such success. A British
captain, Henry Kellett, sailing northwards from the Bering Straits, sighted
an island which he called Herald Island after the name of his ship. To the
west of this island he saw land, which he thought—as had Wrangel—must
be part of the Arctic continent. An American, the whale-hunter Long,
reached this place in 1867. Using astronomical calculations he established
the location of its western coast, wrote a detailed description of its southern
parts, and entered it on the chart under the name of the well-known explorer
as 'Wrangel Land'. In the summer of 1881 one of Long's countrymen,
Captain C. Hooper, landed there and annexed the territory for the United
States under the name of Columbia. In the same year Captain R. Berry,
of the United States Navy, discovered that Wrangel Land was an island.
Thirty years after its annexation by America, in 1911, the Russians built a
lighthouse on it. In 1921 Canadians arrived there, looking for a flying route
over the Pole. They were followed in 1923 by a group of Eskimos, led by
a trapper from Alaska. This did not prevent the Soviets, in the summer of
1924, from deporting all the inhabitants of Wrangel Island, using ice-
breakers for the purpose. The flag with the Soviet star was hoisted, and the
island declared Russian territory. In 1926 the Soviets colonized the island.
A party of six Russians, with fifty-four Eskimos and Chuktas, disembarked
there.

In 1872 an Austrian expedition sailed from Bremerhaven on board the
Tegetthoff, and provided the East with yet another 'Russian island'. Their
ship attempted to force a passage through the ice to the east of Spitzbergen,
but was caught in drifting ice north of Novaya Zemlya at 76°30′, and
drifted to 80° latitude, where one whole year later land was sighted. Using
dogs and sledges, the leaders of the expedition, Julius von Payer and Karl
Weyprecht, explored the rocky, ice-covered coasts of this group of islands,
which they called Franz Josef Land. Payer reached a point 82°5′N. These
islands were later occupied by the Soviets, and renamed Lomonossov Land.
It became the site of the most important Arctic airfield for Russian trans-
polar flights. But the greatest problem confronting Russia in the Arctic
regions was the North-East Passage, that 'northern sea route' for which
the Dane, Vitus Bering, had searched in vain.

From 1870 onwards this search drew closer to its objective, though this
was not due to any Russian explorer. In 1870, a Norwegian, Captain
Johannesen, circumnavigated the island of Novaya Zemlya, and in 1874 an
Englishman, Wiggins, sailed through the Kara Sea as far as the mouth of the
Yenisei. In the following year a Swede, Erik Nordenskjöld, in his sail-boat
Pröven, also went from the Kara Sea to the Yenisei. He repeated this journey
in 1876 in the steamship *Ymer*, and sailed up the river to 71°, thus opening
the Yenisei to shipping. Then Nordenskjöld set out on his last expedition.

With two ships, the *Vega* and the *Lena*, he sailed through the Kara Sea to the Yenisei in July and August of 1878 and thence, without trouble, to Cape Chelyuskin, the northernmost point of Asia, where he made landfall on 19th August. Nine days later both ships reached the mouth of the Lena. Here the *Lena* separated from the *Vega* and steamed up-river to Yakutsk. Thus the Lena River was also opened to shipping. At the end of September, when only one hundred and twenty miles from the Bering Straits and the Pacific, the *Vega* was caught in the ice. During the next ten winter months Nordensklöld and his colleagues carried out extensive research, paying particular attention to the almost unknown tribe of the Chukta.

By the middle of July 1879, the sea route was free of ice, and the *Vega*, braving the constant danger of being crushed by pack-ice, reached the Bering Straits in two days, arriving there on 20th July 1879. The North-East Passage had been found.

During the years that followed, the history of Arctic exploration contains many achievements by men of all the European nations and of the United States, but no Russian national is numbered among them.

In the same year of 1879, while Nordenskjöld was discovering the northern sea route, the first International Polar Conference met at Hamburg. This was due to the Austrian Weyprecht, and its work was continued by the International Polar Commission, presided over by Georg Neumayer, head of the German Marine Observatory. A third conference was held in St Petersburg in 1881. The Swiss meteorologist, Henrich Wild, now presided. He had been appointed head of the Russian Central Physical Observatory in St Petersburg, and had been carrying out a total reorganization of the Russian meteorological service since 1868; he had founded the Meteorological and Magnetic Observatory at Pavlovsk in 1876. At this 1881 conference a programme was drawn up for the International Polar Year of 1882–83. Russia was to be responsible for two of the twelve scientific stations in the Arctic region. The head of one of these was a lieutenant with the not very Russian name of Jürgens.

Ten years later the long series of German, Austrian and English expeditions culminated in the most daring one of all. In the years 1893–96, Fridtjof Nansen in the *Fram* drifted westwards in the pack-ice. From the newly discovered Siberian islands the ship drifted past the Pole to 85°N. With his companion, Johansen, Nansen reached 86°13′6″, where all further progress became impossible owing to impenetrable ice barriers. This expedition confirmed the fact that the area immediately surrounding the North Pole was deep ocean, covered by a layer of ice only ten or twelve feet thick.

Nansen's voyage in the *Fram* gave a strong new impetus to further Arctic exploration, and a Russian expedition was organized, the so-called Murman Expedition. It had a very obvious practical purpose—to investigate the possibilities of fishing and seal-hunting in the Bering Sea, using Kola

Bay as a base. Its leader was a Baltic German, Leonid Breitfuss, one of the greatest experts on Arctic conditions.

That was all Russia could achieve, but the West went on. Numerous expeditions followed one another, notably those of the American, Jackson (1888, 1893, 1894–97), of the Swede, Andrée, whose balloon flight to the Pole ended in disaster in 1897, of the Italian, Cagni (1899–1900), of the Norwegian, Amundsen, who traversed the North-West Passage in the years 1903 to 1910, and of the American, Wellman, who tried to reach the Pole by airship in 1906, 1907 and 1909. The years 1908 and 1909 brought the climax of all these courageous Western European enterprises, when two Americans, Frederick Cook (possibly) and Robert E. Peary (certainly), set foot on the Pole.

In 1904 the Russo-Japanese War brought home to the Tsar the imperative necessity of opening a sea route to the Far East, out of reach of any enemy. The Russians now recalled that the Siberian North-East Passage provided such a natural sea route on their very doorstep. Professor Breitfuss, the expert on Arctic questions, gave a lecture to a group of scientists and naval officers at the Imperial Navigation Society, which was enthusiastically received. Looking far ahead, Breitfuss produced so extensive a programme that to this day the Soviet government has been unable to carry it out in full. Breitfuss went into great detail, touching on such matters as the establishment of polar stations and a shuttle service of ice-breakers for convoys. He intended to render the Siberian rivers, Ob and Yenisei, navigable. He also planned to build a canal across the Chelyuskin Peninsula, making use of the existing rivers. Thus ships would be protected from the danger of ice. As a preliminary to all military and economic plans for the North-East Passage, Breitfuss presupposed thorough scientific exploration of the coastal regions.

The Tsar's government immediately began to put Breitfuss's plans into effect. Sixteen polar stations were set up for systematic meteorological observations. Two new ice-breakers were ordered. Since 1899 this vast country had only one such vessel at its disposal, the *Yermak*. On Breitfuss's advice, an 'Expedition for hydrographic research in the Arctic Ocean' set sail with the two new ice-breakers. In 1914 the Permanent Polar Commission at the St Petersburg Academy took over the planning. Breitfuss set up the first wireless stations, two on Novaya Zemlya, one on the Yamal Peninsula and one on Dickson Island.

Thanks to Professor Breitfuss, the Soviet government later had at their disposal not only several wireless and meteorological stations and ice-breakers, but also many trained scientists and research workers and, furthermore, a schedule planned for many years ahead. The Soviets also profited by the systematic exploration of the Arctic regions which was continued by men from all civilized countries, once 'the rush to the Pole' had ended. When we hear of Lenin's 'brilliant' idea of opening up the

North-East Passage, we might recall that he derived this idea from Leonid Breitfuss.

'Till the age of fifteen, I worked as a shepherd boy,' Khrushchev told an American audience in Los Angeles on 19th September 1959. 'Then I worked in a factory owned by a German, after that in a coal mine that was the property of a Frenchman, and in a chemical factory belonging to Belgians.'

This list of Khrushchev's employers gives a good insight into the development process which had begun long before the turn of the century. The rapid industrialization of the country was mostly carried out by Western Europeans. After the Crimean War, according to Schwartz, 'a consistent policy of encouraging and facilitating foreign capital investment, the import of technicians and technology from abroad, brought rich returns'.

Up to the First World War the West built, for the Tsar, all those economic and industrial bases which enabled the Soviets to carry out their policy of 'socialist development', after having seized, without compensation, the billions invested in Russia by the foreigners.

Economic development of the vast country was unthinkable without modern means of communication. Russia had almost no good roads, and in the year 1855 the total railway track was a mere 646 miles. It was therefore of vital importance to build more railways; there was at that time not so much as a link between Moscow and the south.

But where was the money to be found for this? After the Crimean War Russian finances were in a chaotic state. It was now that foreign countries came to the rescue, particularly France. A 'Russian Main Railway Company' was founded in 1857, for which the Paris firm, Crédit Mobilier Pereyre Frères, provided the greater part of the capital. As a result work could be started on two and a half thousand miles of new track.

'The government had realized the inadequacy and inefficiency of the nation's industrialists and therefore preferred to leave the construction and management of the railways to Western Europeans who had gained experience in building thousands of miles of track,' a Russian, A. A. Golovachov, wrote at the time. 'So the actual management of the Company was centralized in a committee which operated in Paris. To administer the railways a board with twenty members was set up in Russia, only half of whom were Russian subjects. A French engineer named Collinonne was appointed Director General. All the important posts—and many minor ones—were given to French technicians and engineers, who received enormous salaries.'

In 1901, when the Imperial Government had taken over most of the railways from the private companies and nationalized them, the extent of foreign loans used for the construction of railways amounted to 72 per cent of the national external debt—£213m., or $1,039m.

The whole Russian railway network cost 6·2 billion roubles (£656m., or 3·2 billion dollars at the value of the times), the Minister, Count Witte, announced. One-third of this enormous sum was raised in Western countries.

New impetus was also given to the mining and metallurgical industries as more and more foreign contractors poured into the country. In southern Russia an important new industrial centre developed when large coal deposits were found in the Donets Basin and iron ore was discovered in the Central Ukraine, near Krivoy Rog.

For seventy years, from 1797 to 1869, the Russian government had totally failed to exploit even the rich Donets Basin, where the coal deposits extended over an area of nearly 4,000 square miles and the iron ore contained 67 per cent pure iron. Here too it was all left to the ability and initiative of Western Europeans.

In the north, Germans and Dutch, and in Russian Poland Germans, laid the foundations of a heavily capitalized iron industry. The English, and later the French and Belgians, did the same in the south on an even larger scale.

In most countries one man wins the reputation of 'king' in each major industry. The 'iron king' in Russia was an English entrepreneur, John Hughes.

'The Hughes factories', we read in a letter of acknowledgment from the Russian government, 'were the first organizations in South Russia to undertake coal mining and metallurgy, and became firmly established at once. The credit belongs to Hughes who started the first iron foundry in South Russia using mineral fuel, where he introduced the manufacture of rails. He had no fear of the formidable, and often unexpected, obstacles which he encountered. For example, he had to import all his tools and equipment from England, via the port of Taganrog, over hundreds of miles of bad roads. He had to engage Russian workmen, as well as those who came from England, and to provide dwellings for them in the desolate and uninhabited steppes. But Hughes mastered all these problems, and thus inaugurated the production of railway tracks in the South of the Empire, using exclusively locally-produced raw materials.'

The significance of Hughes's achievements is apparent when it is recalled that up to 1870 all equipment for the Russian railways had been imported—duty-free—from foreign countries.

In the period 1836–65 deliveries from abroad amounted to 352,000 tons of rails, 485 locomotives, 1,140 passenger carriages and 4,788 goods wagons. Only when the men from the West had done their work in South Russia were the Russians able to use their own iron.

The flourishing town of Yuzovka is a memorial to the great English industrialist. Thanks to him the districts of 'Donbas' and of Krivoy Rog were linked industrially after 1870, and became a vastly important coal, iron- and steel-producing region. His name has been eliminated. Yuzovka (Hughesovka) has been renamed Stalino.

After Hughes, ironworks seemed to 'shoot up like mushrooms' in the south, according to Tugan-Baranovsky. However, of the seventeen steel mills in this district at the turn of the century, only two were genuinely Russian factories. The others belonged to the foreigners—English, French or Belgians—or had been built by foreigners in co-operation with Russians.

Not content with obliterating the Western past by renaming Yuzovka Stalino, the Soviets have also suppressed the record of what the foreigners achieved in South Russia. The figures are impressive:

In the years 1886–98, which was the period of the revolutionary transformation in South Russia, iron production increased fourfold. It rose from 1,191 million lb. in 1886 to 4,148 million lb. in 1898, an increase unequalled by any other country in so short a time. The iron industry in South Russia increased its production figures in the years 1875–98 by 9,448 per cent. Western initiative in Russia led to an increase in productivity far surpassing anything that the Soviets had ever achieved.

In addition to their industrial revolution, the social and political innovations introduced by the foreigners were of great importance.

'During our journey through South Russia,' B. Brandt, a knowledgeable witness, wrote in 1900 from St Petersburg, 'we got the impression that in the coal-mines belonging to the foreigners, the Russian workmen were much better paid (with the exception of one or two of the older factories) and that the welfare—both mental and physical—of the workers was better cared for than in the Russian concerns, where the workers still lived in the most miserable and primitive conditions.'

Describing workmen's dwellings in the industrial districts of South Russia, Brandt says: 'An official in St Petersburg might well envy the workmen their houses provided by the foreign factories.'

Where industry was in Russian hands, as in Moscow and the north, the workers still lived in great gloomy barracks, even after 1900, while the non-Russian factory owners in Poland, South Russia and elsewhere provided their men with bright, clean houses each of two rooms, parlour, kitchen, cellar and lavatory, at a negligible rent of two to four roubles per month, or sometimes even rent-free. The 'capitalists from the corrupt West' looked after their workers in other ways as well. Schools and hospitals were built, and health-insurance and pension schemes introduced.

The miserable barracks surrounding the Russian factories in the north became the forcing-beds of revolutionary anger. The Revolution was to break out in the north, not in South Russia where Western Europeans had created decent living and working conditions.

Russia also owed to the West the exploitation of its most valuable raw material: oil.

Some time after 1870, huge wooden structures began to rise towards the sky where the spurs of the Caucasus mountains fall away to the Caspian Sea. Where Marco Polo *en route* to China had seen the field of 'flames which are never quenched', at Baku, a group of Swedes directed and administered the first exploitation of the oilfields. The Nobel brothers, and particularly Ludwig, produced capital, machines and technicians. They sank borings and brought into being the Baku oilfields, then the most modern in the entire world. The shores of the Caspian almost belonged to the 'Nobel Brothers Naphtha Company'.

Before the arrival of the Nobel brothers, conditions were extremely backward on the Apsheron peninsula. All the oil wells combined had a yearly output of a mere eight thousand tons of petroleum, which was transported in the most primitive Asiatic manner, using skin bags or wooden barrels, loaded on a two-wheeled cart or *arba*.

All this was changed by the Nobel brothers, and Alexander II sent Professor Mendeleyev to America in 1876 to 'collect ideas' concerning the vast oilfields of Pennsylvania which had been producing since 1859. The Nobels built the first pipeline on Russian soil, a pipe some seven miles long.

Alfred Nobel, the inventor of dynamite and founder of the Nobel Prize, developed a new method for the continuous distillation of oil. His brothers, Robert and Ludwig, had iron 'tanker wagons' built for transport of the oil by rail, and the first iron-built tanker, the *Zoroaster*, for sea-borne transport.

In 1886 another very large foreign company was floated, under the auspices of the Paris banking house of Rothschild, 'The Caspian Black Sea Industrial and Trading Company'. Just as naphtha production had become a major technical industry thanks to Nobel, so the Russian naphtha industry was now developed into an international export trade by Rothschild's. Dr Ischchanian says: 'A historian, writing of production and trade development within the oil industry on the Apsheron peninsula, can correctly describe these two European companies as the "apostles of the Russian naphtha industry".'

There is overwhelming statistical evidence of what the foreigners achieved here. In 1860 the United States produced 70,000 tons of petroleum, the Russians a mere 1,300 tons; twenty-five years later the total production of the United States was 3·12 million tons, while that of Russia was already 2 million tons and in 1901 Russian production was 12·17 million tons, which exceeded the American total of 9·92 million tons. Russia, in fact, had jumped to first place among the oil-producing countries of the world.

Accepting in good faith the 'guarantees' given by the Russian government, Western Europe now invested more and more capital in the country. In 1887 France raised a sum of 500 million francs for Russia, and further large loans followed in 1889 and 1891, liberally subscribed to by the French public.

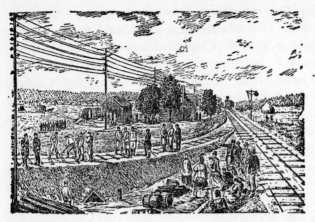

The building of the Trans-Siberian railway, predominantly financed by foreigners, and principally by France, which provided the chief engineer, Collinonne, and the top technicians. The telegraph line was erected and operated by Danes.

Millions were also invested by Belgium, England and Germany. In 1900 half of the enormous capital of all the Russian joint stock companies came from Europe, a fortune which the Soviets wiped out with one stroke of the pen in 1917.

Thanks to assistance from the West, Russia was able to contemplate another great project, the linking of the vast, trackless wastes of Siberia with European Russia by means of a railway running across the whole country as far as the Pacific. On 17th March 1891, Alexander III ordered that this gigantic enterprise be begun. In May the Crown Prince, who was later to be the last Tsar of Russia, Nicholas II, presided at the ceremonial inauguration of the project, in distant Vladivostok, the designated terminus of the railway.

In this same year of 1891 a terrible disaster occurred. St Petersburg informed the world that twenty million people were threatened with famine. The previous year's harvest had been exported, down to the last sack. The granaries of this huge agricultural country—where 85 per cent of the population worked the land—were completely bare.

In order to raise the capital needed for the ever-growing imports of machinery and technical equipment, and to pay the interest on previous loans, Russia had drastically increased the taxation levels. The peasants were being forced to hand over more and more of their crops, which Russia then dumped into the world market. 'We may be hungry but we must export,' were the words of the Minister of Finance, Vyshnegradsky, half a century before Stalin let the Ukrainian people starve while exporting grain to buy American machines. Then, as later under the Soviets, Russia could rely on help and salvation from the West, whenever a cruel and inhuman policy resulted in disaster. Only a few weeks after the famine broke out, help from the West was on the way. From all Europe gifts of food and money poured in, and the United States sent shipload after shipload of flour to the Russian ports.

Massive assistance from the West was apparent everywhere in Russia at the end of the century. Harry Schwartz has provided some statistics:

'The average annual rate of growth of industrial output in Russia between 1885 and 1889, and again between 1907 and 1913, substantially exceeded the corresponding rates of growth during the same period in the United States, Great Britain, and Germany. In roughly two out of every three years between 1868 and 1919, 1,000 kilometres or more of railroad lines were completed: in 1899, 5,257 kilometres; in 1900 and 1901, over 3,000 kilometres each year; in 1908, 8,390 kilometres were finished.'

By the outbreak of the First World War, Western Russia was covered with a relatively dense network of railways, which served the interior, handled foreign trade, and last but not least was of great strategic value. The Trans-Siberian Railway was also completed. 'Rapid development was a characteristic feature of the whole period from 1861 to 1914.'

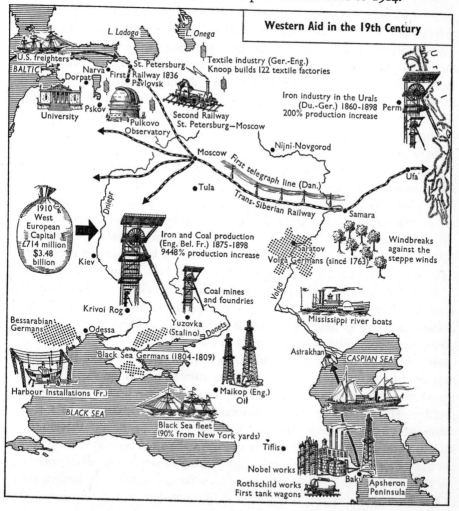

Travellers who visited Russia at the turn of the century were astonished at the progress they saw on every side.

'In the twenty years that have passed since last I travelled along the Volga, much has changed,' Baron Korff wrote in 1900. 'Villages that then consisted of a few cabins are now towns with 40,000 inhabitants and well-paved streets. National costumes have been replaced by Russian workmen's clothes. There is electric light everywhere. . . .'

'It is quite incredible,' Korff tells us, 'to what extent traffic and trade have developed upon the Volga. The river boats are huge, with two or three decks, like Mississippi steamers. Samara, Kasan and Nijni-Novgorod resemble the port of Hamburg.'

The *Baedeker* of the period recommends the 'A. A. Sevecke Steamship Company' for trips down the Volga and also the 'Kavkas and Merkur Company', remarking: 'The steamers of these two companies, equipped in the American fashion, are by far the best and the most comfortable.'

Korff tells us much about the tremendous rate of progress throughout the vast empire of the Tsar. He saw 'English agricultural machinery on many of the railway stations.' He watched a regiment of soldiers firing on the range, 'the targets being manufactured by Gustav Kühn of Ruppin.' He noticed that the rifles of the Russian infantry were sometimes the products of Tula, Isborsk and Okhotsk, but that many were from Krupps. He observed 'a dozen Bechstein pianos, or a complete set of apothecary's instruments, or perhaps the contents of a music shop', being loaded on to Volga ships.

Korff also visited Baku: 'Here one can smell the petroleum. From far away one sees a forest of 80 ft. wooden towers which hold the drills for boring oil wells. Twenty thousand metal tanks or wagons transport the oil to the huge reservoirs. . . . The crude petroleum is purified in the refineries and becomes petrol, benzine, kerosene, fuel oil, machine oil, etc. The Nobel Company produces daily 818·5 tons of kerosene and dispatches three trainloads per day, each of thirty 10-ton tank wagons. Twenty of Nobel's ships ply the Caspian Sea, twelve sail up the Volga. . . . The existing wells produce more petroleum than can be used. Over one and a half million tons are produced, refined and sold. . . . Three-quarters of all petroleum production is in the hands of Nobel. . . .'

At that time oil and its by-products were among the most important exports. In 1900 oil brought in 46 million roubles of foreign currency, and was second only to wheat, which brought in more than double, 104 million roubles. The import figures of 1900 show machinery as coming first, to a value of 76·703 million roubles. 'Certain classes of heavy machinery, such as Russia could not yet construct, were admitted on easy terms,' says Bernard Pares; 'also agricultural implements.' Henry A. Wallace writes: 'In 1901 an American made a study of how farm machinery manufactured in the United States was being used in Russian agriculture. He reported

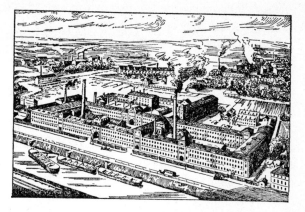

*American rubber goods
factory in Russia, an
example of industrial
development by the West
of the land of the Tsars.
(Late 19th-century
lithograph.)*

seeing in Siberia millions of dollars' worth of American-made machinery.'
Many of these were probably still in use in 1920 when, under the Soviets,
the latest combine harvesters from the United States were being imported.

The increasing number of workers reflected the tremendous growth of
mining and industry. In 1860 they numbered 800,000 but by 1913 there
were three million—an increase of nearly 400 per cent. Furthermore, in
1910 there were one million men in the Russian building trade, and the
railways employed 400,000 men by 1900. 'In total, therefore, over 4,500,000
Russians were engaged in the major branches of the non-agricultural
economy before World War I' (Schwartz).

The future ideology of the Slav State was born in the West during the
nineteenth century. German philosophers drafted the 'World Programme',
that is still inscribed upon the banners of the Soviet Union. For, as everyone
knows, the progenitors of Communism, men still worshipped by the
Bolsheviks, were Karl Marx and Friedrich Engels.

Despite the great numerical increase of the 'industrial proletariat' in Russia
during the second half of the last century, the importation of Western
ideologies intended for consumption by this proletariat was not particularly
successful at first. The first volume of Marx's *Das Kapital* was translated into
Russian a year after its original publication in German. This translation, the
first into a foreign language, was done by Mikhail Bakunin, 'the professional
revolutionary', in 1868. He had listened to Schelling at the Friedrich-
Wilhelm University in Berlin in 1841, and had studied Hegel's philosophy.
Karl Marx, with whom Bakunin was on friendly terms at the time, may
have been rather astonished that his book was translated first into Russian.
He had certainly not had the Slav State in mind when he wrote it, and
doubtless recalled the words of his teacher, Hegel, who had said about

Russia: 'These great masses are irrelevant to the problem, in that they have not yet emerged as an independent force in the formation of ideas.'

A group of Russians wished to know Marx's own views on Russia, for they were quite unable to apply to their own country the Marxist concept of the transition from feudalism, through capitalism, to socialism. The Slav Empire in the nineteenth century had a capitalist economy far less developed than in any West European country; and furthermore a German by the name of August Baron von Haxthausen had described the common ownership of the land (the *mir* system, peculiar to the Russian peasants) as unique. In view of these two factors peculiar to Russia, the lack of a capitalism ripe for 'expropriation' and the fact that communal property already existed, the Marxist theory could obviously be of no practical interest to Russia.

A socialist, Vera Sassulich, asked Marx for his solution to this problem. Marx found it a difficult question. After five false starts, he wrote: 'The inevitability of this transition [from capitalism to socialism] is limited to the countries of western Europe.'

This was a negative reply. The fact that his doctrine has nevertheless conquered the East so totally is explained by the Russian philosopher, Nikolai Berdyayev, as follows: 'It appeals to the Russian desire for a Messiah, for it is a sort of secular religion.'

Das Kapital in the Russian edition was not widely read in the Tsar's empire. Because of the strict censorship it remained known only to a very small circle within the Russian intelligentsia.

Nevertheless it was the West which created and fostered the movement that later raised the Bolsheviks to power. Russian Marxism was born outside Russia, in a foreign country. At Geneva, in a liberal and a democratic country, in the year 1883, Georgi Plekhanov—together with other Russian emigrants such as Pavel Axelrod, Vera Sassulich and L. G. Deutsch—was allowed freely to found the first Russian Socialist Party. He was soon giving instruction to his Russian compatriots, who found their way to Switzerland in ever-increasing numbers. Inspired by Plekhanov, the first propagandists for Marxist socialism returned to Russia.

It was not until 1885 that a Social-Democratic Party was founded in Russia, in St Petersburg. It remained largely inactive until 1890. Then the influence of Lenin began to make itself felt. In 1895 he organized the 'League for the Liberation of the Working Class' in St Petersburg. But progress was still very slow. Only nine Russians attended the first Socialist Congress in 1896. In 1898 the first Party Congress of the Social-Democratic Workers' Party was held at Minsk, a very modest affair. The second congress of the Social-Democratic Workers' Party of Russia was held in London in the year 1903. At this congress Lenin and his supporters won the majority, and from that moment they called themselves 'Bolsheviks', which simply means 'the majority'. This congress was to have incalculable effects in the future. Fourteen years later the Germans transported Lenin and several of his supporters from Switzerland to Finland at Germany's expense, and thus the Bolshevik world reformers finally entered the Empire of the Tsar.

In 1900, when Lenin published in Munich the first number of his illegal propagandist newspaper, *Iskra* ('The Spark'), the West was pouring money and talent into Russia.

On 1st January 1900, 265 foreign joint stock companies were functioning in Russia, 162 Belgian, 54 French, 30 German and 19 English. A further 40 more were registered in the same year, 25 Belgian, 6 English, 4 French, 3 German, one Swiss and one Swedish.

Foreign capital investments and financial assets in Russia, later expropriated by the Soviets, amounted to the enormous sum of £714,000,000,000, or 3,480 billion dollars.

From 1907 to 1913 the increase in the industrial productivity rate in Russia exceeded that of the United States, England or Germany. At that time 2,049,871 Europeans, among them 1,782,946 Germans and 266,450 Swedes—to name only the two largest groups—lived and worked in the Slav state.

'The Russian revolution of 1917,' Schwartz says, 'came not at the end of a long period of stagnation and decay, but rather after more than a half-century of the most rapid and comprehensive economic progress'—progress for which the West alone had provided the whole driving force.

Front page of a widely read German-language St Petersburg newspaper, first published 1726.

Spitzbergen

Bear Island

Murmansk
Kola Pen.
Novaya Zemly

Liepaja
Königsberg
Riga
Kronstadt
Dorpat
L. Ladoga
Pskov
Leningrad
Novgorod
Volkhov
L. Onega
Archangel
Kholmogory

Vitebsk
Smolensk
Dniepr
Rybinsk Res
Vologda
Vorkuta
Kiev
Kaluga
Dubna
Jaroslavl
Kostroma
Kotla
Pechara
Tula
Moscow
Vladimir
Odessa
Krivoi Rog
Poltava
Kolomna
Gorki
Volga
Dnjepropetrovsk
Kharkov
Lipetsk
Kazan
Molotov
Zaporozhe
Voronezh
Ob
Simferopol
Stalino
Saratov
N.-Tagil
Sevastopol
Taganrog
Voroshilovgrad
Asbest
Kerch
Rostov
Kuibyshev
Sverdlovsk
Tobolsk
BLACK SEA
Don
Stalingrad
Ufa
Chelyabinsk
Maikop
Salsk
Magnitogorsk
Batum
Astrakhan
Khyaturi
Tiflis
CASPIAN SEA
Omsk
Tom
Baku
Aral Sea
Novosibirsk
Irtysh
Kuznetsk
Karaganda
Balkhash
L. Balkhash
Tashkent
Alma Ata
Samarkand

New Siberian Is.

Uelkal

Kolyma

Seimchan

Berelyakh • • Magadan

Petropavlovsk

Okhotsk •

Yakutsk

Lena

Yeniseisk

Bratsk

Krasnoyarsk

Angora

L. Baikal

Komsomolsk •

Amur

Khabarovsk •

Irkutsk • • Ulan Ude

Vladivostok •

Part Two · From Lenin to Gagarin

THE CREATION and development of the first Russian state, the kingdom of Kiev, was due to foreign help on the part of the Swedish Goths. It was swept away by the Mongolian invasion.

Five hundred years later Russia rose again, and again thanks to help of every sort from every Western land. As a result it proved possible to create, within a period of some four hundred years, a mighty Slav empire out of a Muscovy hitherto almost unknown to Europe. The revolution of 1917 marked the end of this phase.

In retrospect, these first two periods of Russian development appear mere dress-rehearsals for what started forty years ago.

For foreign, that is to say, Western, help has provided the basis for the third upsurge of power in the East—the might of the USSR. It has enabled them to create the second strongest industrial potential in the world.

The history of the USSR provides a unique example of the rise and development of a great power. It took its declared mortal enemy as a model, and legally or illegally adopted all the technical, industrial and scientific achievements from the whole of Western Europe and America for its own use, claiming them as its own.

The documents of the German Foreign Office, only recently published, reveal in letters and memoranda, papers and receipts the first squalid financial transactions. Help was given from abroad towards the birth of a new Eastern power. Lenin was 'imported' into Russia, and the Bolshevik revolution was financed by Imperial Germany.

In January 1915 the German Ambassador in Copenhagen, Ulrich Count Brockdorff-Rantzau, reported to the Foreign Office in Berlin that he was in contact with a 'Russian expert' by the name of Dr Parvus. Parvus was, in fact, a Russian socialist called Alexander Helphand, one of the leaders of the 1905 Revolution. The Ambassador requested the appropriate authorities to listen to Parvus's proposals.

Shortly afterwards Parvus, or Helphand, presented Berlin with a confidential memorandum on the tense situation in Russia, and recommended that financial support be given to the Bolsheviks in Switzerland—that is to say, Lenin and his circle of émigrés—and that contact be established with the revolutionary groups active in Petrograd and in the Ukrainian towns.

In the strictest secrecy feelers were put out, and the first moves made.

In August 1915 Brockdorff-Rantzau was able to report to Berlin that 'Dr P's organization' was functioning. This was the Research Institute for the Study of Russo-German Industrial Problems, a cover organization set up by Parvus in Copenhagen. Parvus had eight men working for him in Copenhagen, and ten in Russia. 'Up to now our security has been so good that not one of the men in the organization has any idea that our Government is behind it all. Parvus has heard that Lenin wishes to travel from Switzerland to Stockholm. He is unable to do so, however, because Lenin has no money.'

A few months later Brockdorff-Rantzau reported that according to Parvus's estimates the cost of financing a 'total revolution in Russia' would amount to twenty million roubles. And on 29th December 1915 Parvus signed the following receipt: 'Received from the German Ambassador in Copenhagen the sum of one million roubles in notes, for the purpose of promoting the revolutionary movement in Russia.'

Meanwhile the German legation in Berne had made contact with the Bolsheviks in Switzerland with the intention of approaching Lenin. The Secretary of the Swiss Social Democrat Party, Fritz Platten, was in Lenin's confidence, and also in that of the German Minister, von Romberg. Lenin himself took great care to avoid all direct contact with the Germans. Platten arranged the financing of Lenin's party by Imperial Germany. Later he became a declared Bolshevik. He died in a slave labour camp near Archangel in 1939.

On 30th April 1917 Romberg sent a report to the Foreign Office in Berlin of a discussion with Fritz Platten. 'From what Platten tells me it is clear that the émigrés have very little money for propaganda, while their enemies naturally have unlimited means. The funds collected for the émigrés are mostly in the hands of socialist patriots. I am taking steps to arrange that a contact man solve the very ticklish question of how to give them money in such a way that they will not be offended. . . .'

One day Lenin, through his contact man, requested of the German legation that he be permitted to travel through Germany to Sweden, with ultimate destination Russia. Permission was given by the German government and the Army High Command. The Army High Command only stipulated that the journey must be made in a special train with reliable guards. The Bolsheviks themselves had to promise not to reveal their names, nor give their opinions on the progress of the war, nor indeed talk to any Germans during the transit.

Despite all precautions the plan was not kept quite secret. As the special train pulled out of Zurich station, a number of socialists shouted after Lenin, 'German spies! Paid agents of the Kaiser!' Guarded by an army officer and with curtains drawn, the train carrying Lenin and thirty-three other Russians passed through Germany to Sweden.

In Stockholm Lenin deliberately gave the impression that he and his group were without funds. He applied to the Emigrés' Committee for financial assistance. He was given the amount he asked for.

'*Izvestia*', *27th October 1917. Black headlines tell of resolutions on peace and land distribution, passed unanimously by workers', soldiers' and peasants' deputies. '*Izvestia*' and '*Pravda*' owe their origin to massive German subventions.*

Lenin arrived in Petrograd on 16th April 1917, exactly one month after the revolutionaries had dethroned the Tsar.

With this 'importation' of Lenin an unhealthy seed was planted whose growth no man could then foresee. The vast sums of money placed at his disposal by the German government were of decisive importance. When Lenin first set foot once again on Russian soil, in April of 1917, his small party played only a minor role on the periphery of events. By the end of that year the German Foreign Office had paid him—through various secret channels—at least twenty-two million marks. For it was believed in Berlin that only the Bolsheviks could arrange a separate peace.

Thanks to German money, within a few weeks *Pravda* was appearing in editions of 300,000 copies per day, and Bolshevik newspapers were springing up in the provinces like mushrooms after rain. Lenin was thus in a position to build a large and effective propaganda machine, and his Bolsheviks were enabled to act on a great scale. With the dictatorship of the proletariat and the immediate realization of socialism as his slogans, Lenin overthrew the democratic régime of his country so recently freed from the Tsars. In November of that same year, Bolshevism was an accomplished fact.

From this period dates the famous telegram which the German Foreign
Secretary, Richard von Kühlmann, sent to Kaiser Wilhelm II: 'Russia
appeared to be the weakest link in the chain of our enemies. Our task was to
further weaken this link and, if possible, to break it. This was the object of
the revolutionary activity organized by us behind the enemy lines: the
promoting of separatist tendencies, and the support of Bolshevism. Only
when the Bolsheviks had received money from us were they able to create
their main mouthpiece, *Pravda*, to produce an effective propaganda, and
significantly to extend the originally narrow bases of their party. The
Bolsheviks are now in power. But how long they will remain in power no
man can predict. . . . It is in our interest to exploit their period of power,
which may be brief, by arranging a cease-fire, and, if possible, a peace
treaty . . . There can be no question of supporting the Bolsheviks in the
future. . . .'

Lenin, urgently in need of a respite, signed a peace treaty with Germany,
despite Ludendorff's harsh terms, on 3rd March 1918 at Brest-Litovsk. The
idea behind the signing of the treaty which made it tolerable to the Soviets
was the firm conviction that it was a purely temporary measure. The men
who had so recently moved into the Kremlin were convinced that Marx
and Engels had prophesied correctly, and that the 'proletarian masses' in the
great German industrial centres were ripe for revolution and would, in the
immediate future, become the first true representatives of the Communist
world revolution. The revolution could only really succeed in Germany.
Despite all the industrialization of the last fifty years, Russia remained
predominantly agricultural. It was Germany that counted. Revolutionary
agitation on a large scale began in Germany, with Russian support.

For the German government the Treaty of Brest-Litovsk meant that the
financial support given to Bolshevik leaders and Lenin's 'importation' were
justified. 'The Bolsheviks have fulfilled their obligations to Imperial
Germany.' This was the view taken by the German Social Democrat,
Eduard Bernstein.

But this was not the end of the story. Dispatches from the new German
Ambassador in Moscow, where the Soviet government had moved in 1918,
described the desperate plight of the Bolsheviks. Count Mirbach believed
that it was still imperative to support the Bolsheviks if the Treaty of Brest-
Litovsk were to remain valid.

'It is not in our interests,' Secretary of State von Kühlmann informed him,
'to support any group of monarchists who would only reunite Russia. On
the contrary, we must try to prevent, as far as possible, any reconstitution
of Russia. Therefore we must support the parties of the extreme Left.'

Trotsky watched every move of the German Embassy officials in Moscow,
for he feared lest they might also be in touch with the opposition. But the
German government did not favour the overthrow of the Bolsheviks. In

An F-13 near the Afghan frontier. These aircraft, built by the Junkers works at Fili, near Moscow, were the first airliners of the USSR. Tupolev built the first Russian all-metal aircraft, the ANT-2 in 1924, after the design of the F-13.

As late as the early thirties Hindenburg welcomed Soviet officers as guests at German army manoeuvres. Chief of the General Staff, Marshal Tukhachevsky (2nd on left), as well as Marshal Zhukov, the conqueror of Berlin, attended the General Staff courses of the German army.

The Red propaganda giant Magnitogorsk. The Mackee company of
Cleveland, Ohio, built the 800-
million rouble showpiece of the Five
Year Plan, one of the biggest
smelting works in the world.
Above: view of the site in 1929.
Left: the huge blast furnaces under
construction. Below: the finished
smelting combine in operation.

June, 'because of strong competition on the part of the Allies', Mirbach asked for the sum of three million marks per month earmarked for continued support of the Bolshevik propaganda apparatus. In the same month he was given a fund of some forty million marks to be used in Russia. Four weeks later he was assassinated, the murderer being a left-wing anti-Bolshevik socialist.

What no member of the Imperial German Government then realized was that some of this German money was already secretly coming home, that it was being used to finance revolution inside Germany. Moscow foresaw a Communist Germany as her ally, and acted accordingly. The men in the Kremlin prepared for a general strike in Germany, for street fighting, and for civil war. On Soviet maps, Germany was already divided into six military districts. Hundreds of Red Army officers were secretly smuggled across the borders, as were countless Soviet agents and agitators, and specialists in the art of civil war. Germany collapsed in November 1918. 1919 was to be the year of destiny.

It was no mere chance that at this time German was the language of international communism. And Russia's leaders, Trotsky, Lenin, Zinoviev amd Bukharin, all spoke in German at the meetings of the Communist (Third) International, the Comintern, founded in 1919. Banners then fluttered above the Moscow streets proclaiming in enormous letters 'Germany's October is due!' (The 'Victory of the Great Socialist October Revolution' took place, according to the Russian or Julian calendar, on 25th October 1917, and according to the Western or Gregorian calendar, on 7th November.)

When the Spartacists' (Communists') attempt to carry the German revolution of 1918 one stage further misfired, Moscow waited for the next chance while continuing to carry out violent subversive activities.

Hope was not definitely abandoned until 1925. In October of that year the carefully prepared strikes and uprisings failed, the revolution shrank to a riot in Hamburg, and Germany remained loyal to the Weimar Republic. The Soviet advisers returned to Russia. The plans for world revolution were shelved. Instead of Germany, the great hope now was the Far East—China.

Even while the Soviets were attempting to make Germany ripe for the Communist revolution, and street fighting, strikes, and rioting followed one another in almost unbroken succession, the Russian Socialist Federal Soviet Republic (RSFSR) concluded the famous Treaty of Rapallo with the German Reich on 16th April 1922. This treaty offered Germany a possible means of escape from the apparently hopeless situation in which she had been placed by the harsh conditions of the Treaty of Versailles. The Paris Conference of January 1921 had fixed the amount that Germany must pay in reparations at two hundred and sixty-nine billion gold marks, to be paid in forty-two annual instalments, and a duty of 12 per cent to be levied on German exports. A French occupation of the Ruhr was threatened, which could mean a further splitting of the Reich. Disaster appeared inevitable.

In such circumstances the Russian offer seemed highly attractive, with commissions for the German factories and jobs for the German technicians and craftsmen. The Treaty of Rapallo was signed. It was obviously of the greatest importance to Russia as well. It opened the door for them to a land of immense industrial capacity. They needed both German goods and German brains for the development and expansion of Communism. Article Five of the Treaty stated that each government would meet the industrial requirements of the other country on a basis of mutual good-will.

The Treaty of Rapallo enabled Russia to exploit Germany's industrial potential. In March of 1921, Russia had already concluded a Trade Agreement with Great Britain, and in the same year similar agreements were made with Norway, Austria and Italy.

Russia was ready to receive the flood of industrial materials from the West which she needed to keep the Soviet state alive. She was to get them, in abundance.

THREE YEARS after the revolution nobody in the free world considered that the Bolshevik state had a chance of survival.

When H. G. Wells travelled by train through Russia in 1920, he saw from his compartment window a miserable landscape of untilled fields and idle factories. All was chaos in Russia.

'Russia in 1920,' he wrote, 'presented an unparalleled example of civilization in a state of complete collapse; the railway tracks were rusting and becoming gradually unusable, the cities were falling into ruin.'

After three years of Bolshevik rule, the situation had become hopeless. Industry was completely disorganized, production had been reduced to one-seventh of the pre-war level. Most of the factories stood deserted, and the mine-shafts were flooded. The condition of the metal industry was catastrophic, with the output of pig iron down to a mere 3 per cent of pre-war. Stocks of metal and industrial products were exhausted, and there was an acute shortage of consumer goods, of heating fuel, and of foodstuffs.

Such, then, was the result of radical socialization; thus had Lenin faithfully carried out Marx's doctrine of the 'expropriation of the expropriators'.

'We feel as though we were in prison . . . As human beings we are lost and have become slaves!' This was said in a resolution by the Petrograd workers in 1920.

'For democracy, against the Bolshevik dictatorship!' That was the slogan of the workers and sailors who rose at Kronstadt in March 1921.

'Our programme was right in theory, but impracticable,' Lenin was forced to admit. Marx and Engels had never worked out a programme for the actual creation of a Communist state.

'Marx himself,' Lenin complained, 'never considered this problem nor wrote a word on the subject.' The Soviet régime faced disaster. The press of the free world awaited its imminent collapse.

Lenin behaved in typically Russian fashion and ordered a complete about-face. Without the hated capitalists, as he now clearly saw, there was little or no prospect of rebuilding the national economy. Therefore the Red rulers did exactly what their predecessors had always done. They followed in the footsteps of the two Ivans and of Peter I, trusting to the old-established and tested policy: 'Come to our country . . .!'

In 1921 Lenin announced his 'New Economic Policy', known as NEP. Once more the cry came from Russia, now uttered by the new Red despots: 'Our country is rich, but we have no order. Come to us . . .' In present-day language this meant: 'Concessions'. Lenin called upon the mighty industrial powers of the West, with their engineers, research scientists and technologists; they must come to Russia so that 'Bolshevik Progress' might begin.

On 23rd November 1920, *Definitions of the Economic and Legal Conditions Governing Concessions* appeared. These underlined 'the urgent need of absorbing technical personnel and materials from the more advanced countries, so that Russia might regain her importance as one of the main sources of raw materials for world industry, and also develop her own rate of productivity, which had declined as a result of the War'.

Moscow set about luring foreigners by means of these concessions, which Lenin cynically described as 'industrial co-habitation with the capitalists'. For the Soviets this was merely a means to an end. The final objective remained the same. Lenin was in no doubt about this: 'Instead of using guns and tanks, we shall wage an industrial war,' the Red dictator announced in 1920. 'I am convinced that Soviet might will catch up with capitalism and will overtake it, and that we shall not only win economically. . . . This is a new sort of war, an economic struggle between two systems, the communist and the capitalist. We shall prove that we are the stronger. . . . And as soon as we are strong enough to overthrow capitalism, we shall immediately seize it by the throat.'

What was intended was achieved. The Westerners took the Russian bait. They accepted the 'concessions' and began to rebuild the Russian economy, the whole power of which was later to be used against them. They saved the Bolshevik experiment; their plans, their engineers, their machines, their equipment and their skills made Communism viable.

In 1921 famine once again swept the country. Since the revolution five millions had already starved to death. Even before the West took a hand in Russia's industrial development, famine relief was being organized on a grand scale. A future President of the United States, Herbert Hoover, set up an international organization.

The first cargoes of foodstuffs began to arrive in St Petersburg. The Quakers had collected money, and the great Norwegian Arctic explorer, Fridtjof Nansen, had also organized large-scale relief. The figures are lost, and it is no longer possible to say how much foreign help was given to the millions of under-nourished or starving Russians. It is known, however, that the United States alone sent 700,000 tons of foodstuffs.

While food from abroad was arriving in the Russian ports, while hundreds of thousands of German and Austrian prisoners-of-war were put to building the Murmansk railway, sixty-eight concessionary agreements were signed with the purpose of reviving Russian industry.

The first of these concessions were for 'the exploitation of hitherto undeveloped industrial fields' and the creation of 'new industries'—the production of metal alloys, the manufacture of machine tools and heavy machinery, of motor-cars, synthetic fabrics, etc. Every foreign concessionnaire was obliged to 'maintain his particular branch of industry at the highest possible technical level, in accordance with the most modern developments'. (*Trud*, No. 11, 13th January 1929.)

Next came 'technical aid', and a new group of concessions were agreed. Here the concessionnaire acted as adviser in the organization of the new enterprise. He was obliged to make available all technical knowledge already in his possession, as well as any which might come his way in the future.

Such 'technical aid' from foreign companies, required by the Communists to get their industries going and to set standards, increased greatly in later years. By 1929 there were seventy such concessions, of which thirty were with world-famous German firms. (*Ekonomicheskaya Zhizn* of 29th September 1929.)

'If the concession policy is successful,' Lenin had said, 'we shall, thanks to it, be able to create new, model, industrial enterprises, comparable with those of the most modern capitalist states.'

Lenin was right, for the West took the bait. It began to create an ultra-modern industry, for which everything needed was made available—from drawings and blueprints for the installations to the supplying of all machinery and plant, and even the training of the Russian personnel. It was the same story in agriculture, in forestry, in mining, even in the fisheries and in the breeding and trapping of animals for their furs. There were thirty-nine principal concessions for the development of agriculture and fisheries, and for fur-trapping.

The modern *Nyemetskaya Sloboda*, where the industries of all Europe and of the United States were represented, did a magnificent job. It was to Russia's advantage that the post-war years had created serious economic problems in many Western European countries. Not a few well-known firms were glad to accept money from Moscow in exchange for production secrets, the newest patents, or essential technical knowledge. Moscow was later to use all such acquisitions from the West to compete in world markets against the West.

The state of crisis of the European economy meant that the great hope, often the only hope, for the many unemployed engineers was the USSR. Here was a virgin country, where every sort of technical skill and every new idea was welcome.

A British engineer, Arnold Tustin, Chief Engineer at the Metro-Vickers Works in Sheffield, and their leading engineer in the locomotive section of the Soviet Kirov-Dynamo Works, made an entry in his diary which expressed the views of many such technicians: 'For an engineer, working in a Soviet factory affords enormous satisfaction . . . Here the various jobs are integrated into the development of the industry. So each engineer knows for sure that a use will be found for the work he does. Every single useful idea is tried out in practice.'

His compatriot, the chemist G. C. Eltenton, describes the lack of interest with which his experiments with carbon were received in England, whereas in the Soviet Union he received every encouragement. 'I have worked for three years in the Soviet Union, and experimented with the influence of ions on chemical reactions . . . I put in a lot of hard work and I am proud to have earned the title of the best shock worker in the Institute. . . .'

The USSR profited. Large numbers of technicians volunteered for work in Russia.

The economic situation in Germany grew ever more catastrophic. It became increasingly difficult for German firms to deal with their equivalents in Western Europe. From the early twenties the more enterprising German firms therefore began dealing with Russia.

'We are scarcely in a position to discontinue the policy of better relations with Russia,' the German Foreign Minister, Walter Simons, declared in the Reichstag in March 1921, when referring to warnings received against supplying the Eastern power. 'And the reason we cannot is that every other country will also, sooner or later, enter into trade relations with Russia.'

Krupp, the AEG, the 'Steel King' Otto Wolff of Cologne, the Linke-Hofmann Works (leading manufacturers of rails and rolling stock), all these concerns were able to maintain their position principally by exporting industrial plant and equipment to the Soviet Union. Engineers, constructors and technicians went to the USSR. Technicians from Krupp's taught the Russians how to produce special types of steel. Diesel engines were made in Russia under German supervision.

America also supplied help. There were still no diplomatic relations between Moscow and Washington. Even after the creation of NEP, Secretary of State Charles E. Hughes, who knew about Communist propaganda, brusquely rebuffed the overtures of Georgi V. Chicherin, the Soviet People's Commissar for Foreign Affairs. But America's system of free enterprise enabled the American industrialists to make private agreements with the Soviet Union. Thus United States firms acquired the 'gold-prospecting rights' on the Amur, the Standard Oil Company won an oil-boring concession, and other American firms set about diminishing Russia's very considerable export trade credit balance. The International General Electric Company sold Moscow electrical equipment to the value of over twenty million dollars. From 1921 to 1925 alone, thirty-seven million dollars' worth of machinery and equipment was pumped into the USSR by American industry.

Triumphantly Izvestia of 6th November 1928 wrote: 'We only permit such concessions as are calculated to hasten our economic development!'

Lena Goldfields Ltd. was the name of a large capitalistic island deep in the Communist ocean. This English company invested 18,129,000 roubles in a

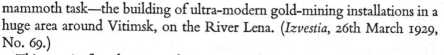
German technical journals of the 1920's cashed in on the development of the USSR with special Russian editions.

mammoth task—the building of ultra-modern gold-mining installations in a huge area around Vitimsk, on the River Lena. (*Izvestia*, 26th March 1929, No. 69.)

This was in fact the renewal, on an even larger scale, of a project which another British firm had already begun under the Tsar, in 1908. Everything that this other firm had built had been destroyed in the revolution. The original plant had rotted away and many pits were waterlogged. The new project involved the creation of a shipping route along the Lena and its tributaries, the building of a railway network, the equipping and administration of copper and iron-ore mines in Lysert and Revdinsk in the Urals, and forestry in the Altai Mountains.

A staff of geologists, chemists and engineers employed by Lena Goldfields set about their various tasks. Expeditions were organized, to survey the whole district systematically, using the most up-to-date prospecting and boring equipment; samples of ore and soil were collected and subjected to thorough analysis. Every sort of machinery, dredgers, sifters and conveyor-belts, were brought from England. The new gold-mines came into being.

The end of this great concession has been forgotten. It was typical. When Lena Goldfields Ltd. had completed its valuable pioneer work, when everything was at last ready, the modern equipment installed, and the huge undertaking with all its ramifications had at last begun to produce—what happened? Without any sort of warning, the Soviets arrested many of the leading technicians. The foreigners were accused of 'industrial espionage'.

But why? Of what use to experienced technologists were the industrial secrets of a country still in a state of medieval backwardness?

The accusation was merely a threadbare pretext. The company was soon forced to discontinue production as a result of the imprisonment of its principal engineers and technicians. Then the order came from Moscow: Lena Goldfields Ltd. was to leave the country—the company was guilty of 'sabotage'.

In August 1930, in London, a court of arbitration retried the case and established without a shadow of doubt that the Soviets had prevented the functioning of the English enterprise. *Pravda* and *Izvestia* with one voice described the London inquiry as a 'legal farce'. Lena Goldfields Ltd., they said, 'consisted solely of capitalist pirates'.

It was the same story with the big American industrialist, Averell Harriman, who built mines to work the richest manganese ore deposits in the world, at Tchiaturi in the southern Caucasus. As soon as the mines had been equipped with American machinery and were in working order, Harriman was deprived of his concession. The work was thenceforth carried on as a 'progressive Soviet enterprise'.

There was scarcely a Western country that did not help 'Communist development' during the NEP period. Not only big companies in Germany, England and the United States, but also leading firms from Sweden, Denmark and Austria contributed to the rebuilding of Russia, while even Fascist Italy sent electrical equipment and machinery for the manufacture of cars. Professor Lomonossov bought locomotives, wholesale, in Sweden, while other Swedish firms supplied machinery and plant, and the world-famous SKF ball-bearing works provided the Soviet Union with a pilot factory. The Danes' most important concession was Trans-Siberian Cables, a subsidiary of the Great Northern Telegraph Company.

There was at that time no telegraphic network embracing all Russia. So the Danes, who had laid the cables during the building of the Trans-Siberian Railway under the Tsar, accepted a monopoly from the Bolshevik rulers of all communications with the Far East. Communications were so important that Lenin was ready to award so vast a concession. He laid down that the Danish personnel at the relay stations were to be granted more or less extra-territorial rights, for Russia had no trained communications personnel of her own. This situation soon changed, however, when Lenin, after reading a report from London in *Izvestia* of 19th March 1922, decided to introduce wireless telegraphy into the USSR.

'An engineer has discovered a procedure,' the London report stated, 'which makes it possible to keep telegrams secret, even when transmitted by wireless. Successful experiments have been carried out between London and Birmingham. The telegrams reached their destination undistorted and secret.'

This new discovery, and the fact that it was secret, greatly excited Lenin. 'If we could buy this invention, then communication by radio telephone and radio telegraphy would be of the greatest possible advantage to us from a military point of view,' Lenin wrote to Stalin.

So the Soviet Union acquired the new invention, and the Danish concessionnaires were soon expelled from the country—after they had instructed the Russians sufficiently for them to carry on.

Not only in industry and in the technique of communications was 'Bolshevik development' entirely dependent on the West. It was the same with agriculture. The Soviet Union owed its first large, completely mechanized agricultural scheme to the firm of Krupp. North of the Caucasus, in the Salsk area, there was a model development area covering some 125,000 acres, the result of a concession made in 1923. What the Soviets attempted with their *Kolkhozes* and *Sovkhozes*, that is to say, completely mechanized agricultural projects, was first demonstrated by German farmers and technicians.

When this Krupp concession started, Russian agriculture was in a desperate plight. An agricultural country, almost 80 per cent of whose population lived on the land, and which, in the 'black earth country', possessed the most fertile soil in the world, produced the poorest harvests. Russian acres yielded only one-third of the English and German equivalent, only a quarter of that of Denmark.

On the model Krupp estate the latest agricultural machinery was installed, for ploughing and harrowing, manuring, sowing and harvesting. There were even some of the famous tractors, which were later to become a sort of Russian symbol. There was a model herd of Merino sheep. In September 1928, when Moscow ordered the complete collectivization of the Russian peasants, the Krupp development scheme became the 'Russo-German Agricultural Group of Manych-Krupp'.

And this is now all forgotten. In Western Europe and America each firm kept its own records, and so it is impossible to give any total figure for the vast quantity of supplies which came to Russia. As for the Russian records, they are definitely not available . . .

Included in the 'concessions', a very special project was started in Russia in 1922, which was to be the beginning of the Soviet aircraft industry. The firm of Junkers began to operate in the East.

The story behind this was that the Treaty of Versailles had forbidden Germany to carry out any further development in certain branches of modern industry and technology, including the construction of military aircraft. This prohibition was extended to include civil aircraft by the 'London Ultimatum' of 4th May 1921. All aircraft already in existence were to be handed over, those under construction to be destroyed. For Germany this had only one meaning—the complete discontinuation of a development process which had hardly begun.

Early in 1919, the first transport aircraft in the world was under construction at the Junkers works at Dessau. This was the F-13, an all-metal low-wing monoplane with cantilever wings, known as the 'tin donkey' in the history of the aircraft industry. Professor Hugo Junkers had realized, before the end of the war, the great future that aircraft must have in the transport of freight and passengers. His F-13 was a brilliant original design, and the F-13 was soon flying over every continent. By 1925 forty per cent of the world's air transport network was to be served by the F-13. Furthermore, Junkers had already started to build a four-engined aircraft, when the ban on aircraft construction imposed by the 'London Ultimatum' threatened to destroy all his work and all his hopes.

The German aircraft manufacturers felt compelled to accept the only alternative rather than discontinue their work. They moved abroad.

Rohrbach founded a new company in Denmark and leased his patents in England. Dornier went to Switzerland and also built a factory in Italy. Junkers moved to Russia.

In 1922 Professor Junkers was granted a concession to build a factory for the Soviets, to meet the future aircraft requirements of the USSR. He, in return, gave the Russians the blueprints as well as the fruits of all his aeronautical, practical and technical experience. His most highly skilled workers were to go to Russia with him, and there build an industry for the Russians. Junkers's other great assignment was to lay the foundations for a Russian air transport network, using Junkers machines.

He had to function in what was virtually a vacuum. Since 1917, when the Russian aeronautical engineer, Igor Ivanovich Sikorsky, had emigrated, Russia had had, for all intents and purposes, no aircraft engineers and therefore no aircraft industry.

So the best men from the Junkers factory at Dessau set off for Moscow. In the next few years there were more German aeronautical engineers and technicians in Russia than in Germany.

At Fili, near Moscow, the Russian Junkers Works came into being, in very difficult conditions. They were given the premises of a former automobile factory. The complement of German specialists and trained Russians soon rose to one thousand three hundred and fifty men.

On Soviet instructions, priority at Fili was given to the building of special military aircraft. This was a difficult job, both technically and constructionally, for the new types—among them the two-seater low-wing model Ju-20 and the two-seater high-wing model Ju-21—had to be built without benefit of the testing installations previously available at Dessau, and the test flights of the prototypes were carried out in primitive conditions. Despite all obstacles, the Junkers works at Fili produced one hundred and seventy aircraft of the new types. Dessau, where the Junkers-Motorenbau GmbH (the Junkers Engine Company) now functioned, supplied the engines.

Thus was Soviet air power born.

Thanks to Fili the first air transport network in the Soviet Union came into existence. Airfield after airfield was built, civil aircraft flew ever greater distances in all directions, criss-crossing the vast land mass of Russia. For Junkers, Russia became the great testing-ground for future world airlines. In view of the date there were already a very large number of aircraft. Apart from the machines built by Junkers in Russia, Dessau had supplied fifty of the famous F-13 models. In the summer of 1922 Junkers opened the first Russian airline from Moscow to Nijni-Novgorod (now called Gorki). Air communications with the Ukraine, the Crimea and the Baku oilfields followed. New airfields were quickly made operational in the Urals, on the Kirghiz steppes, beside the Caspian, Lake Baikal, and as far as the distant borders of China. Junkers aircraft were first used for aerial surveys of this vast territory, parts of which had scarcely been trodden by the foot of man. Aerial surveys of the polar seas were also begun.

Arctic flights were carried out by the international Aeroarctic Company, founded in Berlin in 1924 by the airship constructor, Walter Bruns. Both airships and planes were to help in a geographical and meteorological survey of the Arctic regions, in which all nations would take part. Particular attention was to be paid to the possibilities of an eventual air route over the Pole. Naturally the Soviet Union immediately sent representatives to Aeroarctic. 'Their task', says Constantin Krypton, then employed in a Soviet Institute, 'was to get all information possible from the capitalist countries and at the same time to conceal Soviet data, even of a purely theoretical or scientific character. Written instructions to follow this practice were issued to Soviet personnel at the Arctic Institute.'

For three years, starting in 1922, Junkers and his staff were engaged upon a gigantic undertaking. The foundations for a modern aircraft industry were laid by these experts from Dessau. Large numbers of Soviet engineers and workers were trained, many hundreds of Russian pilots thoroughly in-structed by German test pilots, and the first great airline network created. All that the Junkers experts knew, their methods of testing, their models, their still secret plans and blueprints, were given to the Soviet Union. The Russians even had free access to the works and to all that might interest them in the parent factory at Dessau, as well as Junkers's Swedish factory at Limhamn, where the first twin-engined fighter plane, the S-36, and the first dive-bomber, the K-47, were built.

Then the Soviets began to cold-shoulder the Junkers people, exactly as they had done in the case of the other concessionnaires. The foreigners from the 'corrupt West' had fulfilled their function. It was time they went.

After 1925 the USSR was withdrawing one concession after another and breaking the agreements made in the original contracts. Junkers lost their concession, which had been guaranteed to last for thirty years.

It was not only the Germans who were treated in this way. Other foreign firms and organizations were told to quit. The projects had been started, the plans and models delivered, and the foreigners were not needed any more. The Russian learns very quickly for he is a past-master at mimicry, and adept at imitation. In the same year, 1925, that Junkers were kicked out, the Kremlin's policy in these matters changed. The era of the *Spets*, or specialists, began. Brains were now required for large-scale planning of the whole industrial development plan. A year later Colonel Hugh Cooper arrived from the United States with a staff of assistants. It was he, an organizer of genius, who was to be one of the essential creators of the future Five Year Plans.

Only one foreign 'concession' was permitted by the Soviet Union to continued unmolested. It was of a very special sort and shrouded in mystery. In the greatest secrecy the German Army, in 1920, had put out feelers towards Russia—naturally this had not been publicized in Germany—and had later made a significant contribution towards the modernization of the Soviet Army and the creation of a modern armament industry in the USSR.

By the terms of the Treaty of Versailles Germany was forbidden to make arms of any sort, and the small German Army was not even allowed to possess armoured fighting vehicles or military aircraft. On manœuvres cardboard dummies built upon motor-cars had to substitute for tanks. Training in the use of modern weapons, essential to any army, was as impossible as was the development of new weapons and equipment. The Allied Control Commissions saw to it that the ban was strictly enforced.

Communist Russia offered Germany a unique chance of avoiding total stagnation. And the Bolsheviks well knew what they were doing when they allowed military activities in their country which in Germany would have been immediately stopped by the Control Commissions. It was of the greatest possible advantage to them to learn from the German Army. At that time the Red Army was new and its equipment out of date.

Moscow willingly made suitable training areas available to the German Army so that its training might continue undisturbed behind the Iron Curtain and its weapons be improved and tested on manœuvres.

Three German specialist training schools were created after 1923, the Lipetsk Flying School near Voronezh, the Armoured Vehicles School at Kazan, and a Chemical Warfare Research Institute at Saratov. Year after year the German Defence Ministry sent secret military missions to Russia. Serving officers were ordered to Lipetsk and Kazan.

Large-scale production of the new tanks and military aircraft developed by the Germans in Russian factories was agreed. The German Defence

Ministry had already given Russia over a hundred million marks, from secret funds, for the building of aircraft and armament factories. In 1923 an agreement was concluded with the Soviet Union aimed at the development of a larger armaments industry. But it came to nothing. The Soviets refused to give preference to German industry in the development of their own armaments industry and also refused to exclude all other foreigners from projects in which German firms and German specialists were engaged.

As Karl Radek explained to the German Ambassador in Moscow, Ulrich Count von Brockdorff-Rantzau: 'You cannot expect us to bind our policy exclusively to yourselves in exchange for the few wretched millions you are giving us. As for the monopoly for German industry you ask for, we have no intention of giving you any such thing. Quite the contrary, we take whatever our army needs, wherever we happen to find it. We have bought aircraft in France, and we shall also accept supplies from England.'

There was, in fact, already a French military mission in Moscow. The Allies, who had originally supported the various anti-Bolshevik counterrevolutionary armies, now began to supply the Soviets with munitions. They too helped develop the armaments industry which must provide the backbone for the Red Army. Meanwhile the camouflaged German General Staff, the so-called 'Army Office', filled the gaps in their knowledge of military tactics and strategy. German officers secretly trained and taught the Red Army. It is forgotten today that many of Russia's best senior officers were taught for years by officers of the German Army.

Not only Marshal Tukhachevsky, Voroshilov's deputy as Defence Commissar from 1931 until his execution in June 1937, but also many other Russian generals attended the staff courses organized by the German Army. Among these were Uborevich, Kork and Eidemann, all of whom were later executed during the Great Purge. Others survived to use the knowledge they had acquired from German teachers in the war against Germany. Perhaps the most gifted of these was the man who later became the military commander of Russian-occupied Germany, Grigory Konstantinovich Zhukov.

In 1936 the Kremlin appointed him to command the Red Army units fighting in the Spanish Civil War. On 21st October 1941, when the German armoured spearheads were outside Moscow, Stalin entrusted him with the defence of the Red capital, where he won the first Russian victory of the war. In 1942 Zhukov was given the command at Stalingrad. In 1943 he commanded in the summer offensive the Army Group that recaptured Kharkov, Kursk, Orel and Smolensk. In March 1944 he became Supreme Commander of the 'First Ukrainian Front'. He then took over Supreme Command on the 'First White Russian Front', broke through the German positions on the Oder, and led the Red Army to Berlin, entering that city as its conqueror on 2nd May 1945.

Lenin's most publicized concept, which has been described repeatedly as the cornerstone of 'Bolshevik development', dates from the NEP period.

On 22nd December 1920, Lenin made a speech in the Moscow Bolshoi Theatre. He was addressing the delegates of the eighth Congress of the All-Russian Soviets. He said: 'In my opinion, our second Party programme is . . .' and after a pause came the famous words: 'Communism—that means Soviet power plus the electrification of the whole country . . . Then, and only then, when the country is electrified, when industry, agriculture and communications are firmly based on modern, technical, large-scale industries, shall we have finally won through.'

He then held up a sheaf of documents, the so-called GOELRO Plan. During the next ten or fifteen years thirty heavy industries were to be created. Fundamentally, the Academician Alexander Winter has said, 'This was the first industrialization plan . . .' But the slogan of 'Soviet power plus electrification' did not originate with Lenin nor even in the Soviet Union.

On 8th November 1882, Karl Marx wrote to Friedrich Engels, 'Dear Fred, What do you think about Deprez's experiment at the Munich Electrical Exhibition? It is almost a year since Longuet promised to send me Deprez's works. (I'm particularly interested in what he says about the possibility of employing electrical power over great distances simply by means of telegraph wires.)'

Engels replied, on 11th November 1882: 'Dear Mohr, . . . The more I consider the Deprez experiment in Munich, the greater my interest. . . . This thing will suddenly make available the gigantic, and hitherto untapped, mass of power available in water.'

What had happened was that at Miesbach, in Upper Bavaria, Marcel Deprez and Oskar von Miller, using a water-driven dynamo, had succeeded in sending an electric current along a telegraph wire for a distance of over thirty miles to Munich. There it powered an electric motor in the Electricity Exhibition which drove a centrifugal pump feeding an artificial waterfall six feet high.

Marx had not merely been interested in these early electrical experiments. In his writings electric power was already described as the future basis of socialist technology. This, then, was the origin of the 'new' idea propagated by Lenin, and propagated, incidentally, at a time when every industrial country in the world was already brilliantly lit by electric light. But the Soviet Union could no more carry out this plan on its own than any of the others. The large-scale electrification of Russia only began some ten years later, when teams of American engineers were invited to the country. They built the mighty Dniepr power-plant, where a single turbine produced six times as much power as the total output of Russia's entire hydro-electric system as it had existed in 1920.

12 The First Five Year Plan

IN 1913, under the Tsar, Russia's gross industrial product was valued at 16,200m. roubles. The Soviet Union required eleven years to reach this figure, very small by world standards, and was only able to increase it slightly, to 18,300m., by 1928. Even this was only possible as a result of opening the 'ventilators of capitalism', by co-operation with important foreign firms during the NEP period. But from 1928 onwards the Bolshevik production curve climbed rapidly. Output increased fivefold in less than ten years.

How?

In December 1925, at the Fourteenth Party Congress of the CPSU, Stalin produced an industrial plan which created a sensation both inside Russia and in the rest of the world. The purpose of this plan was to 'transform the Soviet Union from an agricultural into an industrial economy'. Two years later, during the festivities to celebrate the tenth anniversary of the October Revolution, on 7th November 1927, Stalin made a great speech concerning his new programme. It contained some fantastic figures. He outlined his two major objectives, the radical collectivization of the peasants and the creation of a mighty industrial system. A month later the Fifteenth Party Congress took over the colossal task of forced industrialization and of drafting the first Five Year Plan, which was inaugurated in 1928. Such is the background to one of the most ambitious undertakings of the century.

Pyatilyetka (*pyat* = five and *lyet* = years) was the word which was to revolutionize the Russian domestic economy. On 1st October 1928 the first Five Year Plan officially began.

Stalin had one principal objective for his peasant country, so recently ravaged by bloody revolution. In January 1929, 125,188,800 out of a total population of 153,955,600 still worked on or close to the land. His objective was to catch up with the industrialized capitalist countries. This was to remain the objective of all the Five Year Plans.

The Western governments and press took note of this project, but not seriously. They realized what was carefully not mentioned by the Russians, that so vast a project was impossible without the active help of Western industry with its unlimited supplies and its expert technical knowledge. By the time the first Plan was announced, the essential contracts had already been signed by Western firms, which was why the Soviets could appear so confident.

From the moment that the vast Plan was conceived there was feverish activity in Moscow. At the Ministry of Foreign Trade, where the Armenian, Anastasy Mikoyan, presided over Russian commerce, the lights burned late into the night. Countless filing cabinets were filled with the confidential reports of Soviet ambassadors and trade missions, with prospectuses and catalogues, with the details of supplies and the names of technicians, until a complete catalogue existed of all industrial and technical sources of assistance available in the West. These were to be the real raw materials of *Pyatilyetka*.

Orders in cypher were sent to the Soviet representatives in America. Unobserved by the American public, the vital preliminaries for 'socialist development' were set in motion in the very centre of 'capitalist corruption'.

Mr A. Ruckeyser was surprised one day to find himself seated across the table from a group of Russians who had come to see him in his New York office. His interest quickened when the foreigners spread a map of the Urals upon his desk, and the subject of their visit turned out to be asbestos. Ruckeyser was an engineer who had had experience in this field all over the world. He had specialized in asbestos-mining, and had even invented a special method of working this valuable raw material. He was quoted as an authority in international engineering handbooks.

A few weeks after this conversation an invitation from Moscow brought the engineer to the Urals. In Asbest, a place not then shown on any map, he inspected the huts and the insignificant mine-workings. 'Must be entirely replanned!' advised Ruckeyser. Why? the Russians wanted to know. 'It will repay you ten times over!' the American engineer replied. Ruckeyser was given a record contract, payable in dollars into his bank at home.

Many other American experts followed Ruckeyser, including Major P. D. Carter, under contract with the Soviet Union for the installation of the important Moscow–Khabarovsk telephone cable; a senior constructional engineer from Detroit, John K. Calder, who was a great expert on factory-building; and his experienced colleague, H. F. Mitre.

The Soviet Union also won over some of the largest American industrial concerns, which were steadily insulted in the Soviet press as 'the last strongholds of imperialist capitalism'. Orders worth millions of dollars poured into the offices of these great firms. Bolshevik agents appeared at their head offices, negotiating, calculating costs, and bringing with them orders of such incredible scope that even the Americans rubbed their eyes.

For many years Henry Ford had been a favourite target for furious attacks. Now the representatives of the Soviet Trade Mission were exchanging smiles and friendly talk with the capitalist. In 1928 the Bolsheviks had contacted the Ford Company, and there had been bargaining ever since. Russians are tough traders by nature, and what they now demanded in the way of quantities, of follow-up services, of delivery dates and so on was almost beyond Ford's capacity to meet.

Yet on 1st May 1930 the Bolsheviks pulled it off. The Bolshevik motor-car industry was born in the United States. A Soviet representative signed

Kuznetskstroy under construction. With American help and equipment the huge works of Stalinsk and in Siberia were built, also the iron and steel centres of Magnitogorsk, Sverdlovsk and Nijni Tagil in the Urals, during the first Five Year Plan. Below: Panorama of the Kuznetskstroy metallurgical combine in operation.

The Stalingrad tractor works. The shed construction and assembly sheds came from the USA, erected by chief engineer John Calder of Detroit in the record time of 6½ months. US technicians taught the Russians to operate the machinery.

Ford built Gorki, the "Detroit of the USSR". H. F. Mitre, chief constructor of the Austin Motor company, erected the sheds in Gorki, then called Nijni Novgorod, for the enormous car factory. Above: The shed for the press forge department. In this car factory entirely constructed by Ford, the "Volga" model of today is built.

contracts with Henry Ford for patents, licences, technical assistance and advice, and the supplying of spare parts. Ford undertook to supply the USSR with complete designs and technical blueprints of his own models, for the sum of thirty million dollars. He promised in addition to supply, below market price, 74,000 complete sets of motor-car parts ready for assembly, and to put at the Soviets' disposal all the engineers they needed for going into production. He also gave the Russians permission to send their own engineers to Dearborn for training at the Ford Works.

On 19th September 1959, during his visit to America, Khrushchev recalled the part played by the United States in technical instruction and training: 'We sent our engineers over here,' he said in Los Angeles, 'and they learnt from you in your technical institutes. Our engineers came to the Ford Works. The Minister responsible for the motor-car industry in our country himself worked with Ford.'

In drawing up their huge contract with Ford, the Russians cleverly took every conceivable precaution to ensure that their 'socialist development project' of a car factory in Russia should be carried out regardless of setbacks and difficulties. During the first two years, the Soviet works were only to assemble cars from the parts supplied by Ford, under the supervision of Ford technicians. During the third year it was envisaged that they would produce half the parts themselves, in the fourth year 75 per cent, and thereafter Russian production would be entirely self-supporting.

This contract resembled the supplying of a 'do-it-yourself' outfit with directions enclosed. This Ford factory might just as easily have been built and made operational in the African jungle or among the Eskimos. 'When Ford built our first motor-works,' Khrushchev stated at Los Angeles, 'we smashed a great deal of the machinery before we learnt how to handle it.'

But even this Ford contract did not satisfy the ambitious Russians. A few months after it was signed, they pressed the Americans for a still higher rate of productivity. The initial total quota of 100,000 cars a year was now to be raised to 140,000.

At the same time the Soviets shortened the time allotted for the building of the works from two years to a mere fifteen months. This was in a contract with the Austin Company of Ohio and New York. This firm, of world-wide fame, was chosen to build the 'first model Communist town', the enormous factories and groups of buildings needed for the Ford project at Gorki, where the Oka flows into the Volga.

Even these huge contracts were put in the shade by the agreements the Soviets made with another well-known American firm. 'The biggest contract in the history of industry' was made with the Arthur G. Mackee Company of Cleveland, Ohio. This consisted of nothing less than rebuilding the famous city of Gary, Indiana, centre of the American iron and steel industry, on Russian soil. The Mackee Company was to build in this fashion the vital 'key' factory for the carrying out of the Five Year Plan, the huge installations at Magnitogorsk in the Urals. The contract was worth eight hundred million roubles.

Contracts with American specialists mounted up at Amtorg—the department of the Soviet Board of Trade responsible for dealings with America—and in the other Soviet government offices. Hundreds of specialists, works foremen, works managers, technicians and engineers, planners and designers signed up.

Simply to pay the salaries of this army of specialists from the United States cost the Russian treasury in those years some ten million dollars a year. Nowadays American aid is never mentioned when the Russians boast of all that their first Five Year Plan achieved. Indeed, it was never even mentioned at the time.

Together with large numbers of engineers and specialists, great quantities of foreign equipment arrived at Russian ports. There were cranes, hauling and dredging machinery, conveyor-belts, boring equipment, machines, motors, trucks and tractors. They all bore the mark of their countries of origin—the United States, England, Germany . . .

From Leningrad in the north and Odessa in the south, these machines were moved into the interior, unloaded, and transported over poor roads to their destinations. There the foreign technicians and engineers would be waiting to check the invoices and assemble the machinery.

Many such 'destinations' were places not yet marked on any map. One of these was in the Urals, where the Magnitnaya Gora—the magnetic mountain—rises against the sky.

This mountain contained two hundred and seventy-five million tons of 62 per cent magnetic iron ore. The whole mountain, three miles long, two miles wide and fifteen hundred feet high, was a single, solid block of magnetic iron-stone. For miles about no clock kept exact time. This priceless ore deposit was to be the basis of their greatest steel centre.

Iron is, and always will be, the most important metal. Without iron there can be no steel, without steel no heavy industry, and without heavy industry no Bolshevik world power to 'bury' the West. Beside the Magnetic Mountain, the great corner-stone of the Five Year Plan, was built the mighty city of Magnitogorsk. This was to be the show-piece of the 'Bolshevik development' scheme, shown to foreign visitors, photographed and filmed over and over again, the 'steel colossus' of the USSR.

Until 1928 the Magnitnaya Gora slumbered. That part of the Urals was uninhabited. Suddenly it came alive. Endless lines of pony-drawn carts arrived, 'Russian convoys', as they were satirically named. Enormous numbers of Russian workers were moved in. Barracks were built for them. The ground was surveyed. Work began in July 1930. When the American journalist, H. R. Knickerbocker, visited the site a few months later, the

*Products from the West made the
development of Red industry
possible. Kablitz–Berlin was one of
the thousands of firms which helped
in the first Five Year Plan.*

hitherto deserted banks of the Ural River had a population of 35,000, and
an astounding number of buildings were going up.

Knickerbocker wrote:

'Jolting over roads that tested to capacity the springs of the company
agent's Ford, we passed blocks of tents and barracks ... and as we mounted
higher up the mountain-side the panorama of Magnetogorsk spread out
before us. Six miles long and three wide lay a belt of structures, tents and
excavations, brick-red, white and steel-black against the bleak grey
surface of the hard steppe. ... Tents by the thousands, each large enough
to accommodate a squad of men, alternated with flat barracks of double-
walled pine lumber stuffed with clay. Gaping foundation sites, forest of
scaffolds, stacks of railroad ties, an occasional set of brick walls showed
where were to rise the blast furnaces, steel mills, power station, chemical
factory and railroads to make of Magnetogorsk the steel capital of the
Red World.'

Knickerbocker was seeing, spread before him, what the experts of the
Arthur G. Mackee Company told him was the largest construction project
in the world. His countrymen, led by Mr Max McMurray of Cleveland,
had separate living quarters. A sort of 'little America' had been created for
them, a twentieth-century equivalent of the old *Nyemetskaya Sloboda*. Their
houses were comfortable, and good food was supplied in the American
restaurant. 'Breakfast of roast beef, quantities of butter, wheat bread and

coffee proved that the food shortage would not be allowed to touch the foreigners.' For Magnitogorsk, 'on the bare Ural steppe, is one of the most desolate, forlorn spots on the face of Russia,' Knickerbocker commented. 'In winter it could vie with the famous penal settlement, Solovetzky Island, in the White Sea.'

Mr Jack Clark, the American engineer in charge, could already point with pride to their first achievement. Across the Ural River lay a dam five-eighths of a mile long, containing 50,000 cubic yards of reinforced concrete. This initial construction job was completed in a mere four months, and provided the water supply for the future factories. When the river rose in the spring, a lake eight miles long and over a mile wide came into existence behind the dam. The Russians had been taught this particularly difficult building operation by the Americans, and were spurred on by those diabolical means favoured by 'capitalist profiteers' and condemned by Karl Marx—rewards and bonuses. These were more successful than the Red propaganda posters at either end of the building site, on which appeared in enormous letters, 'The right bank must be finished first' on one side and 'The left bank must be finished first' on the other. During the building of the dam, much machinery was used, all of the latest type—pneumatic drills and an enormous cement-mixer, a steam dredger and a nine-ton steam pile-driver from America.

The biggest blast-furnace installations in the world were going up on another part of the site, a job undertaken and completed entirely by the Americans. Eight blast-furnaces were built, each over sixty feet high, with a capacity of 1,500 cubic yards and generating 1,000 tons of iron per day. At that time there were only eight such giants in the whole United States.

The Bolsheviks had been far-sighted. The Mackee Company would only have fulfilled their part of their contract when Magnitogorsk was in full production, with Russian personnel, and running smoothly. The Americans were to run training courses for Russian technical personnel and, further-more, were to send the workers and specialists whom they had thus trained to the United States for further specialized technical instruction.

The contract with the famous Cleveland firm was highly profitable to the Russians. In 1932 there were disagreements between the Mackee Company and the Russian administration. The Soviets thereupon transferred the build-ing of the vast rolling-mills to the German firm of Demag and Klein. The contract for the huge coke furnaces was given to the American firm of Koppers & Co.

There is no mention of all this in the Soviet encyclopaedia, which simply says: 'Magnitogorsk: Industrial town in southern Urals; Population (1939) 145,900, (1947) 270,000, (1951) 500,000; most important mining district in the USSR, containing one of the biggest iron and steelworks in the world; blast-furnaces. Founded in 1930, at the foot of the Magnitnaya Gora.'

Magnitogorsk was the first of many such enterprises. In the Tal steppes, east of the Urals, another city was rapidly built on virgin soil. In Chelyabinsk there arose 'the biggest tractor factory in the world'. The American expert to whom the Soviets entrusted this colossal project was John K. K. Calder, a construction engineer from Detroit.

The first shovelful of earth was dug on 20th July 1930. Calder made a speech, which his contract scarcely obliged him to do. A compatriot has described how Calder 'gave an address from a Red platform decorated with Bolshevist slogans, and surrounded by members of the Communist Youth International holding drawn swords—a symbol of the industrialization struggle'.

Within a few months, and under American supervision (Henry Hendrickson from Cleveland, I. K. MacElroy and R. D. Spencer from Detroit co-operated with Calder), the Russians had dug 780,000 cubic yards of earth, mixed 15,700 cubic yards of concrete and laid the extensive foundations.

The industrial installations at Chelyabinsk were impressive even by American standards.

There is no parallel in any other country to the work done for Moscow by the construction engineer from Detroit. The assembly works were two thousand feet long and six hundred and fifty feet in breadth, and they alone covered an area of thirty acres. Twenty-one American football fields would fit into this one building, with changing-rooms for the players. The nearby foundry was over a thousand feet long and eight hundred feet wide.

The Soviets knew that Calder would get the enormous factory at Chelyabinsk into production in record time. The Detroit engineer had already given them an example elsewhere of American tempo. His first assignment had been the Stalingrad tractor factory. He had got it going in six and a half months, more rapidly even than his contract and the Bolshevik planners had anticipated.

Russia, with her backward agricultural system, urgently needed tractors in large numbers. But Chelyabinsk—as had been stressed by the Soviets in the contracts—could be adapted overnight to the production of another, less innocuous commodity—tanks. If Moscow gave the order, instead of 50,000 ten-ton 60 h.p. prime movers, 50,000 tanks would leave the assembly lines. 'We must create our heavy industries', *Izvestia* stated unequivocally, 'in such a way as to make them capable of producing armaments when needed.'

While the most basic factories were being created in record time, the Soviets also commissioned the building of a 'factory for the production of one hundred experimental tractors per year'.

The Russians thus showed to the Americans their favourite method of ruthlessly exploiting foreign inventions, without paying a single rouble in return. They thus acquired technical knowledge worth millions, at the expense of those nations which had spent long years on research and development.

'The experimental plant constitutes an interesting feature of Soviet industrial practice,' writes Knickerbocker.

'Here in Chelyabinsk, although the tractors to be produced will follow very closely the lines of the machine produced by the Caterpillar Company of America, there have been no arrangements made for payments for the use of the patents . . .

'In the experimental factory tractors of every known make, from all over the world, will be taken down, studied, and the useful features incorporated in the Soviet machines. Freedom from "bourgeois" inhibitions as to private property places Soviet industry in a singularly advantageous position.'

When Knickerbocker made this comment, the appropriation of foreign property, the stealing of patents by the Bolsheviks contrary to all legal practice throughout the civilized world, was just beginning. This robbing of other nations has increased a hundredfold during the past thirty years.

Even after the factories had been planned and built by 'capitalist' engineers and equipped with foreign machinery, the task was not completed. How were they to be kept in production? For this, too, specialists were needed, but the West had a sufficiently large reserve of these.

'The problem of skilled labour for the tractor plant when it opens for operation', Knickerbocker wrote, 'is one that the Soviet authorities intend to solve with the help of America. . . . The Soviet Government is still convinced that the best way to start a Russian factory going is to man it with American foremen.' And indeed arrangements had already been made for the importation of three hundred and fifty or four hundred high-grade American technicians to act as foremen at Chelyabinsk.

Built and bolstered by the foreigners, the 'progressive socialist' industries got off to a good start. For as Knickerbocker says: 'If the plant is erected under American supervision, equipped with American machines, and launched with the help of a large crew of American foremen for a whole year, why should not the plant turn out a quantity and quality of production at least within striking distance of a similar plant in America?'

At Stalingrad—Tsaritsyn, as it used to be—the vast tractor factory was going into production in 1930. Three hundred and eighty American engineers and works foremen were there, to boost production.

This most publicized of all the new factories of the first Five Year Plan 'could not have been better laid out, constructed and equipped, if it had been built in the States', commented the American engineer, Elwood F. Riesing. The assembly works—fourteen hundred feet long and three hundred and fifty feet wide—contained their full quota of turning-lathes, drills, cog-wheel-operated planes and, indeed, every conceivable type of machine-tool; they all bore the trade-marks of American firms.

The Americans had built here a factory to produce one tractor every five and a quarter minutes, that is to say eleven tractors each hour, or 50,000 tractors per year.

For every twenty to thirty Russians, there was an American foreman, whose function was to supervise and instruct the Russians. These Americans were obliged by their contracts to stay until the Russians were capable of operating the machines themselves. Without this initial help, not one production quota could have been met. On 19th September 1959 Khrushchev said in Los Angeles: 'When you helped us to build our tractor factory, we could not keep going even for two years, because all the machines fell to bits.'

The Stalingrad works provided the greater part of the tractors; only the radiators, ignition systems and precision parts had to be imported from the United States. The Soviets, however, planned to manufacture these sections as well, using foreign blueprints. Such a copying process was not confined to parts of machinery. An exact duplicate of the Stalingrad works was built at Kharkov, and another for the 'Selmashstroy' Works at Rostov—the only Five Year Plan factory in the whole of Russia built without foreign supervision—the 'capitalists' supplying only the mechanical equipment. Selmashstroy produced exact copies of those agricultural prime movers which had previously been imported from America.

'Selmashstroy', Knickerbocker commented, 'means a reduction in the import of agricultural machinery by several million dollars at least. Similarly, the construction of the great tractor factories at Chelyabinsk, Stalingrad and Kharkov means that when these are in full production, no more new American tractors will be needed in Russia.'

For hundreds of years Nijni-Novgorod had been the most important trading centre of the East. Now the city began to be overshadowed, for a dozen miles from the vast market-place and fairground—Bétancourt's masterpiece—American engineers set about building the largest car factory in Russia. On the banks of the Oka, the town of Gorki sprang from the ground, the 'Detroit of Russia'.

In 1929, deep in the forests, the air was rent with noise; ten thousand people poured into the district, coming from far and near. A factory was being built, according to American plans, which by 1932 was supposed to produce 140,000 cars a year. In the United States, where there were already twenty-six million automobiles, this might seem an insignificant figure; but in Russia, where there were at that time only about 30,000, apart from the trucks imported from abroad, this new factory represented a colossal step forward. Hitherto Russian production had been pitiful.

In 1929, Amo, in Moscow, turned out 2,585 cars, and the factory at Yaroslavl achieved an output of 711 cars in 1930. And this was all!

'The first Communist "factory town",' the Bolshevik press boasted, 'is emerging very rapidly, and would surely do credit to a far less backward country than Russia. Building has been under way since June 1930. During this period the foundations have been laid for the assembly works (650 metres in length) . . . the repair, machine-tool and maintenance workshops are already installed.'

It is hardly surprising, for the Yankees set the pace at Gorki. They had brought the newest machinery from their own country. Twenty-one American engineers from the Austin Company were there, directing every phase of the building work. The construction engineer, H. F. Mitre, a very experienced man, saw to it that the contract his firm had signed was carried out to the letter, and within the specified time. The Soviets had no grounds for complaint. Next to the shabby barrack accommodation provided for the Russian army of 'ants', the foreign experts lived with their families in a modern *Nyemetskaya Sloboda*, called 'Austingrad' and known as 'Little America'.

As soon as the assembly works were completed, the Austin Company pulled out, and the Ford people moved in. It was their job to see that the wishes of the Soviet Tractor and Automobile Trust were realized, and that they possessed a 'Soviet' motor-works indistinguishable from the Ford factories. For years the Soviet press had mourned the tragic fate of the 'exploited slaves of the conveyor-belt'; now Moscow had commissioned Ford to produce the most modern of conveyor belts for purposes of 'socialist development'.

'America produced the conveyor-belt, the most advanced industrial process in the world,' Khrushchev said in the United States in 1959. However, this admission was made in America, not in Russia, and at a time when Khrushchev was busy wooing the Americans in the hope of securing further assistance from them for his country. Such facts are carefully kept hidden in the Soviet Union.

One of the most brilliant programmes of mystification, designed to fool the rest of the world, was the propaganda in connection with Dnieprostroi— the biggest hydro-electric installation in existence, built in the USSR.

Photographs of Dnieprostroi were printed in newspapers throughout the world. Soviet postage stamps and match-boxes bore beneath the hammer and sickle pictures of the giant dam. No brochure or leaflet issued by 'Intourist' was complete without it. Millions of Russians and foreigners were told about the colossal installations, their vast capacity, and the record time in which this crowning glory of 'Bolshevik development' had been built.

Dam and power station at Dnieprostroi: the show-piece of the Soviets, built by American firms under Colonel Cooper during the first Five Year Plan.

Only one fact was never mentioned: that Dnieprostroi represented the peak of American achievement.

In 1926 Colonel Hugh Cooper, creator of the mighty Wilson Dam at Muscle Shoals, Tennessee, was first brought to the USSR. The Soviets took the famous engineer to the Dniepr, to Zaporozhe in the Ukraine. Rapids, stretching over a distance of forty miles, impeded shipping upon the great waterway, a natural obstacle which annoyed the Russians, and against which they were powerless. Since the early nineteenth century they had been trying in vain to deal with the rapids. Cooper studied the direction of the currents, drew various blueprints, and proceeded to speak of a colossal project which so inspired the Bolshevik planners that his presence was soon requested at the Kremlin. Stalin himself had all the details of the tremendous technical undertaking explained to him by the American engineer. His proposals exactly suited Soviet 'gigantomania' and the Russian passion for superlatives.

A dam, over a mile long and two hundred feet high, was to block the Dniepr, so that the water over the most dangerous shoals would rise to a height of seventeen feet. 1,150 million cubic yards of concrete would be needed. In the mile-long dam there would be nine turbines, each of 85,000 h.p., the 'largest in the world', to be imported from America. Colonel Cooper estimated output at 2,500,000 kilowatts. Cooper was able to assure Stalin that no other hydro-electric installation in the world—not even Niagara Falls—generated so much power. Cooper's own achievement, the Wilson Dam, had a capacity of only 456,320 kilowatts. His Dnieprostroi project would increase fivefold the electrical power output of the USSR, and the Soviet Union would rise from fifth to third place among the power-producing countries of the world, after America and Germany.

Cooper's idea became Stalin's favourite project. Again and again he requested the American to come to the Kremlin, and talked with him for hours on end. Only one other expert from the United States had been thus privileged, the 'record-breaker', John Calder of Detroit.

In May 1927 workmen were ready to start and the enormous excavation was begun. From then on Colonel Cooper was on the spot. He had brought a staff of his compatriots and colleagues with him. Not far from the rapids, near the once-famous island fortress of the Zaporozhe Cossacks, the Russians built a small village of neat brick villas. In this *Amerikanskaya Sloboda* the Dnieprostroi specialists lived. They included Colonel and Mrs Cooper, the engineer Milton Thomson from Montclair, Frank P. Fifer from Baltimore, Louis G. Puls from New York, James Johnson from North Carolina and Henry Wilkinson from Washington. Many had brought their wives and families with them. So attentive were the Bolsheviks to the welfare of the 'capitalists' whose help they needed so desperately, that when some of the American engineers' wives requested it, a swimming pool, six tennis courts and a golf course were laid out.

The time schedule set by Colonel Cooper and his American staff of engineers for the building of Dnieprostroi broke all records.

'We watched them installing the water passages of the turbines, fresh from the American manufacturer,' reports Knickerbocker, who was shown all over the gigantic building site by his fellow-countryman, Frank P. Fifer. 'Twenty-eight feet in diameter, the huge snail-shaped steel structures dwarfed the men at work.' It took a man half an hour to walk across the dam's caissons from one bank to the other. Everywhere mechanical shovels were biting deep into the ground. 'Thirty forty-ton locomotive cranes, ten steam shovels, fifty locomotives, eighty dump cars, all American machinery, presented such a forest of equipment as could not be seen elsewhere on any single construction site in the world. . . . The Dnieprostroi dam . . . is more highly mechanized than any in America.' Seventeen thousand workmen, thus equipped, were preparing to cast more concrete than was ever before cast in the history of engineering. In September 1930 115,000 cubic yards of concrete were produced, in October 145,000 cubic yards; the Wilson Dam record was a 'mere' 53,000 tons a month.

The 'largest installations in the world', completed by Cooper in 1932, were destined to be in operation for only ten years. During the Second World War the Russians blew up the giant dam at the approach of the German Army. Before doing so, they dismantled the American generators and transported them eastwards. After the Second World War, the Soviets reinstalled turbines of their own manufacture at Dnieprostroi; they had, in the meantime, learnt enough from the West to be able to do this.

It is forgotten that America produced the 'giants' of the first Five Year Plan. And even in America the other pioneer projects which helped the Soviets to achieve world power status are also forgotten—the technical equipping of the new iron and steel centres of Sverdlovsk and Nijni Tagil

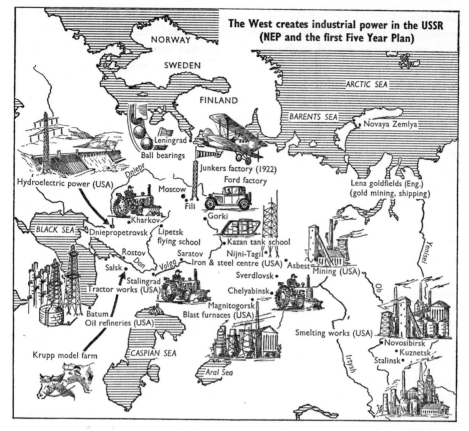

The West creates industrial power in the USSR
(NEP and the first Five Year Plan)

in the Urals, the enormous works at Kuznetskstroi and Stalinsk, north of
the Altai, the vast oil refineries at Batum and the brilliant constructional feat
of the engineer, Ruckeyser, in creating the Ural Asbestos Works.

In the late 1920's, American engineers were working on colossal projects
for irrigating the central Asiatic plains, the great Soviet cotton belt. American
agricultural technicians and agronomists taught the Russians how to use
American combine harvesters and other such equipment in the state
collective farms, *Gigant* and *Verblyud*. Professor E. J. Stirniman of California
University worked as scientific adviser at *Verblyud*.

It seemed at that time as though Europe's and America's greatest wish
was to help 'socialist development'. They vied with one another in supplying
the Soviets with the necessary equipment and technical advice.

Mikoyan's buying agents were welcome all over Europe, and trade
provided the Russians with everything that the Soviet Union lacked. In
1928 German export figures to the USSR reached a new peak, according
to Georg von Rauch: 'In the years 1928–33 tens of thousands of German
engineers and specialists were working in Russia. Owing to the Trade
Agreement of 21st December 1928, and the founding of the Russo-

German Trade Commission, German exports to Russia continued to increase. The importance of Russian trade to the German export industry is shown by the fact that the Russian market actually expanded during the world economic crisis of 1929–32. In these years Russia's share of Germany's total machine-tool exports rose from 10 to 75 per cent!'

In 1931 Mikoyan himself dealt with the Federation of German Industry, and the Soviet Union gave Germany contracts worth some nine hundred million marks. These were for supplies for their electrical industry, for machine-tool manufacture, for shipyards—in fact for whatever was most urgently needed for the fifth year of the *Pyatilyetka*.

The Bolsheviks also ordered supplies from Italy, cargo ships, torpedo boats, light cruisers, submarines and two hundred tugs. They also bought aircraft, seventy-five of the well-known Savoia-Macchetti seaplanes, the 'Balbo' for the South American service and the 'Maddalena' for the air-rescue service at the Pole.

Large quantities of textile machinery came to the Soviet Union from Manchester; Sweden supplied the most modern saw-mill equipment; and the Norwegians built whalers for the Russians.

The Kremlin drew upon the abundance of the West, and copied any inventions which they wished to use. The former Communist, Margarete Buber-Neumann, described one such incident.

When she visited Anastasy Mikoyan in 1932 'he switched the conversation immediately to Germany', she writes in her memoirs, '. . . and to a subject which seemed to lie particularly near his heart. He praised the German synthetic foods, the soup cubes, the dried vegetables, the milk in cartons and the Knorr condensed pea-soup, and told us that he thought of introducing these innovations into Soviet Russia at once, and thus ending the food problem. He further praised the German workers, and likewise the French and Belgians for their efficiency in rabbit-breeding. There was a propaganda campaign in the Soviet Union at that time in favour of keeping rabbits, to relieve the meat shortage.' It produced the results Mikoyan desired:'breeding was started on a vast scale', but 'after a short time epidemics broke out which decimated the expensive animals imported for breeding purposes.'

Having introduced condensed pea-soup and rabbit-breeding from Europe, Mikoyan later imported from America modern bakery installations, meat and vegetable canning plants and, of course, ice-cream, all 'progressive innovations'.

How did the Soviet Union pay for all this? With grain, of which the starving Russian people were deprived, for 'Starve, but export' was still the watchword, as at the end of the nineteenth century. And they also paid with gold.

First came the Lena Goldfields. In 1926 American firms received gold-prospecting rights on the Amur. The real gold era dawned in Siberia on the

eve of the first Five Year Plan, in 1927. At about that time the new gold
centre on the Kolyma River was also opened. On Stalin's orders, vast
national gold-mines were constructed by Professor Serebrovsky, who had
previously been sent to America and South Africa to make a detailed
study of the most modern methods of gold-mining. Two hundred American
mining engineers were 'imported' into Russia. They were followed in the
1930's by the most efficient mining equipment available in America, costing
many millions of dollars. Hundreds of thousands of slave labourers were sent
to Siberia; and in the area once occupied by Lena Goldfields Ltd., developed
by the English and equipped with American machinery and prospecting
gear, gold production began on an ever-increasing scale.

'The Soviet technical expansion was—and is still today to some extent—less
dependent on its own discoveries than on the exploitation of technical
processes discovered and already tried out elsewhere.' So says an American
research paper, published in 1955. 'It cannot be denied that in certain
branches of industrial technology and the applied sciences they have done
some research of their own. By and large, however, Soviet industry in the
last twenty-five years has not been based on their own discoveries, but on
appropriation, exploitation and the improvement of industrial techniques,
models, types and processes which were first discovered elsewhere, namely
in countries with more advanced technical science, e.g. England, Germany
and the United States. . . . This is one of the main reasons for the great stress
which was laid on the learning of foreign languages during the Soviet
development period, and for the amount of translation of scientific and
technical literature done by the Soviets, unequalled in any other country.'

THE HEADQUARTERS of the Bolshevik industrial espionage apparatus in Berlin was a large building on the Lindenstrasse that housed the Soviet Trade Delegation. There were good reasons for choosing 22–24 Linden-strasse. This enormous nineteenth-century building, with its hundreds of offices and its vast entrance with the brass plate bearing the words 'Soviet Trade Delegation', could be easily watched by the German police. But for ten years only a very few people knew that there was another entrance to this office block, through which men could pass in and out quite unobserved.

When the Soviets signed the lease for the building in the Lindenstrasse, they also, and secretly, rented another building. It was in a street which crossed the Lindenstrasse, the Ritterstrasse, and it housed a small jeweller's shop. The courtyards of the Lindenstrasse and Ritterstrasse buildings backed on to one another. Anyone wishing to visit the Soviet Trade Delegation unobserved did so by way of the jeweller's shop.

The Bolshevik Trade Delegation soon developed into a vast export-import organization, handling business that amounted to hundreds of millions of marks annually. This was equally vital to the USSR and to many branches of German industry. The Lindenstrasse dealt with the leading firms, I.G. Farben and Krupp, BMW, Junkers and numerous other organizations. The Soviets handled so much business that they had to open three branch offices—in Leipzig, Hamburg and Königsberg. Besides all official and semi-official business, however, the Trade Delegation was the operational head-quarters for an apparatus employing hundreds of agents, who neither bought nor sold—at least, not openly.

For two years all went well. Then the Lindenstrasse ran into trouble. In 1924 the Trade Delegation became stupidly involved in a political scandal which led to a police raid on the building.

A German railway technician, Hans Botzenhard, was convicted of Com-munist activities and dismissed. In order to make further use of this unemployed comrade's special qualifications, the German Communist Party arranged that he be given a job with the Soviet Trade Delegation. The man who arranged this job for Botzenhard was the late Wilhelm Pieck, who became President of the East German Republic after the Second World War.

Botzenhard, who was sent to South Germany as an agent, was again arrested and convicted at Stuttgart in the same year. He was transported, via Berlin and under police escort, to a prison in Pomerania. While in Berlin he found that the policemen were taking him, on foot, close by the Lindenstrasse. Thinking rapidly, Botzenhard decided to profit from this.

The South German police officials, in the capital for the first time, let Botzenhard persuade them to go to a restaurant which he knew well for a drink and a bite.

No sooner had Botzenhard entered this restaurant than he broke away from the police escort, shouting: 'Comrades, it's Botzenhard! I am here. They're taking me to Stargard.' In a few seconds a group of Soviet Trade Delegation officials surrounded him, got in the way of the policemen, and led him to safety through a back door.

The police escort sounded the alarm, and the Berlin police carried out a thorough search of the Trade Delegation building. They found nothing. The fugitive had disappeared. The police were, however, astonished by the large number of officials legitimately employed in the Soviet service.

The search had been in full swing for some two hours when it was suddenly called off. This was on the direct orders of Stresemann, the Foreign Minister. Germany wished to avoid any dislocation to her industrial dealings with Russia.

Moscow's reaction was characteristic. The Botzenhard affair was inflated into a diplomatic incident. Routine tactics were employed. The Soviet Ambassador in Berlin, Nikolai Krestinsky, lodged a formal protest with the Foreign Office. He produced the same arguments which the Soviets have always and indignantly used all over the world, when accused of espionage or of stealing patents. The Soviet Trade Delegation, he said, was a part of the Embassy and therefore had extra-territorial rights. The German police were guilty of unauthorized trespassing, for which the USSR expected an official apology. At the same time Krestinsky put a stop to all the purchasing activities of the Trade Delegation. This was a blow aimed at German industry, in the belief that the industrialists would exert pressure on the German government to make them accept the Soviet version. Centralized control became even more apparent when Moscow ordered that the ambassador return immediately to the Kremlin 'to report'.

Krestinsky left the German capital. Simultaneously the Soviets brought another weapon into play, the obedient German Communist Party. On the day the Soviet Ambassador departed, newspapers in the Ruhr announced: 'Strike called by Communist Party, 300,000 miners out.' This was a demonstration strike 'against the raiding of the Trade Delegation premises'. In Moscow a quarter of a million people were ordered to stage a 'spontaneous' mass demonstration, which Krestinsky himself attended in his official capacity.

Moscow continued to insist, and after almost three months of negotiations its object was achieved. A 'protocol' was signed. It contained an official apology by the German government and a declaration to the effect that the police officer responsible would be relieved of his post; it also granted to the Trade Delegation and some of its more important officials extra-territorial rights in future. The public had no idea why this was done, nor why the Soviets insisted on diplomatic privileges, that is to say, immunity from interference by the police, for their Trade Delegation.

All too soon, in the horrors of the pre-Nazi and the Nazi period, the Botzenhard affair faded into oblivion, and with it the peculiar role played by the Soviet Trade Delegation.

Despite the regular exchange system existing between the German and the Russian Armies, and despite the German military schools functioning at Kazan, Lipetsk and Saratov, the Soviets missed no opportunity of sending their agents to military objectives and of planting their spies in any organizations of 'military importance'. An engineer named Alexandrovski, employed by the Red Air Force, then still in its infancy, had a secret office in Berlin. As his top agent he employed a young German engineer, Eduard Ludwig, an aviation expert. When Ludwig was at the Junkers Works at Fili, near Moscow, in 1924–25, the Russians had promised him a professorship as an incentive, if and when he 'proved himself'. Back in Germany, Ludwig moved rapidly from one famous aircraft factory to another. Within a few years he was equally conversant with the processes used by Junkers at Dessau and by Dornier at Friedrichshafen, and also with the research being carried out in the Institute for Aviation Research at Adlershof, Berlin. From late 1927, in his new job at Adlershof, he had access to many secret documents. These he had copied, for the Red Air Force. When he was brought to trial in July 1928, Ludwig produced an argument that the world was to hear so often twenty years later, during the trials in connection with the betrayal of atomic secrets to the Soviet Union. His argument was that science is international, and that therefore nothing should be concealed from the USSR which would exclude them from new scientific discoveries.

Everything that was, or might be, of importance in the sphere of armaments interested the Kremlin and its 'outpost' in the Lindenstrasse in Berlin. Even bullet-proof glass, about the production of which the USSR knew absolutely nothing, appeared on the enormous list of successful thefts committed in the name of 'socialist industry'. In 1930 a chemist named Theodor Pech, an agent, supplied from the Neutex Glassworks at Aachen all relevant documents, including descriptions of tests and models. And when Germany built her first big battleship, the much-publicized 'Armoured Cruiser A', particulars of all the important building sections, photostat copies of constructional drawings and details of the ship's armament were in the Russian Admiralty long before the launching. Shortly after the project was made public by the German government, a group of engineers and technicians, headed by Willi Adamczik, had passed the plans to the Lindenstrasse.

This systematic robbing of a great industrial power by mass espionage is unparalleled in history. The Federation of German Industry estimated the financial cost in 1931 alone at some 800 million marks.

German industry tried desperately to protect itself against Russia's large-scale robbery campaign by taking counter-measures. A start was made by I.G. Farben, who set up their own detective agency at Leverkusen. A number of German firms followed their example, in an attempt to check this wholesale plundering. But such private protection schemes in industry did not meet with much success. The Soviet apparatus even managed to install a female agent in one of the private detective offices as secretary.

Why were so many Germans prepared in those days to rob their own people in the interest of a foreign power?

The results of the defeat of 1918 were still to be felt. The spectre of unemployment was everywhere, for the number of unemployed had passed the million mark. Large sections of the population were desperate. And the membership of the German Communist Party increased rapidly. For hundreds of thousands, it meant the hope of better times to come, in a 'Workers' Paradise' imported from Russia. Part of the intelligentsia was also fascinated by the apparent originality of the Bolshevik idea. The German Communist Party included thousands of writers, scientists and artists.

Thus the German Communist Party—and consequently the Kremlin—had a following which included men from every profession, unconditionally obedient to its orders. Communist propagandists never ceased to extol the virtues of Communism. A German legal document dated 29th October 1932 gives this extract from a Communist speech: 'Russia must . . . be able to carry out her Five Year Plan. . . . The fulfilment of this objective presupposes that she must possess the necessary machinery and materials, as well as acids, gases, phosphorus, light metals and so forth. Consequently it is the duty of all members of the Communist Party, in their place of work, to study whatever is to be studied in the way of machinery and plant, to observe the means of production. . . . Russia needs a great deal for her Five Year Plan and her armaments production. Therefore not only must the workings of these industrial organizations be understood in every detail, but their sources of supply and markets must also be studied. One way this can be done is by listing everything which goes in or out on the railway trucks. . . . Nobody should worry about committing acts of espionage of this kind. The Party will take anyone who gets into trouble straight to Russia.'

An enormous amount of information from all branches of industry was supplied by such Communist 'worker agents', at Moscow's demand. Towards the end of 1928 there were thousands of such agents reporting regularly from works and factories.

Furthermore there was all the information that German scientists, with the best intentions, supplied to Russia, in letters to their 'colleagues' in the East, or through the revelations of German scholars cleverly appointed by Moscow as 'Corresponding Members' of scientific societies in the USSR.

And it was not only in Germany that the Russians succeeded in organizing espionage operations on a hitherto unparalleled scale. Similar stories can be told about their activities in all other countries.

In 1926 and 1927 came the first setback. A whole series of arrests and trials of Soviet agents took place, from England to China. At the end of 1926 it was Czechoslovakia, in March 1927 Poland, a week later Turkey, and in April Peking, then Switzerland and in May Lithuania and Austria.

On 9th April 1927 France uncovered a Soviet spy-ring; this was the 'Cremet' case. Over a hundred people were involved. A month later decisive action was taken by Great Britain. The British ordered a police raid on the Soviet Trade Delegation in London, Arcos, and even broke off diplomatic relations with Moscow.

But it did not worry the Russians. Undeterred by such setbacks, and using new agents, they continued their espionage activities. Nor could their victims organize an effective defence. This became obvious in the years 1949–50, when the story of the great betrayal of atomic secrets was made public in a series of sensational trials.

The 'Rusgertorg' company, part of the Soviet Trade Agency located in the Lindenstrasse, Berlin, handled the equipment of factories in the East.

14 Education for Illiterates

'THUS WILL a new life begin, a new type of man will arise and all will be changed. History will then fall into two epochs: from the ape to the denial of God—and from the denial of God'—to the ape again? No—'to the physical transformation of the earth and of mankind. . . . Man will be a god and even his physical characteristics will change.'

These words, which Dostoevsky puts into the mouth of Kirillov in *The Possessed*, sound like a vision of the future, a prophecy of that period of Russian history which began with the revolution of 1917.

With the emergence of the 'new Bolshevik world' fresh perspectives were opened which were so daring as to be almost beyond the grasp of the human mind. The Bolsheviks believed that everything would be transformed, improved and made beautiful. A metamorphosis of human life and of man's character would inevitably result from their 'glorious victory'.

'Mankind will become incomparably stronger, cleverer and more free,' Leo Tolstoy had said. 'The human body will be harmonized, its movements more rhythmical, its voice more musical, and life will acquire a dynamic form. The average man will be an Aristotle, a Goethe or a Marx.' But despite this idyllic picture the Russians had to face certain inescapable facts. The means to the Communist 'Paradise on Earth' were greater productivity. This demanded a large class of skilled farmers and industrial workers. The Pharaohs could build their great pyramids and the Kremlin could dig canals, pave roads and lay rails, with a labour force of illiterates. They might even build a dam in this fashion, but they certainly could not construct an electric power station, let alone an ultra-modern industrial system. And the number of illiterates in Russia when the Soviets came to power was enormous. Among the nations of the world Russia came nineteenth in the battle against illiteracy. Seventy-two per cent of the Russian people could neither read nor write, while in some Asiatic provinces the figure was as high as ninety-nine per cent. These are Soviet statistics. But Tsarist sources tell much the same tale. In 1914 fifty per cent of the young men called up for military service were illiterate.

Lenin was never in doubt about the urgency of this task. He himself had had a strictly Western education. After his brother's execution he was expelled from school at the age of seventeen and was brought up by his grandfather, Dr. Blank; of Swabian-German descent. His mother, the doctor's daughter, taught him and she was a very efficient teacher. She subjected the boy to the severe mental discipline of the German classics and philosophers. After Hegel, Lenin went on to read Marx and Engels. When in later years Lenin was asked by the Council of Revolutionary Students for three watchwords, he replied, 'The first is: learn; the second is: learn; the third is: learn!'

Here we have a clear echo from another decisive period of Russian history. In 1697, when the Tsar Peter at the age of twenty-five set off for Germany, Holland and England to learn the trades of ship's carpenter, pilot and seaman, his personal seal bore the inscription: 'My rank is that of student. I need a teacher.' Eleven years later the first Ten Year Plan of this Tsar proved its worth. At Poltava Russia defeated the Swedish Army, the strongest military force on the Continent, hitherto believed invincible.

Lenin made no secret of his chief objective. When the English author, H. G. Wells, visited him in the Kremlin in 1920, he was told: 'We are determined not to give up the power which we seized in 1917 until Russia has achieved a régime of social justice. But to obtain such a system of government it is imperative that the percentage of illiterates be reduced to zero. The number of scientists in Russia should exceed that of the capitalist countries.'

What was done?

Fantastic ideas germinated in the minds of the leading Bolsheviks of the time. If the environment were changed, then everything would be different, and better—including human nature. Children in a socialist world would suddenly and miraculously become ardent seekers after knowledge, and workers would be able to study at the universities without having first received a basic education. The East believed that revolutionary enthusiasm was enough and that all former educational theory could be scrapped.

The Lunacharsky educational decrees, the first of which was proclaimed on 29th October 1917, that is to say, four days after the Bolshevik Revolution, laid down compulsory education for ten years, with communal instruction, without examinations and without punishments, in an atmosphere of complete freedom. Study groups of schoolchildren were to be formed, known as 'brigades'.

Teaching in an atmosphere of complete freedom—such was the reaction to the methods employed in the capitalists' schools. The bourgeois schoolmasters of the West, it was said, had produced mere automatons trained to blind obedience through beatings and intimidation. The mental development of the pupils was thus deliberately stultified in order to make them into capitalist lackeys, the slaves of the aristocracy.

The new teaching methods were launched on a vast wave of propaganda, and they caused much interest and won considerable admiration in the West. They were truly revolutionary methods, hitherto quite untried.

Young people were allowed to attend university lectures at the age of sixteen without passing any examination, and large numbers availed themselves of this opportunity. Special workers' faculties, called *Rabfak*, were created, where male and female workers aged between eighteen and thirty, who had had only elementary schooling, attended three-year courses at the universities. There were competitions between students and teachers, and university students and schoolchildren formed 'brigades', in which they worked out their problems together.

Soon the names of famous teachers from the West began to appear in this educational system. The Soviets employed the teaching methods of the liberal educationists. One such system was the 'Dalton plan', well known in Anglo-Saxon countries, a method of instruction designed to encourage individual development.

But the greatest achievement in the 'educational revolution' according to Soviet propaganda, was the mastery of the problem of the *Bezprizorniki*, or abandoned children.

During the chaotic years of the revolution, civil war and famine, tens of thousands of children had become delinquents. Bands of youthful criminals terrorized the countryside and were a major source of anxiety to the Russian Government. Hordes of these homeless children roamed the land, moving north or south according to the season. They lived by looting and theft, and were often guilty of assault and violence. On the squares and streets of Moscow daylight robbery was quite common. Swarms of *Bezprizorniki* would raid trains at lonely stations, robbing the passengers.

The police were unable to deal with the *Bezprizorniki* crime wave. The use of force was then strictly forbidden, as were punishments of all kinds. The Bolsheviks maintained that punishment was superfluous in a 'communist state'. Such problems had now to be solved by entirely different methods. Were not the *Bezprizorniki* a striking example of the heritage of an evil past? They had surely become social criminals owing to their former environment under the Tsarist régime. In the new socialist world, however, even immoral characters would be reformed and juvenile delinquents transformed into useful members of Soviet society.

A documentary film was made and exported so that the West might see the new system, which promised so much. This film, entitled *The Road to Life*, made by the Russian director, Ekk, showed how a gang of juvenile delinquents was transformed into a group of happy, hard-working adolescents. There was no discipline, no authority, no punishment. 'The only cure is work, belief and communal life.'

The film had an enormous success all over the world. It was supposed to show the West the socialist attitude towards crime, the abandonment of the old system of reprisal and intimidation, in favour of new and progressive methods for protecting society. Such was the fundamental doctrine of Soviet penology during those early days, and also of Soviet education.

For nearly ten years this educational experiment, which had been inaugurated with such a fanfare—the 'Educational System of the Future', as it was called—was continued. New educational centres were established in the farthest corners of the vast country, on both sides of the Urals, in Siberia and Soviet Asia. For almost a decade the famous 'educational revolution' from which the Bolsheviks hoped for so much was given every opportunity to prove its worth. But at long last it was realized that the results of all these new methods and educational theories were worthless. It had been a colossal failure.

Nobody had really learned anything. There was almost no basic knowledge being taught either in the elementary or in the secondary schools. The students coming to the universities were more or less illiterate. The removal of the authority of the teachers meant, all too often, that they were terrorized by their pupils. Discipline was non-existent.

Complete freedom in the planning of the school curriculum had led to fruitless discussions and endless political argument rather than to serious teaching.

At the end of ten years—the 'revolution's holiday' as Lenin once described this period—the results of the educational experiments were seen to be disastrous. Soviet statistics said the last word. In 1927 eighty per cent of Soviet citizens were still illiterate. This meant that the number of those who could neither read nor write had increased, and that the educational level had sunk, since Tsarist days. 'This daring experiment which chose to disregard the experience of other countries,' wrote Sidney and Beatrice Webb, 'continued to flourish until 1931. There was no discipline; the pupils were in charge, and the teachers had to do what the pupils wanted.'

The experiment had failed. The Bolshevik thesis of 'a new and perfect education' was on the rocks. Once this failure became apparent, the Kremlin did not hesitate to execute a complete about-face. There was a drastic change of policy, and the Soviet system of education was re-established on a new and solid basis, a Western one. Stalin himself gave the orders and proclaimed the new objective.

At the first All-Union Conference of Industry in February 1931, Stalin said: 'The Bolsheviks must master technology. It is time the Bolsheviks became specialists. We are fifty to a hundred years behind the advanced countries. We must catch up in ten years. We must become specialists, and scientists.'

In his realistic fashion Stalin brushed aside Bolshevik self-deception and Utopian illusion, and concentrated on the facts.

This marked the beginning of a new period. Stalin's order was the signal for the training of the *Spets*, or specialist, the scientific, technical and industrial experts. An efficient Soviet intelligentsia was essential, if the capitalist Western Europe were to be surpassed. The experts from the capitalist countries who were organizing the industries of the Soviet Union were living examples of Western education and training.

Thus from 1931 an entirely different atmosphere prevailed in the Russian schools. Lunacharsky's famous educational theories were scrapped. Under Bubnov, who took over in 1931 as Lunacharsky's successor, education was on a solid, Western basis. Everything formerly banned as typical 'relics of the capitalist past' was now triumphantly reinstated under the slogan of 'Socialist Progress'.

An examination system copied from the German schools in Tsarist times was reintroduced. The *Rabfaks* and 'brigades' disappeared, as did the 'free workers' schools'. Only the 'mad bourgeoisie', it was now announced, could accept the theory of 'educational freedom'. To the tumult of a gigantic propaganda campaign, a rigid system of school discipline was introduced. This was 'the true spirit of Marxism'.

'We declare war on the sentimental and spineless type of teacher,' it was announced, 'and we condemn the teacher who is reduced to pleading and persuasion. Soviet education expects of its teachers a rigid and inflexible authority. The Soviet school must surpass all other schools by its strict discipline. The higher the standards of a society, the stricter the discipline in the children's schools. The Suvorov system, according to which punishment can even include imprisonment, is approved by the teachers.'

There were to be tests, diplomas and end-of-term reports in the schools, just as in the days of the Tsars. There were also to be prizes and the public announcement of distinctions won by the best scholars, to encourage maximum effort. Even children's books emphasized this, mocking children who could not rise above the average.

'What could I expect from life?' says the girl Ustya, the principal character in a novel of the same name by Lev Kassil. 'It was such a shame that I only got an average for mathematics, and just before May Day, too. It looked as though I was going to get three averages in my report at the end of the year. Everything about me was "very ordinary". I was considered a poor pupil and nobody took any notice of me. They were forever praising my schoolmates who did well, publishing articles about them, writing about them to the local State Education Officer, and hanging their photographs on the walls . . .'

What the Soviet Union needed even more than efficient primary and secondary schools was a modern system for training the specialists and engineers indispensable to the development of industry, and the creation of a vast 'technical intelligentsia' hundreds of thousands strong.

In former times Europe had provided Russia's teachers. Göttingen and Marburg in particular, but also Holland and England, while France, too, had sent professors and teachers to Tsarist Russia.

Since then, however, Europe had lost its supremacy to America in those fields which mainly interested the USSR. The United States were now the strongest political power in the world. Therefore the Soviets determined to take advantage of the experience of this super-industrialized state, which the Kremlin hoped to surpass. Although the Soviets never concealed their intentions, the Americans did not hesitate to share their knowledge and experience with the Eastern state that was dedicated to the destruction of capitalism. When the Soviets asked permission to send delegates to America to study their training methods, Washington readily offered to supply them with all the information they desired.

Soon large numbers of Russian experts were arriving in America and working to a detailed plan. One delegation studied with the Department of Child Psychology at Iowa University, under Professor George Stoddard. Other groups spent several months in Detroit, centre of the American motor-car industry. The most important Soviet delegation went to the University of Cincinnati, where they learned all about 'Co-operative Study', a system being perfected by Dean Schneider.

This system divided a thousand students into two numerically equal groups, A and B. While group A were learning in the lecture-halls and laboratories, the students of group B worked as factory hands. After a period of six weeks the two groups were interchanged, the students always working in pairs. Thus all lectures had to be given twice. Every student was visited by a 'Co-ordinator' every six weeks, who examined all his problems with him.

After one Soviet commission had studied Dean Schneider's method, another arrived a year later asking for much more detailed information both from the American professors and from the industrial concerns. They were given it at once. A year and a half after the commission had left the country, the University of Cincinnati received a book from the USSR. It contained a comprehensive report drafted by both Soviet commissions concerning the methods of the 'engineer Schneider'. Enclosed was a letter, informing the American professors that hundreds of thousands of technicians and engineers in the Soviet Union were already being trained on the lines of Schneider's 'Cincinnati Plan'.

The Soviets had picked on the most effective and most up-to-date American system. Not only the Soviets, but also the biggest capitalist enterprise in America adopted this system of 'co-operative study'. General Motors organized their training establishment at Flint, Michigan, on these lines. The 'General Motors University' at Flint contributed greatly to General Motors' enormous success. Some three thousand employees between the ages of seventeen and sixty were here given theoretical and practical training according to Dean Schneider's methods, thus laying the foundation for General Motors' inexhaustible 'reserves of talent'.

After 1931 the Soviets concentrated on the construction and improvement of engineering colleges. They spent huge sums on this, far exceeding corresponding investment in the whole of Western Europe. The plans and the technical books needed for this enormous 'talent expansion' came from the West, as did the teaching methods.

While spectacular statistics concerning the development of industry achieved under Western auspices by the first Five Year Plan and the successes of the new teaching methods were being trumpeted abroad, the *Bezprizorniki* experiment came to a sad and silent end, unnoticed by the West. Eighteen years after the revolution Moscow brutally terminated this idealistic socialist experiment.

The boys and girls of those terrible years of civil war had long since grown to men and women, but the gangs of juvenile delinquents had not disappeared from the Bolshevik state. On the contrary, a new generation of *Bezprizorniki* had emerged, children who had been born during the new régime and had been brought up in the new environment. The experiment of trying to show them the 'road to life' by psychological methods, apparently so successful in Ekk's documentary, had in fact failed utterly.

By 1934 the failure was recognized. The Kremlin abandoned all its claims concerning psychological cures through 'work, re-education and communal life'. A decree of 4th April 1935 declared that children from the age of twelve were entitled to 'maximum social protection'. 'Maximum social protection' meant death by shooting. From then on it was the duty of the GPU to liquidate the problem of the *Bezprizorniki*. A law which treats twelve-year-old children as adults in the criminal courts has no parallel in the legal system of any civilized, or indeed uncivilized, country.

15 Bolshevik Science and the Old Guard

'ABOVE MOSCOW', according to an old Russian proverb, 'there is only the Kremlin, and above the Kremlin only Heaven.' From the time of Ivan III until quite recently the Kremlin was the most prominent feature of the old capital. For centuries the domes and belfries on the hill were visible for many miles. To the Russians the Kremlin was a sacred place; it was there that the Tsars were anointed by the Church. When the bells rang out from the tallest belfry, the Ivan Veliky, which rose two hundred and fifty feet against the sky, the populace knew that a new Tsar had ascended the throne of his ancestors.

Almost overnight the familiar silhouette was changed. The Kremlin with its cathedrals took second place. From whatever direction one approaches Moscow by train, car or plane, a new and overpowering symbol now towers above the city, the mighty bastions and turrets of the Lomonossov University.

This skyscraper, eight hundred feet high, modelled on the New York Woolworth Building, is the tallest structure in Europe after the Eiffel Tower and is now the principal landmark of the huge city. The buildings consist of thirty-four separate blocks surmounted by a thirty-two-storey tower. It is a strange, barbaric mixture of American skyscraper, Kremlin steeple decorated with plaster columns, and Gothic cathedral. It contains one thousand seven hundred laboratories and four thousand rooms, as well as whole floors of lecture-rooms and libraries for twenty-four thousand students. In this vast structure, a giant factory of learning, are the high altars of science and sociology, for it is the shrine of the Godless, Bolshevik world. 'The Soviets now worship science instead of God,' as Edouard Herriot once pungently expressed it.

Moscow's super-university is a symbol to the whole Soviet Union and the model for Russia's seven hundred and sixty-six other universities and colleges, with close on two million students.

Lomonossov University, rising almost overnight above Moscow, was intended to show every visitor, including those from the West, that a miracle had happened. It proclaimed that the USSR had managed to create its own ultra-modern centre of learning from nothing. And in the same year that the university was opened, in 1953, the Iron Curtain was partially lifted, on the orders of the Kremlin. After years of utter seclusion, Soviet scholars suddenly began to appear at international conferences and to take part in the discussions. Their contributions were sound and up-to-date.

ДОМ НА ЛЕНИНСКИХ ГОРАХ

The skyscraper building of the Lomonossov University, Moscow.

This was a revelation. The public outside Russia had read often enough in their newspapers and heard on the radio reports of the mighty industrial development and rearmament taking place in Russia. But nothing had been published about serious scientific work being done there. When Russian science was mentioned in the West, as in 1948 at the time of the Lysenko affair, the conclusions drawn were that in the Soviet Union all research was fettered and all scientific work thus doomed to failure.

What had in fact happened was not some 'Red scientific miracle', as many people now believed. It was the result of a systematic development scheme, ruthlessly carried out at prodigious expense amidst desperate poverty. And, as usual, Westerners had laid the foundations long ago.

The public, astonished by this new phenomenon of 'Bolshevik Science', knew nothing of the research carried out under the Tsars as under the Soviets, of the training of scholars and the creation of centres of learning. No books, no magazine articles, no newspaper spoke of such matters. If an occasional warning voice was raised, nobody listened.

Professor William E. Dick (*Discovery*, 1951) writes: 'The impression is often conveyed—sedulously conveyed, one may add—that this expansion of science teaching was something miraculous, as though there had been nothing worth calling science teaching in Tsarist days. This impression does not correspond to the truth.'

Such comments were rare, and were only to be found in technical or scholarly publications. Governments and the popular press ignored them. Thus the Iron Curtain that hid the scientific potential of the Russian state was, in part at least, of Western origin.

This 'huge leap forward' of a nation of proverbial illiterates to the top level of science and research, a favourite theme used by Soviet propaganda to exemplify 'socialist achievement and progress', never in fact took place. A glance at Tsarist Russia shows that the Bolsheviks enjoyed a sound inheritance.

In 1913, 124,600 students matriculated at Tsarist universities. Not until twenty years later did Germany exceed this number. In 1932 there were

133,000 students in Germany, but under Hitler the number declined to 72,000 by 1937.

In 1917 the Bolsheviks inherited from the old Russia a sound basis of technical and scientific research institutions. First, of course, was the Academy of Sciences with its various institutes and museums, observatories and meteorological stations, in existence since 1725. Russia also had excellent universities in Petrograd, Moscow, Kazan, Kiev, Kharkov and Odessa. There were a number of technical institutes in Petrograd, Kharkov, Perm, Omsk and Kiev, and, of course, the Moscow Engineering College, all of which were comparable to the famous technical colleges in Zurich and Charlottenburg, Berlin. There were also first-class modern institutes of electrical engineering, constructional engineering, hydraulics, forestry and mining.

The new Soviet rulers did not hesitate to make use of this legacy, and to multiply it.

'From the very first months of Soviet rule,' the President of the Academy, Professor Sergei Ivanovich Vavilov, has stated with perfect truth, 'new universities and colleges were founded in our cities as well as in the provincial towns and in outlying districts. Soviet science began to prosper and flourish, to shoot out new branches, just as a plant starts to grow when rain falls after drought . . .'

Even in the confusion of the first weeks, Lenin realized the vital importance of a strong scientific and technical *élite* to develop a modern industry. He issued his instructions accordingly, and the projects were carried out.

The Soviets invested large sums of money in this. They gave Russian scholars the widest opportunity for further research and arranged the teaching and training needed to produce the next generation of scientists and engineers.

In 1918 the first students crowded into the lecture halls of Moscow, Smolensk, Voronezh, Nijni-Novgorod (Gorki) and Irkutsk. In 1920 the universities of Sverdlovsk in the Urals and Vladivostok were opened. After the 'liberation' of the territories occupied by the White Army, new universities were immediately opened at Tiflis and Baku, Erivan and Minsk. But teaching and research were not allowed the same freedom as in the West. From the inauguration of the first Five Year Plan all the teachers at the various institutes and laboratories, and all the students too, were 'under orders'.

By 1928 there were fourteen universities. By 1935 the number had increased to twenty-eight, including thirty-five faculties. The number of professors and lecturers increased even faster. In 1939 620,000 students were attending lectures and training courses in the USSR. In addition to the universities hundreds of special institutes for industrial research had been opened, with a total staff of 33,000, by 1935.

The Physical-Technical Institute in Leningrad, under Professor Abram Th. Joffe, a pupil of Röntgen, enjoyed an international reputation long before 1917. By 1930 it had managed to produce two thousand assistant professors and lecturers. These were the men who then created similar institutes at Kharkov, Tomsk and Samarkand. It was the same story with chemistry and agricultural research: with the help of a huge staff of trained scientists, the botanist and geneticist, Nikolai Ivanovich Vavilov, made the world's largest collection of wheat varieties.

Scientists were churned out in a colossal programme of cellular reproduction, as it were. There was something almost sinister and unnatural about such forced cultivation.

The West, one day to be threatened by the results of such Bolshevik scientific development, was unaware of what was going on. Not that the Soviets did not publish data and statistics, but these were disregarded. In other countries nobody believed that such fantastic results were possible. The West, which had never really noticed the considerable scientific progress in Tsarist Russia, now became the victim of its own ignorance. 'As late as 1930 the popular foreign stereotype of the Soviet Union and its people was a land of illiterate peasants, ignorant of machinery and modern technology,' wrote Professor Harry Schwartz, the American expert on Russia, in his work, *Russia's Soviet Economy*.

So far as the world press of the 'thirties was concerned, the attention of the journalists in Moscow was focused on the bloodthirsty story of a revolution which 'devoured its own children'. The public was only interested in the political angle. Contemporary descriptions from the 'thirties give the impression that during the revolution all scientific activity, and indeed all the scientists, had been wiped out. Such is still the general opinion. Were it so, the Soviets would indeed have performed a miracle.

But the facts are different. At the principal Russian research centre, the Academy of Sciences in Leningrad (Petrograd), work had gone on uninterrupted despite revolutionary disturbances and personal tragedies. This is revealed in the files of the periodical *Izvestia*, published by the Academy, which gives current reports on work done. A study of these files reveals that the Academy's work was not interrupted by the riots of the 1917 February Revolution, nor by the events of the following October, when the Bolsheviks took over. It was the same in the universities and research institutes.

Of course, many scientists died or fled abroad. But of the great number of scientists, mathematicians, chemists, physicists and engineers active before 1917, very few vanished. Of those who left Vladimir K. Tsvorykin and Igor I. Sikorsky were the most prominent. They went to the United States in 1919, where Tsvorykin achieved fame with his research into television and electronic microscopy, while Sikorsky became the leading helicopter expert in his adopted country.

Large numbers of writers, philosophers, theologians and historians were liquidated or emigrated. The Communists let them go, since they served no useful purpose in the 'building of socialism' and the creation of industrial power. For this they needed the scientists; and the professors from Tsarist days, all of whom had studied in the great universities of Europe, were later exhibited to the West as the 'Soviet scientific *élite*'.

The extent to which these scientists from Tsarist days contributed to the success of Bolshevism is shown by one example, given by Professor C. L. Boltz: 'In fact many modern physicists in Russia are old men carrying on in the old tradition so far as they can, and it is scarcely a coincidence that up to 1945 only six scientists born in the twentieth century had been elected to the Academy of Science.'

Thus the reliable 'old guard' from Tsarist times, Western-trained, even today provides the backbone of Soviet scientific development.

They received and receive help from the West. The laboratories and libraries of Russia contain all the learned publications of the West. Every basic handbook is available. Visitors from the West have noticed this again and again. Russian scientists have no trouble in using such works from Europe and America, for every scholar in Russia has an adequate knowledge of German, English and French.

Just as Western technical literature is found in all the libraries, so Western apparatus and instruments are used in all the laboratories of the institutes and universities. Microscopes, scales and X-ray equipment, testing apparatus, spectrometers and precision instruments are all available, the products of famous foreign firms. In its early years the Soviet Union could not hope to produce such equipment at home. But this was not allowed to hold up work nor hinder the establishment of new institutes. The required goods were on offer from famous firms in the West, nor did any such firm ever hesitate to fill an order from Moscow as quickly as possible. Thanks to Europe and the United States the Soviet laboratories and institutes were thoroughly equipped.

Such contributions from the West are never mentioned, any more than are the Western scientists and experts who took an active part in the scientific development of the USSR.

'Only in co-operation with the West has Russia ever managed to produce either scientists or scientific work of any value,' Professor Boltz comments.

This contact with Western scientific and technological progress was never broken. When at the end of the first Five Year Plan the Kremlin sent its army of foreign industrial helpers back home, when hordes of engineers, technicians, industrial planning consultants and works managers from Europe and America were ordered to leave the country after having first effectively instructed the Russians and then been replaced by them, the scientific links remained intact. The Iron Curtain might prevent the West from observing what was going on in Russia. It has never stopped the Russians from observing and studying what goes on in the West.

Professor Eric Ashby, of Manchester University, visited Russia in 1945. He has written in his *Scientist in Russia*: 'It was my good fortune to work for a short time in two laboratories of the Academy of Sciences, and my chief impression was one of reassuring familiarity. A Soviet laboratory, when one is accustomed to it, is like a laboratory anywhere else in the world. . . . Precision instruments, especially microscopes, refractometers, spectroscopes, etc., are not Russian-made. Departmental libraries are excellent. It is rare to find the laboratory without half a dozen British, American or German journals on the table, and some zealous young research worker puzzling over them with a dictionary. . . . I once had a card which admitted me to the Lenin Library and found great pleasure in looking through the collection there. Not one foreign periodical—however unimportant or unusual—seemed to be missing. The Russians can easily obtain everything published in the West, and, usually, everything which is manufactured there too. . . . A competent Russian scientist will know all about what is happening abroad in his own field.'

When Professor Ashby made these observations scarcely a month had passed since the Russians occupied Berlin. Even during the war the flow of technical literature from all over the world had continued without interruption.

IN JULY 1941 Harry Hopkins flew to Moscow from Scotland, via Archangel. As Roosevelt's representative, he was to tell Stalin that the American government were firmly resolved to give the Soviet Union every possible form of assistance as quickly as possible.

At this date 75 per cent of the armaments industry in the areas Leningrad, Moscow and Kiev was directly threatened by the enemy. Russia was desperately in need of anti-aircraft weapons, machine-guns, rifles, indeed of weapons of all sorts as well as of basic commodities such as petrol and aluminium. As the German Army penetrated deeper into the most important industrial centres, conditions in the USSR grew critical. Just how critical was revealed in a confidential talk between Stalin and Hopkins on 30th July. Stalin said that there was only one possibility of defeating Hitler: America must declare war on Germany. American troops, even exclusively under American command, would be welcome on any sector of the Russian front.

The very existence of the communist dictatorship was threatened, and it saw its hope of salvation in support from the hated and despised capitalist West. The essence of the tragedy was the fact that Germany had temporarily ceased to be a civilized Western nation and had itself accepted a barbarous dictatorship. The free West, in self-defence, sent aid to Russia on the largest scale. American help, based on the Lend-Lease Act, saved the Soviet Union at the crucial moment. A vast flood of armaments, raw materials and foodstuffs flowed from West to East.

In July 1941, Roosevelt ordered large convoys to be immediately made ready for Russia. During the next three months goods valued at $145,000,000 were released for Russia. In September 1941 an American delegation led by Averell Harriman went to Moscow to discover what sort of armaments and raw materials were most urgently needed. Stalin's fears for the survival of the Soviet Union were clearly shown when the Red dictator asked Lord Beaverbrook, who had accompanied Harriman, whether Great Britain could not send troops to the Ukraine.

According to the 'Moscow Protocol' the United States engaged to send goods to the Soviets to the value of $1,015,000,000 during 1942. Roosevelt declared the USSR to be a 'suitable partner' for a lend-lease agreement and earmarked $1,000m. as an interest-free loan.

The immense industrial potential of the United States was put freely at the disposal of the Soviet Union until 1945. The Soviet Union was given top priority. A special decree of Roosevelt's laid down that armaments be

Colonel Cooper (inset on right) built what was then the biggest power works in the world, Dnieprostroy (Dnieproges today) for the Soviets, with his American staff of engineers, as part of their first Five Year Plan. In the foreground: the then most powerful turbine in the world, 85,000 HP, brought over by the Americans.

200 combine harvesters—the pride of the Soviet state farm, "Giant" the biggest grain factory in the world. The Russians forgot to touch out in this photograph the foreign trademark HOLT.

Lindenstrasse 22/24 in Berlin. This large office building, rented by the Soviet Trade Agency, was the centre of Red industrial espionage in Germany from the late 1920's until the early 1930's. Here in 1930 Botzenhard escaped from the police through a secret passage. He was given his job with the Soviets by Wilhelm Pieck, later President of the post-war East German Republic.

The Besprizorniks—the wretched, neglected Russian children. Their allegedly successful re-education as a result of progressive methods was shown in Ekk's propaganda film The Road to Life and much admired in foreign countries.

supplied to the Red Army even before they were issued to the military forces of the United States.

What did America send to Russia? Between 1st October 1941 and 31st May 1945, 2,660 ships with a total cargo of 16,500,000 tons left American ports for the Soviet Union. 427,284 army trucks, 13,303 tanks, 35,170 motor cycles and 2,328 other vehicles were shipped in the American Arctic convoys.

Tankers, making a wide detour round Norway, brought vast amounts of mineral oils to Russia, 2,500,000 tons of high-octane aviation petrol as well as fuel for every type of land vehicle. 15,033 aircraft were provided by the United States, 4,570 by Great Britain. According to an article in the *Journal of the Air League*, altogether twenty thousand aircraft were given to the Soviet Union.

The Russian transport system, which had almost broken down, was completely re-equipped. Nineteen hundred steam-engines and sixty-six Diesels were sent by the United States, together with ten thousand railway trucks, all brand-new and, of course, adapted to the Russian broad gauge. Shipload after shipload of machine tools, complete industrial plants, spare parts and armaments, textiles and footwear, was unloaded in Russian ports.

Of inestimable value were the supplies of foodstuffs. Nearly 4,500,000 tons of tinned meat, sugar, flour and fats were sent from America. The United States fed the Red Army for several years. Stalin was able to give each of his twelve million soldiers half a pound of high-quality American rations per day.

The United States did not only send armaments, machinery and foodstuffs in enormous quantities. They also had to guard the cargo ships sailing in convoys by means of warships and aircraft. Therefore they built, at record speed, one of the world's longest trunk roads to the Arctic, the famous Highway No. 1 to Alaska.

Up this route moved the lend-lease goods which were then flown to Russia over the North Pole. It is officially estimated that the United States sent the USSR lend-lease goods to a value of 10,800 million dollars. At the time of writing Russia has not repaid a single cent.

Amazing as these figures are, in fact it was only a fraction of the stream of goods which flowed from West to East. It will never be known how much the Soviet purchasing commissions transferred privately from the United States to their own country.

During the war American citizens visiting Soviet Asia were amazed at the quantities of American materials stockpiled everywhere. One such visitor was no less a man than the Vice-President, Henry A. Wallace. His tour was, of course, carefully organized by the Soviets. He wrote: 'In travelling through Siberia we were accompanied by "old soldiers" with blue tops on their caps. Everybody treated them with great respect. They are members of the *Nkvd*, which means the People's Commissariat of Internal Affairs. I became very fond of their leader, Major Mikhail Cheremisenov, who had also been with the Willkie party.'

Henry A. Wallace had set off from Washington in a Skymaster on 20th May 1944. His mission, as laid down in Roosevelt's instructions, was to proclaim to the Russian people in Soviet Asia 'the desire of the American people that co-operation between the two nations may outlast the war, and continue into the post-war years and the period of peace'.

Vice-President Wallace flew to Siberia along the new ALSIB (Alaska–Siberia) air route.

Not only did the Americans construct and supply a chain of new airfields connecting the north-west United States, Canada and Alaska with Irkutsk and Soviet Asia, over the North Pole, but they also supplied and improved the Siberian ports in the Soviet Union. They then created a sea route from Seattle through the Bering Straits and the White Sea to Murmansk. 'So vital did our government consider this new strategic waterway that lend-lease food was shipped in to help maintain the permanent residents at the new Siberian arctic ports,' Vice-President Wallace states.

Thousands upon thousands of bombers, straight off the American assembly lines, followed the ALSIB route across the Bering Sea. Their fuel, also from America, was either moved along Highway No. 1, through the Rocky Mountains and Alaska, or through the Canadian oil pipeline, CANOL, which started at Norman Wells near the Polar Circle, and ran to White Horse on the Pacific, some five hundred and fifty miles.

Wallace was told that on the large American airfield at Ladd Field, near Fairbanks alone, 'up to the summer of 1944, more than six thousand warplanes had been transferred through lend-lease to Russian pilots, who flew them across Siberia to the Russo-German war front'. At Ladd Field the Americans even built barracks for the Russians.

Vice-President Wallace took the same route as those aircraft. His Skymaster flew over the Bering Sea from Alaska to the Russian airfield at Uelkal. Proudly, Major General Ilya S. Semyonov pointed out the new equipment on the airfield, 'all built to help speed lend-lease planes on their way'. Eight hundred miles to the south-west the Skymaster landed again on the airfield of Seimchan, in north-east Siberia. Here Wallace notes: 'I had to pinch myself again when, on entering the local warehouse, we found Penick & Ford Corn Oil from Cedar Rapids and Pillsbury enriched flour from Minneapolis. The food had been transferred under lend-lease.'

On his tour through Siberia the Vice-President met familiar faces everywhere, even in places not marked on the map, for wherever he stopped he found American products.

In Magadan Wallace saw the new ice-breaker *North Wind*, built in America. The huge warehouses beside the port were stuffed with lend-lease goods, among them Studebaker heavy-duty trucks. 'They will be used on the Kolyma Road', Wallace was told.

In Kolyma, the centre of the gold-mining area worked by tens of thousands of slave labourers, Wallace visited the town of Berelyakh. 'We were surprised to find the Kolyma gold miners wearing United States rubber boots, because our lend-lease policy had always denied anything requested for gold mining anywhere in the world, including Soviet Russia.'

In a shipyard at Komsomolsk, the 'Youth-town' founded in 1932, Wallace saw an eight-thousand-ton light cruiser and three anti-submarine vessels under construction. 'Inside the cruiser were American lend-lease compressors and electric fittings.'

The aircraft factory in the same town, where Stormovik bombers were being built, owed both its existence and its production to the United States. All the machine tools and all the aluminium came from America. When Wallace saw the factory he remarked: 'It looks like the old Boeing plant at Seattle.'

For the offensive against Japan in Manchuria, which began in August 1945 and lasted only two weeks, America gave further massive help. 'Our lend-lease shipments had helped them', confided the Vice-President, 'for after V-E Day we stepped up our shipping schedule to Soviet Siberia, moving supplies across the North Pacific at the rate of 300,000 tons a month. Huge stockpiles were built up like the one we saw at Magadan, to which vessels went with vital goods. . . .'

Even in Ulan Ude, capital of the Buryat Autonomous Soviet Republic, Wallace found lend-lease parts in a locomotive repair shop. At Novosibirsk, the famous Yak aircraft were being built, with wings made of plywood from Siberian pines. 'The plant director pointed to a new building that was being used as a paint shop. "Donald Nelson urged us to build it", he said, adding characteristically: "Our output is now twice what it was when he was here last October." '

In the coal-mining district of the new Soviet town of Karaganda Wallace was shown, with pride, a special piece of mining machinery. Looking at the trade-mark he discovered that 'it was a Bucyrus Erie electric shovel, one of three at work here, and had been shipped in under lend-lease from the United States'.

In the copper town of Balkhash, in Kazakhstan, where copper-mining mechanical shovels and electric drills 'made in USA' were also in use, Wallace was told: 'We could use more.'

'Soviet Asia will see the rise of its own Pittsburghs, Clevelands and Detroits', Wallace wrote after his return. He might have added that his own country had supplied not only the models but the means.

In Alma-Ata, the capital of Soviet Kazakhstan, the distinguished American heard the following remarks made by Nurtas Undasynov, the president of the Supreme Council of Kazakhstan, 'The Kazakhs who will run the steel mills are being trained at older mills—Magnitogorsk and Kuznetsk. That's how the Uzbeks also trained their native steelworkers.' Those 'older mills' were the first models for Russia's industrialization, built with American help and later copied throughout the Soviet Union as part of the Five Year Plans. American engineers had there trained the first Soviet specialists. And Wallace has this to say on the subject: 'His remarks served to remind me of a rather interesting example of how interdependent our world economy is today. In the 1930's American engineers from Cleveland and Chicago went into Siberia on technical aid contracts to help the Russians found their first steel mills behind the Urals. Their know-how in modern steel-making is now being passed on to the Uzbeks and the Kazakhs.'

The Skymaster returned to America on 5th July 1944, landing on the huge airfield at Great Falls in the State of Montana.

This airfield, too, had been built for the purpose of accelerating the dispatch of goods to Russia, and was one link in the chain of ALSIB air bases. 'Lend-Lease warplanes, produced all over the United States, were flown into Great Falls, assembling there for the long flight across the North to Siberia, the Russo-German front in Europe, and the Far Eastern front against Japan', Wallace remarks in his book.

It is ironic that Wallace should have ended his mission to Soviet Asia at Great Falls. Great Falls was one of the vital transhipment points through which the Soviets were even then sending to Russia American industrial and armaments secrets and American goods on which there was an export ban. It was not until several years later that the disastrous story of what had happened at Great Falls became generally known.

Seattle was one of the principal ports from which, year after year, huge American convoys set sail, loaded with the supplies the Russians so desperately needed. And it was from Seattle that Henry Wallace addressed the American people over the radio on 9th July 1944. It was a coast-to-coast hook-up:

'From Magadan on the coast of the Pacific to Tashkent deep in Central Asia . . . in the factory and on the farm . . . everywhere I found American machinery, some purchased before the war but most of it obtained under lend-lease. The way in which American industry through lend-lease has helped Russia to expand production in Soviet Asia has given me an increased admiration both for the United States and for Russia.

'I found American flour in the Soviet Far East, American aluminum in Soviet airplane factories, American steel in truck and railway repair shops, American machine tools in shipbuilding yards, American compressors and electrical equipment on Soviet naval vessels, American electric shovels in open-cut coal mines, American core drills in the copper mines of Central Asia and American trucks and planes performing strategic transportation functions in supplying remote bases. . . . I am convinced from what I saw in Siberia and Central Asia that lend-lease has helped the Russians in many difficult and even critical situations on the industrial front as well as on the military front.'

The American Vice-President's broadcast was redolent with optimism. This was the period when Roosevelt was dreaming of a peaceful reconstruction of the global economy after the war, a process in which the United States would take a leading part. In 1944 a future 'Billion Dollar Market' was under discussion. The Russian market was to be opened to American production. America was pleased that she had been able to give the Russians decisive aid in their struggle against the German aggressor in the form of goods and foodstuffs. None of these lend-lease supplies were to be paid for by Russia, any more than the debts incurred in Tsarist days. But this did not worry the Americans. They foresaw the opening up of a vast new market, and enormous profits. They had not yet realized that every piece of machinery and every ton of raw material which they had supplied would be used exclusively to rebuild Soviet totalitarian power, which was very soon to be turned against Russia's benefactors in the West, either secretly or openly. . . .

The future that the Soviets were planning was very different from the optimistic dream. Some of their real intentions, however, were becoming apparent even then.

FBI reports piled up in Washington, revealing some very curious aspects of this industrial co-operation with the Russian ally. They showed the first moves of a large-scale campaign of theft from America. But the United States government kept these reports confidential. It was only several years later that the American people were to hear about them.

On 6th July 1944, Vice-President Wallace left the airport of Great Falls where, on the previous evening, his tour through Soviet Asia had ended. As it happened, on this same day, after Wallace's Skymaster had taken off in the early morning for Washington, a top secret conference took place in the capital, with Great Falls as the subject. Men from the FBI, customs officials and defence experts met in the State Department.

For some time confidential reports had been arriving in Washington, all stating that great quantities of goods were continuously leaving the United States without any kind of control. Soviet officials firmly and successfully refused to let the American officials examine these goods, which they declared were 'diplomatic bags'. Recently these packages had increased to such an extent that sealed crates marked 'diplomatic bag' and weighing several tons were not unusual. Washington resolved to go into the matter more thoroughly. The reports mentioned Great Falls as one of the main loading points.

At Great Falls, far away in the north-west of the United States and near the Canadian border, a huge airfield had been built for the 'air-lift' from America to the USSR early in 1942.

This was, of course, known to the men attending the Washington conference. But nobody could answer the question as to who was officially in charge of customs control at Great Falls. No department had been officially designated to carry out this important job. There was not one American authority at Great Falls with inspection rights. 'It appears', so the protocol of this conference of 6th July 1944 states tersely, 'that the authorities mainly concerned—the State Department, the Customs and the Immigration authorities—had no idea of what was going on. . . .' One fact was plain. The Soviets could, without interference, export from the United States whatever they wished, openly, and in bulk. It seemed for a moment, on 6th July 1944, that the curtain would be lifted, and a dark secret revealed. But the men assembled in Washington, all senior American officials, did not carry their investigation any further.

'They agreed', says the protocol laconically, 'to collect information about conditions prevailing there, to act accordingly and, if necessary, to contact other departments also concerned in the matter.'

It was not until years later that the truth came out about what had actually happened at Great Falls. By then lend-lease was almost forgotten and the headlines were filled with the espionage activities of the Russians against their former allies in the West.

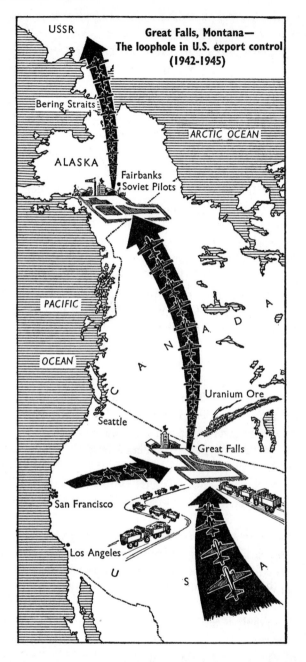

Great Falls, Montana—
The loophole in U.S. export control
(1942-1945)

The details of this extraordinary smuggling operation through Great Falls can now be pieced together from the testimonies of eyewitnesses, confidential reports and interrogations.

No sooner were the runways completed than scores of American aircraft came in to land. They were straight off the assembly lines. Squadron after squadron landed, refuelled, and immediately took off again for Fairbanks in Alaska. There a Russian, Alexei Anissimov, was stationed with several hundred Soviet pilots under his command. These pilots flew the bombers to the Soviet Union, for the Kremlin would not permit American pilots to fly them in. Soon planes from Moscow were flying as far as Great Falls without any questions being asked. After all, were not the Russians America's allies? Only a single civilian official was stationed at Great Falls. This was Randolph Hardy, a representative of the United States Treasury, in charge of customs and excise. Randolph Hardy was seventy years old and his office was five miles from the airfield. He was not empowered to carry out any inspections at Great Falls, nor was his solitary 'colleague', the liaison officer appointed by the United States Air Force. His only instructions were to assist the Soviet mission in every possible way.

Until 1944, Major George Racey Jordan was the liaison officer. During this period Sergeant Andrei Vinogradsky represented Anissimov at Great Falls. Vinogradsky pretended that he knew almost no English and could communicate only by signs or through interpreters. Nevertheless he often travelled into the interior of the country quite freely, as was normal in America. Where did he go? He was frequently to be seen in San Francisco, where he met the Russian Vice-Consul, Grigory Khaifetz. This man was head of the Soviet espionage apparatus on the west coast of the United States, a fact which only became known much later.

It appeared strange to Major Jordan that the planes arriving regularly from Moscow always carried so many Soviet passengers. He was unable to discover who they were, though he tried hard to do so. The Russians always disappeared the moment the planes landed.

'I would see them jump off planes, hop over fences and run for taxicabs,' Major Jordan later stated. 'They seemed to know in advance where they were headed and how to get there. It was an ideal set-up for planting spies in this country.'

From early 1943 strange items of baggage began to arrive at Great Falls. Trunks, large and small parcels, wrapped in brown paper, carefully tied with string and 'officially sealed' with bright red sealing-wax. Sergeant Vinogradsky was always present when they were loaded into the planes leaving for Russia.

Major Jordan tried to find out what these mysterious parcels contained, but without success.

The first of the 'black trunks' that attracted Major Jordan's attention—there were six of them—belonged to a Soviet officer, and were being loaded into an aircraft ready to take off at once. 'Personal baggage,' was the Russian's answer to Jordan's question. Soon it became almost standard practice for the Russians to have these large black trunks with them when returning to their own country. Major Jordan has said: 'The units amounted to ten, twenty and thirty, and at last to standard batches of fifty, which weighed almost two tons and consumed the cargo allotment of an entire plane. The officers were replaced by armed couriers, travelling in pairs, and the excuse for avoiding inspection was changed from "personal luggage" to "diplomatic immunity". Here were tons of materials proceeding to the Soviet Union, and I had no idea what they were.'

Major Jordan finally approached the Soviet Colonel Kotikov stationed at Great Falls, first with questions, then with protests. He always got the same reply. The trunks with the red seals were of 'purely diplomatic character'. The Soviet colonel stuck to this even when Jordan pointed out that all this mysterious 'diplomatic baggage' being exported by the ton did not come from the Soviet Embassy in Washington. It originated in fact with the Soviet Purchasing Commissions, which were active throughout the United States.

Major Jordan even had to grant the Soviets another request, by assigning them a shed in which they could lock up their 'black trunks'.

Major Jordan's curiosity was now really aroused, and he was determined to find out, on his own if need be, what was in the trunks. His chance came in March 1943. Colonel Kotikov had invited the American officer to a small party, and a new batch of trunks had just arrived. While the vodka was circulating, Jordan slipped out unobserved. He ran to the airstrip, and rapidly went through the contents of one of the 'black trunks'.

'There were groups of documents which, on the evidence of stationery, had been contributed by the Departments of Agriculture, Commerce and State. All such papers had been trimmed close to the text . . . I decided that this was done either to save the weight, or to remove "Secret", "Confidential" or "Restricted" stamps that might have halted a shipment, or for both reasons . . . Bewildering, to say the least, was the discovery of voluminous copies of reports which American attachés in Moscow had forwarded trustfully, in diplomatic pouches, to their superiors in Washington. I asked myself what these officers would think if they knew their most secret dispatches were being returned to the Soviet capital . . .'

During his rapid search by the light of an electric torch, Major Jordan made another discovery. 'For the first time in my life, I met the word "Uranium". The exact phrase was "Uranium 92".'

Lieutenant Robert K. Califf, responsible for supervising the clearance of all goods at Washington Airport, fared little better. He was frequently told not to check Russian consignments. 'I was prevented from examining these articles by higher authorities, on the ground that they carried diplomatic immunity.'

A special agent of the American Intelligence Service, whose report was brought to official notice far too late, stated that 'an unbelievable amount of diplomatic mail is being sent to Russia via Great Falls'. This report,

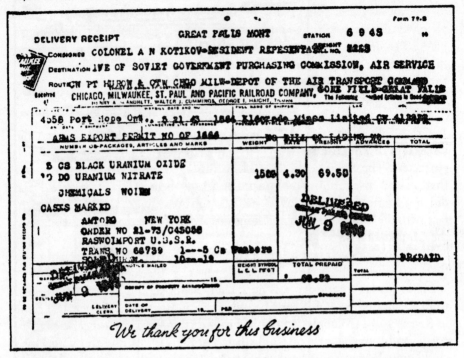

Two documents showing (left) how Moscow managed to obtain uranium for its atomic development and (right) the Canadian state railway's bill of lading of 21st May 1943 for uranium oxide and uranium nitrate, consigned to the Soviet Colonel A. N. Kotikov, Great Falls, USA. A certain measure of irony may perhaps be read into the polite footnote to the delivery receipt.

dated 28th March 1944, continues as follows: 'On January 29th, 1944, mail weighing 3,563 lbs. was sent to Russia on a C-47 aircraft. On February 17th 4,180 lbs. of mail was dispatched, and on February 28th 3,757 lbs., also by C-47s. None of this mail could be checked owing to diplomatic privilege ... It was not unusual for these Russian consignments to be accompanied by two men, who admitted openly that they were under orders to ensure there was no check ... One slept while the other guarded the freight, taking it in turns. These consignments were delivered by members of the Consular Service, by Russian Army officers, Russian engineers, Russian families passing through, and other people ...'

In one trunk the Russians sent 'detailed technical reports on American ships and shipping problems'. To his questions, Major Jordan received the answer: 'The Russian economic system is at present modelled on the German system and the Soviet government wishes to change over to the American system.'

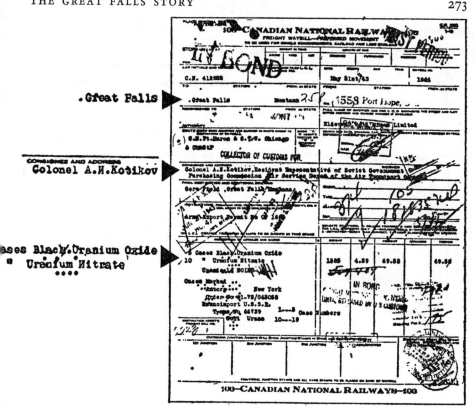

At last Washington began to take notice. On 28th July 1944, a memorandum was handed to the Soviet Embassy, pointing out that only packages addressed to the *Narkomindel* (*Narodny Komissariat Inostrannykh Dyel* or People's Commissariat for Foreign Affairs) and accompanied by a diplomatic courier would be exempt from customs control.

This memorandum was ignored. The Soviets continued to move these vast quantities of 'diplomatic baggage' and the American authorities, incomprehensibly, let it through. In the very heartland of the United States, under the noses of the security police, the Russians calmly continued to pilfer documents and charts from government offices and armaments factories. Meanwhile reports were now pouring into Washington. One, dated 21st September 1944 and signed by the Security Officer at Great Falls, stated: 'Aircraft No. 8643, Type C-47, left on September 20th. Destination Russia. One passenger of Russian nationality on board together with 3,800 lbs. of mail: these documents have not been checked . . .'

The Soviets brazenly sent uranium ore to Great Falls. They bought it in Canada and it crossed the frontier, unchecked, in the goods trucks of the Canadian railways. This ore, the exportation of which was strictly prohibited by Washington, was flown across the Arctic and into the Soviet

Union in American planes, which took off from Montana, USA. In the Soviet Union it was processed. This uranium made possible the production of the first 'Soviet nuclear reactor', an exact copy of the Western models.

For many years, long after the end of the war, the Russians were able to export by air everything they could lay their hands on.

Great Falls was only one of the many points through which the Soviets set out to bleed the Western world, a world infinitely their superior in the technical and scientific fields. The war gave them a perfect opportunity to do this.

From the beginning of the German-Russian conflict, the United States, the most highly developed industrial power in the world, became the most important target for Soviet espionage. American supplies to the USSR and the extensive trade agreements between the two countries gave Moscow unlimited possibilities of exploiting their great capitalist ally.

The Soviets immediately seized the opportunity and sent their agents everywhere—on an apparently legal basis. They knew that this 'coexistence with the West' was a transitory matter of expediency. From their point of view the sole purpose of the alliance was to save them from Hitler. Mindful of Lenin's teaching, they set out to make the most of this 'economic cohabitation with capitalism'.

In 1942 Moscow's espionage apparatus in America moved into top gear. Month by month the apparatus extended its scope and increased in size. Hundreds of new officials appeared at the Soviet Embassy in Washington. They were then sent to the various consulates or organized into Purchasing Commissions. In each of these groups, warmly welcomed by the Americans, were a few secret agents.

The headquarters of the Soviet espionage ring was in Washington, in the newly created Soviet Purchasing Commission, called Amtorg. This commission was officially concerned with administering lend-lease. Its unofficial activities were far more important.

The personnel of this organization numbered over a thousand. Business connections were established with all major industrial concerns. Every firm in the United States was interested in the colossal orders coming from the Soviets and paid for by their own government.

Fabulous opportunities for purchase were thus offered to the Soviets. Their agents were everywhere, ferreting out things not included in lend-lease: the Americans' industrial and scientific secrets.

Ever more experts arrived from Moscow: experts in aviation, industry and production, shipbuilding and shipping, artillery and ballistics, naval strategy, and, above all, in submarine construction. Among the agents posing as unimportant minor officials were famous scientists and high-ranking officers with special technical qualifications. The suspicions of American industry were not to be aroused. Some of the Soviet experts were camouflaged as ordinary workmen.

The successful campaign waged in Europe in the 1920's was now repeated in the United States. The proved methods of the Lindenstrasse in Berlin and of Arcos in London were used once again in America, and on a much larger scale. On the first occasion the German and British Intelligence Services, and the industrial concerns themselves, had tried to prevent the theft of technical and scientific secrets, and several trials had taken place. America, on the other hand, turned out to be a veritable Eldorado for the Soviets. Nothing was done to stop the spies, who functioned in perfect safety. Until after the war not one of the many cases uncovered was brought to trial. The government watched the activities of the Soviet agents with incredible tolerance. The worst that could happen to an agent was a polite request that he leave the country. In such cases an official of the FBI would accompany the agent to the boat or plane leaving for Moscow, but without checking his luggage or brief-case.

Well hidden in an inconspicuous Washington office building, the Soviet apparatus performed its secret functions. An office on the seventh floor of No. 3355, 16th Street, housed the Politburo of the Purchasing Commission. The brains of this outfit were General Leonid Rudenko, Mikhail V. Serov, the head of Amtorg, Gusev, and the chiefs of the special departments. Secret instructions arrived in code from Moscow.

In late 1943 all the agents of the Soviet Purchasing Commission were summoned to a secret conference. Behind locked doors, with an armed guard outside, Serov read aloud an order which had just arrived from Moscow. It was from Anastasy Mikoyan. The People's Commissar for Foreign Trade, the authority in charge of the Purchasing Commission, instructed all the members to obtain information on industrial development in the United States, and especially on the production and capacity of the armaments factories.

Each person present had to sign a written statement that he had noted Mikoyan's instructions and undertook to do his utmost to carry them out.

From then on a large-scale espionage campaign was under way. David J. Dallin, in his *Soviet Espionage*, writes: 'Among the items obtained were designs of industrial plants, special machines, parts and details; photographs and blueprints of technical processes in the aviation, arms, oil, submarine-building, and many other industries; long-range plans for the development of large industrial units; hundreds of maps of the United States, the individual states, industrial sites, bridges; descriptions of railroads, reports on the building of cities and highways; and so on.'

In the offices of the Soviet Purchasing Commission this campaign, which in scope and achievement exceeded all previous ones, was known as

'Super-lend-lease'. A few years later the items thus collected were reproduced exactly by the Soviets, and presented to the world as brilliant examples of 'socialist industrial development'.

The Soviet agents rapidly learned to know the American mentality, and discovered the best methods of procuring classified industrial information.

Jack Roberts, attached to a group of Soviet engineers as interpreter, has described his experiences.

The man in charge of this 'group of engineers' was a Russian called Vesselkov. In every factory they inspected, Vesselkov always made the same speech, ending with the words: 'There is no rivalry between us. It's quite O.K. for you to show us everything.' He would then drop a sly hint about possible large orders.

Unobtrusively the questions would veer towards whatever it was they wanted to find out. The Soviets operated just as Peter the Great had done. 'Quietly they took out their little notebooks,' Jack Roberts says. 'They were principally interested in new mechanical processes, in laboratory installations and in special equipment for testing metals. They were adept at drawing the Americans into lengthy explanations, by appearing to be impressed and fascinated . . . Questions were asked in a casual way and if no answer was forthcoming, the questions were repeated again and again, in different words. The Russians would then ask for samples of ore, copies of plans, or data about chemical analyses. They even tried to obtain details about water and electricity supplies and about the transport facilities at each particular factory. . . .'

Busy as beavers, this was the impression the Soviet engineers made on Jack Roberts. Even the most unimportant visit to any factory was carefully prepared beforehand.

'They worked hard reading up about the factory they planned to visit, so as to know all about it in advance. When they got there they would try fraternization and comradeship, playing dumb, and then quietly, bit by bit, they'd worm out the most detailed information about production processes. Back in Washington they would spend hour after hour drawing up detailed reports on everything they had heard and seen. This material was then photostated and sent off to Russia at once.'

One of these Soviet agents was a man named Talalayev, an expert on coke-oven locks. He had been sent to the United States on a specific mission, which he soon completed. His job was to find out all about the latest, and as yet quite unknown, type of furnace lock recently developed in the United States.

Roberts gives a vivid description of how Talalayev carried out his mission. On the pretext of ordering lend-lease goods, the Soviet engineer group visited the offices of the Allied Chemical and Dye Corporation in New York. After promising to place a large order, they were shown the brand-new construction model. Mr Wilputte, the engineer designer, himself demonstrated it to the Russians.

Roberts noticed how the inventor became involved at once in a lively discussion with the other Russians while Talalayev quickly examined the model. 'He took it apart, put it together, took it to bits again. He didn't now appear disinterested and bored. I could see he was very excited. His hands were quite steady, but there was an expression of intense concentration on his face, such as I had never seen before. He repeatedly closed his eyes for a few seconds so as to imprint upon his memory what he had just seen. . . . When Mr Wilputte at last broke away from the discussion with the others and returned to the bench, Talalayev showed no sign either of interest or of emotion. He seemed just as indifferent as before.'

Talalayev was soon ordered back to Russia. Roberts, who had heard this news, went to his room. While they were talking, Roberts saw something he had long suspected. 'My eyes wandered towards his desk for a moment. Amidst all the patents and photostats I saw detailed drawings which looked familiar. They were drawings of the Wilputte automatic furnace lock.'

It is hardly surprising, in view of the Russians' methods and the Americans' carelessness, that the quantity of valuable information obtained increased rapidly. Copies, stolen originals, plans, models and samples piled up in the various Soviet departments. It was worth millions. And now their problem had changed. The Russians were now less preoccupied with obtaining vital information than with getting all this loot, which already weighed many tons, safely and quietly out of the country.

Sealed diplomatic bags, the usual means employed, would only hold a tiny fraction of it all. On the other hand their American allies had generously provided diplomatic passports, and, at the Russians' request, documents to the Soviet officials which exempted both them and their baggage from customs control when leaving the country.

General Belyayev, of the Purchasing Commission, could thus take bundles of maps, plans of aircraft factories, and much else out of the States. Semyon Vassilenkov, when returning to Moscow, filled a plane with parcels containing classified industrial documents. Lieutenant-Colonel Motinov, the Assistant Soviet Military Attaché in Canada, flew to Moscow with 'hot' uranium samples.

Even this was not enough. What aircraft could not carry across the Arctic was packed into the holds of Soviet cargo ships. As soon as a ship docked in an American port, all the sailors were given shore leave. They were told exactly what to do beforehand. When they came back on board, they all carried heavy parcels. No customs or other authority stopped these allies and 'comrades' or checked the contents of their mysterious parcels.

With tools, machinery or apparatus too heavy or too bulky for this procedure, the Soviets evolved another technique. They were declared as something other than what they were. Radar sets were declared as truck engines, which were permitted exports under lend-lease, and bulk loaded on to the ships.

'We sent tons of material not only by air, but in the ships given us under lend-lease,' Kravchenko later disclosed.

Thus the Americans themselves provided the transportation in which the Russians carried away the fruits of the most spectacular campaign of robbery ever undertaken. And the stolen goods arrived safe and sound in Russia. . . .

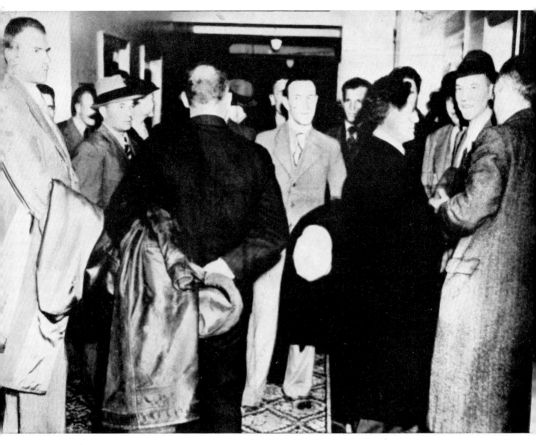

Beginning of Lease-Lend deliveries: Soviet experts arriving in Seattle on the Pacific in 1941 to discuss deliveries to the USSR.

American Lease-Lend 44-ton tanks on the Kalinin front in the Second World War.

Reparations for the East from Western Germany: 50 per cent of the production plant of the world-famous Schweinfurt ball bearing works went to Russia after 1945. A German worker marking one of the cases containing special instruments.

East German industry being dismantled. After 1945 long goods trains rolled across the German–Polish frontier, carrying factory plant.

The kidnapping of German technicians. A Soviet commission interrogating a foreman from the Junkers works.

18　Loot Unlimited

As THE HAZE of smoke slowly lifted from the pulverized cities of Europe, it soon became apparent who had really won the Second World War. The Soviet Union could count enormous territorial gains, and a vast amount of human skill and industrial potential had fallen into its lap. Stalin had every reason to feel pleased.

Germany was defeated, Hitler dead, and of what had so recently been a great industrial power, only heaps of rubble remained. Soviet territory had increased since 1939 by some 180,000 square miles—an area the size of Spain. Twenty million people, the equivalent of the combined populations of Belgium and Holland, had become 'Soviet citizens'. The Baltic countries, Eastern Poland and Bessarabia, Northern Bukovina, Finnish Viipuri, Eastern Karelia and Petsamo were now part of the USSR. So was northern East Prussia. Königsberg had become Kaliningrad.

The Bolshevik fist was closing on territories further afield. There were Soviet troops in Bulgaria, Rumania, Hungary, Czechoslovakia, Poland and Eastern Germany, as well as in Lithuania, Latvia, Esthonia and Finland. The Atlantic Charter had been thrown into the dustbin of history.

Such was the situation when Stalin received the Commanders-in-Chief of the Red Army in the Kremlin on 24th May 1945.

After Peter I had won the Battle of Poltava, he had sent for the captured Swedish generals. First he drank a toast to the Russian victory. Then he raised his glass to the Swedes and proposed another toast: his 'great teachers'. When Stalin raised his glass in the Kremlin on that 24th of May, 1945, he also drank to victory and to the prosperity of the Russian people, 'the greatest of all the nations within the Soviet Union'. Stalin, however, made no reference to those to whom the USSR owed its salvation from complete collapse and disintegration. He did not mention the colossal amount of help sent by the West, and particularly by the United States. If he avoided speaking of lend-lease, of the technical advice given by American engineers in the building of the new Siberian industrial centres, of the millions of tons of supplies sent by land, sea and air, he did so deliberately. He was determined that all this should be forgotten by the Soviet people as quickly and completely as possible.

Nevertheless even after the war was over help from the West continued to arrive in vast amounts. UNRRA sent food and drugs, clothing and shoes to Russia. Great Britain and Sweden put credits at Moscow's disposal for the purchase of raw materials, particularly rubber and tin, and, of course, for machinery and ever more machinery. The bases of Soviet reconstruction were thus laid by the West, which took all possible steps to get Russian industry and rearmament going again with all speed.

The West meanwhile disarmed. In the United States whole fleets of war-ships were decommissioned, armaments turned into scrap, and work on nuclear weapons almost halted. In 1946, however, the USSR started its fourth Five Year Plan.

This Five Year Plan had a plainly announced objective. It was the 'future strengthening of Russia's defences and the equipping of her fighting services with modern weapons'. Russia devoted all her energy to the construction of super-weapons, to counteract the supremacy of the West. These were, principally, atomic bombs, jet aircraft and rockets.

By 1950, the end of the fourth Five Year Plan, production in the Soviet Union was far in excess of the pre-war figure. The Russians had almost caught up with the United States in the field of atomic weapons, and a horrified West had learned that Russia, too, possessed the Bomb.

And the material basis for this astonishing recovery was loot, loot on an unprecedented scale, loot from Europe and loot from the Far East.

In Manchuria they took over a great number of valuable industrial concerns. 'All large power plants, rolling-mills and compressors, indeed the greater part of all equipment used by the heavy industries, which the Japanese had got going before the Second World War, came from Germany,' according to Anton Zischka. Ambassador Pauley, put in charge of repara-tions by the United States, took a staff of experts to Manchuria in the spring of 1946. They estimated the value of the equipment dismantled and removed by the Russians at $858,000,000. The removal of pumps and generators had led to considerable flooding in the mine-shafts. Where the roads to the plants were too bad or the machinery too heavy for truck transportation the Russians laid rails and loaded their loot straight on to flat-cars.

In Eastern Europe, from 1945, the entire economic and manpower potential of the Soviet empire, from Rumania to Czechoslovakia, from Eastern Germany through Poland to the Baltic, was concentrated exclusively on a single objective: the increase of the military power of the Soviet Union.

The former Polish and German coal-mines in Upper Silesia, Saxony's industrial belt, the Rumanian oilfields, and the Skoda armaments works in Czechoslovakia all worked to capacity for 'Soviet progress'.

The satellite states had not only to supply minerals and petroleum, machinery of all kinds, optical instruments and electrical equipment, but also sugar, fats, meat and grain, and in such quantities as to bring them to the verge of bankruptcy. Inside Russia, however, a very different story was put out by the state propagandists.

'The Soviet Union', wrote the Soviet economist, N. N. Baransky, 'is the first socialist country, and therefore the most efficient and progressive, and it is helping the Peoples' Democracies in their efforts to industrialize, to become completely independent of all imperialism, and to build the foundations of socialism.'

The lower the standard of living fell in the Peoples' Democracies, until even basic necessities were unavailable, the louder the shouts about 'progressive socialist development' in and from Russia.

The Kremlin got ten thousand million dollars out of Germany, as compensation for war damage. Their expropriations were worth at least four times this amount.

In occupying Eastern Germany the Soviets acquired 41 per cent of Germany's 1943 industrial capacity. A vast process of dismantling began. Whole factories were demolished, taken to bits and packed up, down to the last electric light socket and the last ashtray from the boss's office.

The great Jena firm of Zeiss and Co., makers of optical instruments, their special equipment, their research laboratories, their archives of documents and specialized information, all were transported lock, stock and barrel to Monino, near Moscow. Owing to this looting of the Zeiss works—the value of the booty is incalculable—the Soviets could henceforth produce optical instruments and equipment which previously would have been utterly beyond them.

The generators from the Siemens-Halske works in Berlin went to Leningrad where they were used to power the much-photographed Elektrosila Works. 'In Kiev we watched the manufacture of precision instruments to a very close tolerance,' an eyewitness, Wilfried Braun, wrote in 1957. 'The machinery had been dismantled at Siemensstadt in Berlin, and reassembled in Kiev. It still bore the Siemens mark. Inquiries at Siemens-Halske confirm the accuracy of this statement.'

In the pump storage works at Niederwartha, on the Elbe, one of the biggest in Europe, the Soviets dismantled the pumps and turbines for use in their mines and tunnels. From Magdeburg-Rothensee, from Leuna, Zeitz and Pölitz huge hydrogenation plants for coal refining were moved eastwards. In the Elbe power station, at Vockerode near Dessau, the Russians seized the D.C. high-voltage installations, built by AEG, SSW and Felten and Guilleaume.

Train after train was loaded with the Siebel aircraft factory from Halle and the Heinkel aircraft factories formerly at Warnemünde and Oranienburg. They were reassembled at Podberezhye on Lake Moscow. The Junkers aircraft works also travelled by train from Bernburg to Kuibyshev. This was also the new location of the Askania Works, a leading firm manufacturing the most modern measuring equipment. The Opel works at Brandenburg on the Havel went to Moscow, where the Russians proceeded to produce their Moskvitch car, a faithful reproduction of the Opel Cadet.

At this time the railway stations and marshalling yards in the Eastern Zone of Germany all presented a strange spectacle. They contained mountains of packing-cases of every size each marked with large Russian lettering. The contents? Machinery, machinery and ever more machinery . . . equipment, apparatus, documents, files . . . the industrial wealth of an entire country transformed into booty. Nor was that all. The transport system itself was not safe. The Soviets seized the railway network, after that of Belgium the densest in the world, and dismantled the tracks, signals and sleepers. Even main lines, such as the one from Berlin to Leipzig, became single-line track.

It was the same story with the huge underground V-2 factories known as Mittelwerke in the Harz, with iron and steel works, chemical works, such as Leuna, shipyards and motor-car factories, the entire equipment of coal-mines, brickmaking factories, electric power stations and cement works.

Nor was this the end. The Western Occupying Authorities had to meet a Russian reparations claim for 26 per cent of the equipment in their zones. From May 1945, equipment from the most modern factories in Western Germany was also being moved by road and rail to Russia. It was not until 1946 that these shipments from the Western Zones to the USSR came to an end.

However, the Western Allies continued to help the Russians by supplying them with the latest German production secrets connected with advanced industrial processes. The Soviets received from the British and American Zones all the patents, open and secret, of both heavy and light industry, and it cost them nothing. Moscow had only to order photostats from London or Washington. The Russians ordered such photostats by the hundredweight.

The very valuable scientific and industrial information collected by Allied teams in Japan and Germany found its way to Russia on microfilm. With the code-names BIOS, CIOS and FIAT three groups of specialists investigated all aspects of science and technology in the two 'Axis powers', as they were then called. Everything of interest in research, development and manufacture was noted. 'This massive collection of information, made available for nothing', Jacques Bergier commented in the English magazine *Discovery* in July 1954, 'represented "know-how" worth millions of dollars before the war.'

The Allies believed in all good faith that the German armaments factories would not be transplanted to Russia, but would be destroyed as promised.

An English eyewitness observer, Gordon Schaffer, in his book, *Russian Zone*, has written:

'In January, 1947, a Commission representing the four occupying powers carried out an inspection of the Soviet Zone on behalf of the Allied Control Commission. Their report, signed by the British, American, French and Russian representatives, said that they were satisfied that every plant producing war materials had been destroyed. War machinery had either been dismantled or destroyed. Plant and buildings had been treated in the same way. . . . No fewer than seventy underground factories were discovered. Scores more war plants were found hidden in the forests. . . . At Plauen the great tank factory is now a mass of wreckage; the Junkers factory at Magdeburg and the Heinkel plant at Rostock have also been completely demolished. The explosive works all over the zone have been reduced to ruins. . . . Thousands of war planes, thousands of flying-bombs and rockets . . . and 80,000 tons of ammunition were also blown up. . . . About eighty-two military aerodromes were ploughed up. . . . The rocket stations at Peenemünde, put out of action by the RAF before the end of the war, have been demolished. . . .'

What the Allied Control Commission who visited the Russian Zone in 1947 were shown by the Soviets were these empty or bombed buildings, depots and dumps. But since 1945 their contents, whether machinery or new rocket planes, V1s and V2s, had been methodically and carefully removed piece by piece, and by 1947 they were already in operation again in the Soviet Union. And by 1947, too, all the German experts had already been transported, to work for the USSR.

The Soviet Union urgently needed technicians, inventors, engineers and scientists, if the Russians were to 'catch up and overtake' the West. Such men abounded in Germany, as the Russians well knew. And they set about obtaining them. Their methods were frequently quite subtle.

Their well-organized secret service soon told the Russians where the most important scientists were to be found. Lists were drawn up of the names of all munition production experts who had previously worked in what was now the Russian Zone. Then their agents had to discover where these valuable men were living, for many had moved and some had gone into hiding.

When at last all was ready the Soviets pulled in their nets. It was often a simple, routine operation. A group of Russian officers would suddenly appear at the front door of a former armaments technical expert. They were friendly, polite and extremely well informed. They would start by asking him his name and his present profession, and would say, casually: 'How'd you like to have your old job back? You could start at once. Your old factory is being rebuilt.'

For the men approached, such an offer often meant the end of unemployment. In a time of great privation it always meant extra money for food. The Russians would even see to it that each such man had a house of his own for his family and himself.

These first overtures on the part of the Russians began early in 1946, throughout the whole Eastern Zone of Germany. In Dresden, Leipzig, Halle and Bernburg, in East Berlin and Dessau and in the country villages where so many people had taken refuge, the Soviet commissions knocked upon thousands of doors. They went to barracks, to bombed houses, to refugee camps. Everywhere the same questions were asked and the same offer made. For almost all of them this meant the chance of a new life, the end of privation and forced idleness.

Very few hesitated, and most of those who did finally agreed when the Russians gave them the names of former colleagues who had expressed their willingness to help in the 'reconstruction work'. Almost all the men thus approached accepted the Russian offer.

GEMA, in Köpenick, a suburb of Berlin, was one of the many centres in which were collected the German specialists working for the Russians. Within a matter of weeks, offices of the former electricity works were humming with new activity. Some two thousand armaments experts were delighted to have a good job once again. There was more than enough work for all, going through and sorting out the mass of blueprints, patents and documents looted by the Russians. The head of this research team of armaments experts was Dr Eitzenberger.

The 'Raabe Institute', at Bleicherode in the Harz, also had its team of experts. The rocket engineer, Helmut Gröttrup, was in charge there, acting as a sort of decoy duck. His function was to 'engage the services' of V-bomb experts from Peenemünde, Nordhausen and the numerous V-bomb production centres formerly located in the Harz and in Thuringia. Such men and their families were promised everything they wanted in the way of food and the other necessities of life.

Soon an army of technicians, scientists and specialists was hard at work.

Next came the prison camps. From June 1946, Soviet commissions combed the camps. Long lists were made, giving the profession of each POW. Then the interesting ones were interviewed separately. The great bait here, of course, was release from prison camp. And the technicians left the camps by the hundred. Many of them received, with their release papers, rations and travel-vouchers to the place where they had previously worked.

On the outskirts of bombed and battle-scarred Berlin were certain remarkable 'islands', the existence of which was not generally known. Niederschönhausen was one of these. A whole residential district, which had been spared the bombing, was sealed off. By night, or in Soviet trucks with blacked-out windows, great numbers of specialists began to arrive there, and were soon installed in pleasant and comfortable houses. The food was excellent, tobacco and drink were available, and it was wonderful to be working again. Only one fact disconcerted the newcomers. The whole district was surrounded by a barbed-wire entanglement, higher than a man, and Red Army guards were posted at the entrance gates. Numerous machine-gun emplacements were dotted about the wire.

One principal fear worried these men engaged on the work of 'reconstruction'. Would they be sent to Russia? Again and again the Russians promised that this would never happen.

During these months the Soviets were preparing for the great *coup* of Tuesday, 22nd October 1946. Nobody could escape. Every house was watched, front door and back, guards having been posted the night before. At 4.15 a.m. the operation began, simultaneously at all points.

Red Army soldiers banged on the door. A Red officer, assisted by an interpreter, shouted at the half-asleep technician: 'On the orders of the Soviet High Command, you are mobilized for work in the Soviet Union. You will go, with your wife and family, to the place in Russia where you are to work. The Soviet High Command will see to it that your furniture and effects are delivered, undamaged, to your new destination. The length of your stay is uncertain, but will not exceed five years.'

All protest against this order was impossible, all resistance useless. The order for the great slave march to the East had hardly been given before the Russians began moving out the possessions of the men's families, chairs, tables, cupboards, lamps and pictures. Soviet trucks were waiting. In the first light of dawn they rumbled away, piled high with household furniture. In other lorries travelled the closely guarded 'egg-heads', the scientists, engineers and skilled workers, with their families.

Long columns of these trucks lumbered through East Berlin to the waterworks, which were surrounded by barbed wire. The Russian organization was very efficient. Special trains were ready to leave. Loading began at once, very quickly and almost in silence. Each train consisted of one passenger coach, followed by dozens of goods trucks for the furniture. There were soldiers in all the trains. The human cargo was handed over and the clearance papers signed. The numbers must be correct, and correct they were. Nobody escaped.

The same scenes were simultaneously taking place in the other towns of the Russian Zone. In the sealed-off station at Halle on the Saale, long trains waited in the dawn of that same morning. Heavy lorries rattled through the night. At Halle all the German aircraft specialists had been assembled, from the former Junkers works at Dessau and Bernburg as well as from Siebel's of Halle. Among the names now ticked off on the Russian list were Heinson, a highly qualified engineer formerly in charge of the construction department at Siebel's, and his colleagues Albert and Kagel, Rössing, the managing director from Halle, the chief test pilot Captain Ziese, and the test pilots Rauschen and Motsch. Eighty-five of the most highly qualified men from the Jena Zeiss works were also put on the train for Russia, enough to start the production of optical precision instruments in the USSR.

Before the break of day—that grey October day—the trains steamed out of East Berlin, following those from Halle and the other stations in the Russian Zone. Six thousand specialists, accompanied by twenty thousand dependants, travelled eastwards. The results of these twenty-six thousand deportations were, however, not to become apparent to the West for a few years.

Ninety-two trains passed through the station at Brest-Litovsk. The journey ended as one train after the other arrived in snow-covered Moscow and drew up in sidings. For days they waited there. Then, suddenly, the trains started again, and the journey went on. Where to? The guards shrugged their shoulders. The iron curtain of silence was rung down on the fate of these thousands . . .

Yet the fate of these twenty-six thousand, despite all the anxieties and injustice to which they were subjected, was infinitely superior to that of hundreds of thousands of Eastern Europeans, from the Baltic to the Black Sea, deported after the victory of the Red Army.

Between the 22nd and 27th of May 1947, three hundred thousand men, women and children were transported from Lithuania to Siberia. Sixty thousand Letts were moved to Siberia and Novaya Zemlya in 1949. A mass deportation of nearly forty thousand Esthonian peasants followed, in the same month. By 1950, about 15 per cent of the population of the three Baltic states had vanished.

There were other mass deportations. After the Fourth Partition of Poland, in September 1939, a million Poles were sent to Siberia. During the war, three hundred and eighty thousand Volga Germans and Germans from Odessa and the Kuban were moved. Many of the Odessa Germans were sent to the Vorkuta–Ukhta district, some two and a half thousand miles from their old homes, and thrown into slave labour camps. A large number of Volga Germans were moved to the Altai Mountains on the Mongolian border, while the Germans from the Kuban were sent to a camp north of Tashkent. And after the end of the war the Russians, for a period of ten years, regularly deported masses of the population from all the countries in their empire to wherever they were needed for 'Bolshevik development'.

'I arrived at Vorkuta in 1951, in one of the regular transports from Germany,' Sigurd Binski wrote, after his return in July 1956. 'There were about a hundred of us, men and women from Central and Western Germany, some justly and others wrongfully accused of anti-Communist activities. We first realized the real reason for our arrest and deportation when we were in the coal-seams beneath the tundra, and learned the truth behind the Soviet penal colonies—an almost insatiable need for workers. The thirty-odd mines in the Vorkuta district were in process of development, and the wastage, in terms of man-power, was considerable. It was necessary to arrest and deport people whenever possible, if the whole economy were not to suffer serious setbacks.

'In our camp, in Pit No. 29, there were prisoners from about thirty different countries: Germans and Poles, Czechs and Hungarians, Rumanians, Yugoslavs, Bulgarians, Albanians and Greeks, Finns, Esthonians, Letts and Lithuanians, Turks, Persians, Chinese, Japanese and Koreans—even some Americans, English and French.'

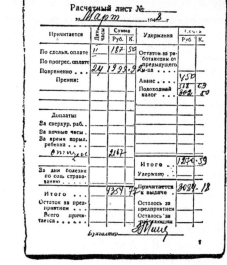

*Wage card of a deported German
specialist in the USSR.*

'During my imprisonment in Vorkuta from 1950 to 1955,' another victim, Dieter Friede, has reported: 'I used to watch the women's section at work on road-building, shovelling away in terrible Arctic snow-storms. Women of many nationalities were driven out to work day after day in thirty or forty degrees of frost—Esthonians, Letts, Lithuanians, Germans, and especially Ukrainians . . .'

Many hundreds of thousands of prisoners of war, Rumanians, Japanese, Germans, Austrians, Hungarians and Italians, worked for the 'progressive development' of the Soviet Union in the foulest of forced labour camps, and the most wretched living conditions.

The deportees from Europe, and the prisoners of war, played a decisive, but officially never mentioned, part in the growing productivity of the USSR after 1945. In Professor Baransky's book, *The Economic Geography of the USSR*, there is no mention of the foreigners in the forced labour camps and their importance to Russian industrial planning. What he does, however, say is: 'In the last few years the development of mineral resources has been considerably increased. Vorkuta coal and Ukhta oil are of great importance to industry and communications in the whole of Northern Russia as far as Leningrad. The Vorkuta coal-fields are already known as the future Donetz Basin of the Arctic Circle.'

In 1932 seventy per cent of Russian coal came from the Donetz. In 1950 the Donetz Basin supplied only thirty-five per cent of the coal requirements of the Soviet Union, while the districts of Vorkuta, Karaganda, Pechora and Tunskaya provided sixty-five per cent.

After 1863 it was the forced labour of thousands of Poles which built the mountain road on the southern shore of Lake Baikal. German and Austrian prisoners built the Murmansk railway during and after the First World War. Similarly, after 1945, millions of Western Europeans performed an immeasurable service to Soviet development in mining, railway construction and industry. But so far no economic survey has calculated the extent and importance of their contribution.

Having exploited the labour potential and the creative capacity of the West, Russia made a mighty leap forward—just as it had done in every previous century throughout its history. Only a few years later, Moscow was able to show the West the most modern weapons and super-weapons. The first was the MiG fighter, then the Soviet jet-bombers, and finally atomic and hydrogen bombs, intercontinental rockets, Sputniks, Luniks and manned satellites.

The impact this made on the West was all the greater in that, since 1945, Soviet Russia had given the rest of the world an example of complete human degradation and intellectual tyranny in her treatment of her scientists. And the West had assumed that the denial of freedom to the scientists could only mean that there would be no scientific development in the Soviet empire.

19   'Russia Leads the World'

ON 16TH JUNE 1945, four weeks after the entry of the Red Army into Berlin, large crowds assembled on the Sverdlov Square in Moscow. The delegations passed between the Ionic pillars of the famous Bolshoi Theatre, Bove's masterpiece. Russian and foreign scholars, among them a group of English dons in academic dress, were attending a festival. The Soviet Union was celebrating the 220th anniversary of the founding of the Academy of Sciences, inspired by Leibniz and created on the instructions of Tsar Peter I.

To the playing of an orchestra, the enormous theatre gradually filled. In the first six rows sat foreign diplomats and Red Army officers, their uniforms ablaze with decorations. The rest of the stalls were reserved for the academic guests from Great Britain, Canada and Australia, America, France and Belgium, from Sweden, Finland and Poland. Among these there were Nobel prize-winners from four countries—Szent-György from Hungary, Joliot-Curie from France, Langmuir from the United States, and Adrian from England.

The celebrations began with the sort of theatrical performance which the world was soon to recognize as a feature of Soviet science. Punctually at one o'clock the music stopped and the curtain rose.

Downstage behind a table draped in a vivid red cloth and picked out by a spotlight, sat the members of the Academy's Senate.

Behind them, in semicircular rows, were the 'Heroes of Red Science', wearing their orders of Lenin and Stalin. There were flowers everywhere, and among them a bust of Lenin three times life-size. Between crimson draperies which formed the backcloth hung a portrait of Stalin, twelve feet high, in the uniform of a Marshal of the Soviet Union.

'An impressive and unusual spectacle,' commented the English Professor Ashby, to whom (as to all his colleagues who came from Western countries with their centuries-old academic tradition) a 'stage performance' of this kind was extremely odd.

The visiting professors first listened to the anniversary address delivered by the President of the Academy, the seventy-six-year-old botanist, V. L. Komarov.

In his résumé of the history of the Academy, Komarov outlined three main phases of development. The 'encyclopaedic phase' under the influence of Lomonossov, the 'positivist', under the influence of Mendeleyev and other nineteenth-century scholars, and the present 'socialist phase', in which 'industrial and social patterns, and even nature itself are being transformed in accordance with a scientific and common-sense point of view'.

There was no mention of Leibniz. There was no mention of the great European scholars who laid the foundations of the Russian Academy, nor of the fact that practically all important Russian scholars had studied in Western European universities.

President Komarov knew all the facts, but was not allowed to speak frankly. 'Progressive Soviet science' had had its instructions. These were that all memory of Western, and particularly of German, influence should be erased. The gathering at the Bolshoi Theatre was less an anniversary celebration than a political stunt.

The foreign scientists, who thought they had come to Moscow to attend an academic festival, found that they were involved, for days on end, in a political demonstration with theme: 'The Triumph of Soviet Science'. Komarov described these triumphant celebrations in a leading article in *Pravda*. Every unguarded remark which the visitors let fall that flattered their hosts, even the most trivial, was reported in the newspapers, and broadcast throughout the world.

It was proudly announced that American delegates had described two of the Moscow Institutes as 'the best in the world', and had stated that 'in most branches of science the Soviet Union is in the first or second place vis-à-vis the rest of the world'. According to Tass, a Frenchman remarked: 'French science has a lot to learn from the USSR'; and Canadian scientists were reported as saying that in their opinion 'the scientific standard in the Soviet Union is higher than in other countries'.

This propaganda stunt was merely a prelude to what followed next. The world was to be stunned by the announcements of Russian achievements.

There were as yet no jet-fighters, jet-bombers, rockets or atomic bombs. The originals from Messerschmitt, the V2s, the German teams of experts, the truck-loads of packing-cases filled with patents and constructional drawings, had not yet crossed the Soviet frontier. The Russians did not then have the final agents' reports or the essential apparatus and equipment for copying the American uranium bomb. Thus the Soviets had nothing with which to bluff and frighten the West. Instead they produced a propaganda campaign, largely for internal consumption, the object of which was to create a scientific past for themselves. Moscow launched the notorious 'inventors' campaign. The absolute 'supremacy of Russian science', which the Soviets had postulated for the future, must now also apply to the past history of science and technology.

'Russia leads the world!' was the headline of an article in *Komsomolskaya Pravda*. Its readers were informed that 'Russia is the birthplace of the internal combustion engine, photoelectric cells and the electric motor'. A paper written by A. Popovsky advanced so many claims for Russian inventors, that if they had been true all the reference-books in the world would have had to be rewritten. He alleged, for instance, that it was not Herschel who

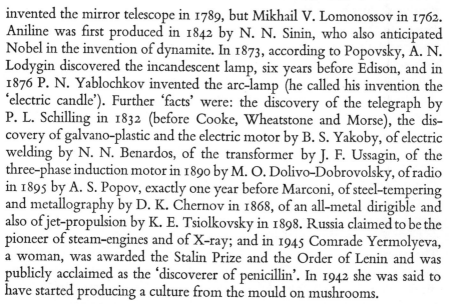

Baron Paul von Schilling, who invented an electromagnetic telegraph in Russia in 1832.

invented the mirror telescope in 1789, but Mikhail V. Lomonossov in 1762. Aniline was first produced in 1842 by N. N. Sinin, who also anticipated Nobel in the invention of dynamite. In 1873, according to Popovsky, A. N. Lodygin discovered the incandescent lamp, six years before Edison, and in 1876 P. N. Yablochkov invented the arc-lamp (he called his invention the 'electric candle'). Further 'facts' were: the discovery of the telegraph by P. L. Schilling in 1832 (before Cooke, Wheatstone and Morse), the discovery of galvano-plastic and the electric motor by B. S. Yakoby, of electric welding by N. N. Benardos, of the transformer by J. F. Ussagin, of the three-phase induction motor in 1890 by M. O. Dolivo-Dobrovolsky, of radio in 1895 by A. S. Popov, exactly one year before Marconi, of steel-tempering and metallography by D. K. Chernov in 1868, of an all-metal dirigible and also of jet-propulsion by K. E. Tsiolkovsky in 1898. Russia claimed to be the pioneer of steam-engines and of X-ray; and in 1945 Comrade Yermolyeva, a woman, was awarded the Stalin Prize and the Order of Lenin and was publicly acclaimed as the 'discoverer of penicillin'. In 1942 she was said to have started producing a culture from the mould on mushrooms.

Moritz Hermann von Jacobi from Potsdam, the inventor of electrotyping and an electro-motor in Russia.

On investigating these claims, these 'inventions' turn out to be a clever mixture of the true and the false.

Professor S. V. Yermolyeva was certainly not the discoverer of penicillin. It was unquestionably the Scotsman Dr Fleming who discovered the bactericidal substance *Penicillium notatum* in 1928; and it was Howard Walter Florey, an Australian, who exploited its therapeutic value. In the case of Boris Semyonovich Yacoby the allegation is equally crude. He did in fact discover galvano-plastic, and his electric motor was among the earliest practical constructions of this type. In this case, it is the 'Russianizing' of his name which has been suppressed. He was actually a German born in Potsdam, and his real name was Moritz Herman von Jacobi. He worked first at Dorpat and later in St Petersburg. The same applies to P. L. Schilling. He did discover the electro-magnetic telegraph, his work being carried

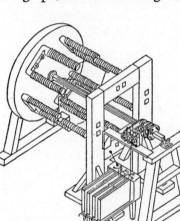

Model of the electromotor invented by M. H. Jacobi, with which he powered a boat for the first time on the Neva in 1838.

further by Cooke and Wheatstone. But this Pavel Lyovich Schilling was the Baltic German Baron Paul Schilling of Canstadt. The Russian claim in the case of N. N. Sinin is similarly ill-founded. It would appear that this Russian was the first to produce aniline (he called it 'benzindam') from nitro-benzol. Five years earlier, however, the chemical genius Friedlieb Ferdinand Runge had produced aniline ('kyanol') from coal-tar. It was, in fact, Sinin who showed Immanuel Nobel the explosive power of nitro-glycerine—the basis of dynamite—after it had been discovered by the Italian chemist, Sobrero, in 1847. Nobel used nitro-glycerine to manufacture mines for the Russian Fleet in the Crimean War, and on his advice his son Alfred began the experiments which led to the discovery of dynamite in 1867.

What about Marconi? Are all the facts as presented by the West false? 'Popov, Alexander, Russian physicist, inventor of the wireless aerial (1895):' such are the facts given in all Western European reference-books. Whereas Marconi is credited with: 'Wireless transmission over distance of five

*The physicist Alexander Popov, whom the
Russians claim as the inventor of radio.*

kilometres (1897); Nobel Prize 1909.' How, then, could Moscow celebrate
the 'fiftieth anniversary of the discovery of radio by A. S. Popov'?

It is often difficult to decide exactly who was the first to produce a particular invention. In the case of Marconi and Popov, two facts are indis-
putable. First, that the foundations of wireless were laid by the German
physicist, Heinrich Hertz, in 1887, and secondly, that it was Marconi who
first put radio-telegraphy to practical use.

The best evidence in support of Marconi's claim is the British Patent
No. 12039, dated 2nd June 1896, which he was awarded. Independently of
Marconi, Popov, who was then working in the torpedo school at Kronstadt,
was experimenting with electro-magnetic waves, as were many other
physicists, for the Hertz experiments had caused an extraordinary sensation.

In 1895, Popov repeated Hertz's experiments. He did not then have a
transmitting apparatus corresponding to the Hertz oscillator. So he had
the idea of trying to receive electro-magnetic oscillations, similar to those
present during an electric storm. As an aerial, he used wire suspended from a
child's balloon; as a receiver he had a battery connected to an electric bell.
On 7th May 1895, he addressed the Imperial Russian Physical and Chemical
Society on his researches, and in January 1896 a detailed report appeared in

Aerial installation with which A. Popov received radio signals.

the Society's periodical. Popov called his apparatus the *Grozootmechik*, or 'storm indicator'. The 'storm indicator' not only picked up distant storms, but also made it possible—as further experiments showed—to receive waves transmitted by means of an oscillator, to a distance of about five kilometres. The reception of Hertzian waves across five kilometres involved the transmission of what was, in fact, a 'wireless signal'. During these experiments Popov had worked with genuine overhead aerial installations.

In the English publication, *The Electrician*, of 10th December 1897, a letter of Popov's, written in English, was published giving extracts from an article published nearly two years earlier in Russian.

This established that Popov had definitely transmitted and received Hertzian waves before 1896. Nobody ever questioned this achievement, just as every technical history also names the other wireless pioneers of the years before 1895, David Edward Hughes and William Preece, Emil Rathenau and Heinrich Rubens, Oliver Lodge, Nicola Tesla and Augusto Righi. And Popov is recognized as the inventor of the wireless aerial. But 'whether Popov had an accurate conception of how the aerial-wire worked is always open to doubt' and above all 'he did not, incidentally, develop his experiments further' (C. V. Klinckovstroem).

Technical history teaches that there is not a single discovery which did not have its precursors. There have been, for example, an incredible number of submarine 'inventors' since the Middle Ages, in fact since ancient times. The classic example is the history of the incandescent lamp. The Russians have stated that the inventor of the incandescent lamp was Lodygin, in 1873. The Germans consider its inventor to be Heinrich Goebel, of Hanover, in whose New York clockmaker's shop carbon filament lamps were in use from 1854. It was Joseph Wilson Swan who first introduced them in England. But the man who really put the carbon filament incandescent lamp into universal use was, and still remains, the American, Thomas Alva Edison. All the others were precursors—all credit to them, certainly, but still they were only precursors.

The Soviets have also stated that a Russian invented 'the' steam-engine. It is beyond dispute that in 1763 a certain Ivan I. Polsunov built a 'steam blast-engine' in a mine in the Altai region. With equal justice the Egyptians could claim credit for the steam-engine. In 200 B.C. Heron of Alexandria built a steam-driven reaction-wheel but this did not constitute a steam-engine. *The* steam-engine, which gave rise to an unparalleled technical and industrial revolution, was the invention of James Watt, who was granted the British Patent No. 913 for it on 5th January 1769. All the other 'inventors of the steam-engine', Savery and Papin with their steam-pumps of 1698 and 1706, Thomas Newcomen with his 'pumping engine' of 1712, John Smeaton and so forth, they are all—including Ivan Polsunov with his 'steam blast-engine' of 1763—merely precursors.

It may be added, that while Papin and Savery, Newcomen and Smeaton are known to have exerted mutual influence upon one another, nobody in the West had then heard of this pioneer in the Altai mountains, and his discovery did not influence Watt's invention in the smallest degree. It is far more probable that Polsunov knew about the 'pumping-engines', which had been in use in Western Europe since 1712.

It is a similar story in the scientific field. Nobody in their senses would deny that Russian research has made important contributions to scientific knowledge. But there was no really great scientific genius: 'Russia has not yet produced one single physicist of the stature of Newton or Faraday or Einstein,' Professor C. L. Boltz has written, 'to name only three from the world of physics in the past three centuries. . . . Nevertheless Russia has nurtured a number of outstanding men whose achievements in physics have been everywhere acknowledged.'

Soviet claims were distortions of the truth, and went much too far. This 'inventor' propaganda, with its nationalistic attitude towards Russian achievements, and the chauvinistic dismissal of Western science, strikes the experienced observer as characteristically Russian, for it is the old theme the pan-Slavists played throughout the previous century. It is the same contemptuous propaganda against the 'foul and corrupt West', in a new and 'modern' form. Despite the 'inventor propaganda', it is not really a preoccupation with the past, but a question of crediting Russia with every new and successful development in contemporary science and technology. Scarcely a day passes without the world being deluged with reports by the Soviet news agency Tass, claiming Soviet supremacy in the sciences.

20   The Rise and Fall of Lysenko

'WE CHANGE NATURE, we create as though we were God, . . . we shall re-shape man until he no longer recognizes himself. And when he reads about how we lived today, he will shake his head and say: "What savages they were!" '

Thus speaks the hero of one of Ilya Ehrenburg's novels, during a digression on the new and allegedly revolutionary experiments in plant cultivation, the so-called Yarovization of wheat.

This over-confident glimpse into the future dates from just after the Second World War, when Russia amazed the world with the announcement that a completely new theory of biology had been evolved, one which dispensed with the time-honoured Western scientific methods, a 'socialist biology'.

'Soviet scientists', says the *Soviet Encyclopaedia* compiled with the co-operation of the Academy of Sciences, 'not only classify natural phenomena, but boldly reshape the course of nature. Conditions have thus been created in the USSR which have never previously existed in the history of mankind.'

What had happened?

For nearly thirty years biological research, like all other branches of natural science, had followed sound, Western European lines. The methods of the West had been taken over, its accumulated knowledge appropriated, and on this solid foundation the science of biology began to emerge in Russia. Successes were recorded, which won proper recognition and gave rise to a certain amount of admiration in other countries. Of the original workers in this field, the only one worthy of note was a research scientist, Nikolai I. Vavilov, soon regarded as the world's leading plant geneticist. Famous scientists went to Russia to work with Vavilov. The distinguished geneticist and biologist, Professor Herman J. Muller, who later produced the radiation genetics theory, was one of them. He continued his research work in one of the most important biological centres in the Soviet Union, being appointed Chief of the Genetics Department in the Leningrad Institute of Applied Botany. (Muller, Nobel Prize-winner in 1946, was in the USSR from 1933 to 1937.)

With this Westernized biology, a 'bacillus' was imported which must have seemed extremely dangerous to the Bolsheviks. For one of the bases of modern genetics is that acquired characteristics are not hereditary. In non-technical language, this means that all the characteristics and capabilities which a man acquires in the course of his life—for example, a highly developed muscular control, or a tremendous virtuosity in some particular art —are not passed on to his children and grandchildren. The son of a smith who had 'acquired' muscular strength far above the normal in the course of his manual work is not born with stronger muscles than the son of an intellectual. And this applies equally to plants and animals. The heredity of all living things changes regularly at a certain rate, but always spontaneously, suddenly in arbitrary and irregular mutations—never in direct and logical response to external influence.

This theory must have been highly unpalatable to the theoreticians of Marxism-Leninism, being exactly contrary to the ideology which they claimed to be the progressive blueprint for the future.

Dialectical materialism is the theory of communism. It asserts the complete dependence of all life on environment and particularly of all human beings on economic conditions. The old *milieu* theory of the Age of Reason is thus exaggerated and raised to the status of dogma. A change of environment changes the way of life, whether it be that of plants, of animals or of human beings.

If the change is carefully directed, then the plants, animals and human beings 'adapt themselves' to the new environment and the change becomes hereditary.

Applied to human beings, this dogma means that if the economic conditions under which people live are changed 'for the better' (in other words, towards socialism, communism, and a 'classless society'), then the people become 'better', and their children automatically follow suit.

All that applies to human beings, according to this theory, should also apply to plants. Through a change of environment and the resultant changes of characteristics due to the responses (which will be passed on to future generations) it should be possible to produce plants which will thrive in the most severe climates, and therefore to transform Siberia and the remote districts near the Arctic into flower-gardens and lush cornfields. The experience of Western European research scientists and growers has always led them to refute this Russian theory.

Any man who could succeed in proving a biological theory compatible with dialectical materialism was certain to win Soviet approval. A Viennese biologist, Paul Kammerer, tried during the 1920's. He committed suicide in 1926 when it was proved that there were falsifications in his experiments to show the inheritance of acquired characteristics. Later the Soviets themselves produced the man. The son of a poor peasant, and thus by his own life-story the perfect prototype of the new Soviet race, his name was Trofim D. Lysenko.

One of Lysenko's biographers has written:

'The old man saw in Trofim the worthy heir to his little piece of land, his house, his cow and his few miserable possessions, acquired by hard work and the sweat of his brow. The father had no thought of anything better for his son. But the Soviet Revolution had other ideas concerning Trofim's destiny. Like so many other young men from the villages, Trofim went to the city to learn. The universities and institutes opened their doors wide to the people. Trofim loved the land, and so he decided to become an agronomist. A man of bold, practical ideas.'

The young man was born in the Ukrainian village of Karlovka, in 1898, and he did receive a scientific education. After studying at a horticultural institute in Poltava, he completed a two-year 'selection course', and learned the fundamentals of every sort of plant cultivation, and the West European theories which decided which plants were best suited to which environment. For four years he worked at the Kiev Agricultural Institute, then moved to the plant selection station at Gandsha in Azerbaijan. As a result of ingenious experiments, which he immediately linked to Marxist-Leninist theory, the young agronomist Lysenko soon attracted the attention of the Party.

The first rung on the steep ladder that brought him fame was his theory of 'Yarovization'—in Russian *Yarovizatsiya*, which might be translated as 'summerization', from *yar* meaning summer wheat. With a process of yarovization of winter wheat, he claimed that he had for the first time caused acquired characteristics to become hereditary in the plant world.

Winter wheat is normally sown in the autumn and grows very slowly, to survive the winter's cold. Lysenko moistened his wheat seed, thus causing it to germinate, set it out in a temperature of 2°–5° Centigrade in continued moisture for several weeks, and then planted it as summer wheat. He maintained that by this process he could transform slow-growing winter wheat into fast-growing summer wheat, that this alteration was inherited, and the harvest yields would thus be increased by 40 per cent.

It appeared that a new method of grain cultivation had been found, which would produce a revolution in agriculture. In further experiments with yarovized seed Lysenko tried to produce types of frost-resistant wheat which would flourish in the dry steppes of south-east Russia. He also worked out methods for sowing summer seed potatoes in the arid regions of the south, claimed that he had trebled the millet harvest, and started wheat cultivation in Siberia and Northern Kazakhstan.

Lysenko's methods of yarovization were welcomed by the Kremlin, and formed the basis of a progressive Soviet 'agrobiology'.

In fact this experiment was neither new, nor the invention of Lysenko. The German botanist Gustav Gassner realized from his researches, begun in 1906, that winter corn, and also summer grains, needed lowered temperatures for a certain period in order to germinate. Gassner had then recommended 'the cold germination process'.

In the 1930's Lysenko's yarovization was tried out on a very wide scale, and endlessly publicized. We hear rather less of it today, for good reason.

Meanwhile Lysenko, encouraged by the men of the Kremlin, who were delighted at the apparent successes of this much-praised 'research' agriculturist, ventured to plunge into theory. Taking as basis the practice of yarovization he maintained that the characteristics of the seed could be changed, the summer species transformed into the winter and vice-versa. He thus formulated the 'new Socialist genetics', and invented a 'biology of practical transformation', the object of which was to 'control the course of Nature'. This fitted the theory of dialectical materialism, which did not acknowledge the laws of chance, as exemplified in the theory of spontaneous and arbitrary mutations as set out by Western biologists.

'All sudden and unexpected phenomena in nature are just about as sudden and unexpected as the birth of a child nine months after its conception', Lenin jeered. 'It is quite clear', Lysenko commented on this analogy, 'that the laws of chance can play no part in the development of a materialistic biology.'

As proof of the validity of his new theory (that acquired characteristics are hereditary) Lysenko quoted, in addition to the 'scientific genius' Lenin, two well-known biologists and plant experts, the Frenchman Jean Baptiste de Lamarck and his own countryman, Ivan Michurin. Lamarck (1744-1829) was one of the pioneers of the modern evolutionary theories, which were to be proved by Darwin's The Origin of Species through Natural Selection in 1859. Michurin (1855-1935) was a successful and reputable plant expert and grower.

The great French scientist wrote: 'Whatever animals gain or lose through the influence of an environment to which they are exposed for long periods and through using, or not using, specific organs, will be transmitted to succeeding generations by propagation.'

Lamarck's most famous example was the giraffe, which tries to eat the leaves high up on the trees and must therefore stretch out its neck. As this process is repeated generation after generation, the neck eventually becomes longer and longer. Lamarck thus postulated what Lysenko was trying to prove: the inheritance of characteristics acquired through the influence of environment. But Lamarck, in contrast to Darwin, was a theoretician, not an accurate and systematic observer. It is appropriate that his book, which ranked him among the precursors of the modern theory of evolution, was entitled Philosophie Zoölogique.

As further evidence of the validity of the new Soviet genetics, Lysenko quoted his compatriot, Michurin. Michurin, then in his dotage, had been in his time a superlative breeder and cross-breeder of plants. He had not only produced new types of fruit and vegetables by crossing and selection, but also some interesting hybrids by grafting, for example, a mountain ash with a cherry tree, gherkins with water-melons, a mountain ash with a pear tree. Three hundred and fifty new types of fruit and berries were cultivated by

Michurin, that is to say ten times more than the number already in cultivation in central and northern Russia. From his vast experience and often
startling success, Michurin, towards the end of his life, had reached the conclusion that the validity of Lysenko's thesis could be proved. He worked out
a 'Theory of the controlled metamorphosis of plants through the transmission of acquired characteristics'.

The greater the Kremlin's enthusiasm, the more non-committal the
biologists became. Now, as before, they based their work on the solid foundations laid in Western Europe. And measured against Western genetic
research and experience in plant cultivation, Lysenko's theory seemed at best
to be a retrogression to the obsolete theories of the nineteenth century. For
Lamarck's doctrine had been disproved by a German zoologist, August
Weismann, before the turn of the century.

In the year 1900 the successful but then completely forgotten experiments
of the Augustinian monk from Brno, Gregor Mendel (1822–84), were
rediscovered.

In classic experiments with peas and beans, Mendel had established the
basic laws of heredity. Even cross-breeding does not alter the inherited
characteristics which are transmitted from generation to generation.

With the rediscovery of Mendel's law, modern genetics came into being.
An American, Thomas Hunt Morgan, experimenting with the fruit-fly,
established the existence of genes, within the so-called chromosomes of the
cell nucleus, arranged like pearls upon a string. There is nothing to indicate
that these genes react in any way to environmental influences. They are
capable of change, of spontaneous mutation, or of mutation caused by some
external force, such as radiation. And such changes are hereditary. But these
changes in the genes, recognizable in all living creatures, have no connection
with the environmental influence.

So Lysenko was unlucky. The 'founder of a new Soviet biology' had
taken as his source Lamarck, a man whose theories had long been proved
obsolete.

What about his second source, Michurin?

He was a most competent practitioner—as Ashby put it, 'he had an eye
for a good plant'—and he cultivated various new species, especially fruit-
trees, which suited the Russian soil and climate. But Michurin was treading
well-worn paths, and his experiments were in no way original. Professor
Theodosius Dobzhansky of New York has said: 'These experiments were all
being carried out by Western biologists and plant growers as early as the
nineteenth century.' And beyond that the gifted Russian could not go. The
theoretical inferences he later drew from his practical work were erroneous
and unprofessional.

But Lysenko received the support of the Party, and Stalin was his patron.
And in Russia the Party decides what is wrong and what is right.

'The supporters of progressive concepts and endeavours in the world of science receive the support of the Communist Party and of public opinion and gain leading scientific appointments', said G. F. Alexandrov, a most influential member of the Academy of Sciences. 'The Party lays down the general line of development and helps to overcome the mistakes and false concepts of those scientists, isolated cases among the Soviet intelligentsia, who are influenced by bourgeois ideology. The forces which direct the developments of Soviet science and culture, by organizing and controlling them, are the Communist Party, with its wise and far-sighted leader, Comrade Stalin, and its Central Committee.'

So Lysenko had a free hand. Western geneticists he attacked violently, and 'Mendelism-Morganism' he insulted as a 'fabrication of reactionary lies and inventions for the benefit of capitalist profiteers'. Lysenko's harsh polemics in *Pravda* led to the dissolution of the Institute of Medicine and Genetics in 1936, which, with its enormous staff of biologists, psychologists and doctors, had done important work in genetics, highly regarded even in the West. The reason for this was that 'the laws of human heredity were represented as though environment had no influence'.

Many Soviet biologists opposed Lysenko's 'new Soviet biology'. Vavilov raised a warning voice. In 1939 he had the courage to say: 'The theories developed by Michurin and Lysenko . . . should not overshadow the whole content of genetics. If a new theory of heredity is to be combined with the modern chromosome theory, it must not be one which puts us back seventy years, but leads us forward, based on facts, on experiments, and on the achievements of world biology.'

Vavilov, though highly respected in the West, had now gone too far with this public attack on the Kremlin-supported pseudo-science. In 1940 Vavilov was arrested, and, on the pretext of being a British spy, condemned to death. As an act of 'clemency', however, the death sentence was altered to deportation, and he was imprisoned in a Siberian camp, where he died in 1943. With Vavilov, a number of other scientists were arrested, among them well-known men such as Karpechenko, Koltsov, Levitski and Serebrovsky.

Lysenko triumphantly entered the ranks of the Supreme Soviet, took over the post left vacant by Vavilov's liquidation as President of the Lenin Academy of Agricultural Science, and also became the head of the Institute of Soil Analysis and the Institute of Genetic Research.

Now the 'Creator of Soviet Biology' could finally dictate to the remaining adherents of Western genetic theory and, he hoped, finish them off.

His plan was cunning. In the autumn of 1947 the Moscow *Literaturnaya Gazeta* invited all geneticists to give their views in open controversy. Many scientists availed themselves of this to confirm the findings of the Western geneticists. In late July 1948, a Geneticists' Conference was suddenly called in Moscow.

Seven hundred scientists, from all parts of the Soviet Union, filled the hall and galleries of the great conference room at the Lenin Academy of Agricultural Science, when Lysenko opened the proceedings on the evening of 31st July. This was to be one of the saddest and most shameful chapters in the chronicles of Russian science.

'The Situation in the Science of Biology' was the theme of his address. He accused the 'scholiasts of the West' of regarding 'all nature as a jumble of disconnected, illogical phenomena, not ruled by any laws. . . . They degrade the science of biology to a matter of statistics. That is why the Mendelian theory is worthless and is not an exact science. The basic tenets of Mendelism-Morganism are false. They represent a perfect example of metaphysics and idealism.' Lysenko deplored the fact that the 'Michurinists'—as he called the supporters of his own thesis—'have not yet seen how to exploit on a large scale all the glittering possibilities offered in our country by the Party and the Government, for a complete exposure of Morganist metaphysics.'

In each of the first nine sessions of this conference other biologists produced arguments for the 'Mendelians and Morganists', which were not refuted but were merely ignored. 'We must help our Party in its exposure of this unscientific and reactionary corruption which is being propagated by our enemies,' was one of the phrases used. 'We must realize that this corruption has already influenced certain Soviet scientists; and it must be torn up by the roots.'

At the tenth session, on the morning of 7th August 1948, Lysenko played the trump card he had been keeping up his sleeve.

'Comrades!' he shouted. 'I may be asked, what is the attitude of the Central Committee of the Party to my speech? I reply that the Central Committee has read my speech and has approved it.'

'Storms of applause, rising to a standing ovation', adds the stenographers' report of the session.

This immediately put an end to all further discussion, for no one now dared to oppose the official fallacy. All those present understood exactly what the Academician's words meant. The Party were unequivocally behind Lysenko.

With one voice the seven hundred scientists condemned Western genetics. All those who were not among Lysenko's fanatical adherents remembered the fate of Vavilov. The biologists I. I. Schmalhausen, B. M. Zavadovski, P. M. Zhukovsky, A. R. Zhebrak, Y. A. Rapoport, N. P. Dubinin and other 'Mendelian-Morganists'—all of whom were present—lost no time in confessing the error of their ways, in a humiliating display of self-criticism, before the assembled delegates.

'My address of two days ago', asserted Professor Zhukovsky, 'was unworthy of a member of the Communist Party and a Soviet scientist. I shall fight for Michurinian biology.' Professor S. I. Alikhanyan said: 'From this moment on, I shall not only free my own scientific thinking from the old, reactionary Weismann-Morgan influences, but shall also re-educate my colleagues and students.' One scientist after the other abased himself in similar terms.

After this well-staged scientific 'trial', the last supporters of Western genetics were banned from the universities of the Soviet Union, and the Academicians Schmalhausen and Dubinin left the Institute of Genetics.

The result was the total collapse of this branch of science in the USSR. The meaningless phrases and dilettantism of the 'new Soviet biology' took the place of pure and exact scientific research.

'The most unbelievable fact about Lysenko's unbelievable career', said Professor Dobzhansky, speaking for the leading scientists of the free world, 'was that neither he nor any of his voluntary or compulsory supporters produced a single new or original idea—true or false. All he offered was a retrogression to worn-out theories and concepts, discarded long ago because they had been proved false. Like the Emperor's new clothes in Hans Andersen's fairy-tale, the "new Soviet biology" simply did not exist.'

After the 'historic' August session of the conference all comment in favour of the real scientists was silenced, and the ambitious dilettante was given free rein to develop his bogus theories. He soon produced a whole series of unbelievable new 'discoveries' and 'theses'.

'There is not, and cannot be, any conflict between individuals of the same species,' Lysenko announced one day. Such was the opening phrase of a paper in which he re-examined the theory of the survival of the fittest. In a wolf-pack the fighting of the wolves among themselves is insignificant in comparison with their joint struggles against other animals. Therefore a thickly sown cornfield thrives better than one sparsely covered, where the standing corn cannot 'defend itself' against weeds. Darwin's theory, whereby competition is one of the fundamental factors in natural selection, is thrown overboard, and is replaced by a Lysenko theory according to which homogeneous plants collectively, so to speak, wage war with other species.

Lysenko did not hesitate to draw conclusions from this theory intended to be of practical use in plant cultivation. For example he anticipated a tenfold increase in yield, if by sowing thickly ('clump sowing', as it was called) the Kok Saghis rubber-plants were helped to resist destructive weeds. Lysenko recommended a similar course during the afforestation of the steppes, 'clump sowing' of oak trees and grain together, as a protection against their common enemy, weeds.

In the experiments of Lysenko's followers, the progressive 'Michurinists', the most amazing biological transformations were said to have been achieved. Species of wheat suddenly bore rye-seeds, while various species of rye were simultaneously transformed into wheat; a common pine reproduced a common spruce, and a hornbeam bore a hazelnut.

Nothing could have shaken Lysenko's position in the Soviet Union—least of all criticism from scientists of the free world—had it not been for an occurrence which caused a violent reaction among the Soviet leaders. His theories failed in practice.

Lysenko's protector, Stalin, died, and the struggle began between Malenkov and Khrushchev as to who was to be his successor. Khrushchev was responsible for agriculture, and at the very moment when he most needed popularity and success the harvest yield decreased drastically. And Soviet agriculture was based on Soviet agronomy, while the basis of Soviet agronomy was the Lysenko theory.

The wind veered overnight. In the popular press as well as in the technical journals, violent attacks on Lysenko began to appear. Khrushchev himself made a report to the Central Committee in which he condemned Lysenko's theories.

In it he said that agricultural methods based on Lysenko's system were foolish and uneconomical. They had had a disastrous effect on production and had reduced the grain cultivation area of the Soviet Union by almost two and a half million acres.

The Party organ, *Communist*, which deals with all questions of ideology, emphasized the necessity for 'completely open discussion of Lysenko's theories'. Lysenko was now the accused. He resigned 'voluntarily' from his official positions in 1954, and disappeared from the scene. Even today, neither agricultural science nor practical agriculture has completely recovered from the results of Lysenko's disastrous methods.

'In the last few years we have seen many governments accept foolish political theories; but the total destruction of the science of biology in the USSR wins the world record.' This was Professor Dobzhansky's verdict on the situation, and he adds: 'Lysenko did great permanent damage to Soviet agriculture, to an extent that only future statistics will be able to estimate. He reduced the work of a whole generation of plant-growers and animal-breeders to nothing, and filled the heads of the younger generation with old wives' tales instead of with modern scientific facts.'

The pseudo-scientific writings of the 'geneticist' Lysenko, over two hundred in number, ran into countless editions and are translated into sixteen languages. Even today they fill whole shelves in the libraries and schools, not only in the USSR, but in Eastern Germany, in Czechoslovakia, and even in China. 'Thus these countries have been robbed of all the agricultural advantages made available to them by modern genetics', says the American Nobel Prize-winner, Hermann Josef Muller, once a colleague of the unfortunate Vavilov.

Lysenko proved very resilient, and bounced up again. He lost his position as President of the Lenin Academy of Agricultural Science, but he did not finally disappear. He quietly went on with his so-called scientific work.

Three years after Khrushchev had accused him of causing serious damage to the nation's agriculture, he was rehabilitated by this same Khrushchev, who had meanwhile achieved supreme power.

'Lysenko is one of our greatest agricultural experts', Khrushchev told a French delegation in the Kremlin. 'But he has the characteristics of a dog.' 'Acquired or inherited?' a French delegate, Philip, asked. Khrushchev ignored this, and went on: 'He is a great agronomist. Many of the pseudo-scientists who criticize him are not worth the dirt under his fingernails.'

In December 1958, Lysenko was summoned before the Central Committee of the Communist Party once again, to give a fuller report on his work. *Pravda* then published a leading article, in which Lysenko's views were defended. For his agricultural programme, Khrushchev chose the 'wonder cow', produced by the 'magician of progress' by crossing big Kostroma cows with the smaller English Jersey bulls.

Why should competent Soviet scientists associate themselves with a tissue of folly such as Lysenko's theory, long proved useless? Why should the Central Committee once again support this charlatan, so thoroughly convicted of fraud? The answer is that Lysenko's thesis of the heredity of acquired characteristics fits exactly—unlike Mendel's law and the modern genetic theories evolved from it—into Communist dogma. When natural laws do not fit the theories of Marx and Lenin, they must be forced willy-nilly until they do fit the doctrines of dialectical materialism. For otherwise the whole Bolshevik programme, with its claim that the future is theirs alone, would collapse like a house of cards.

But even so, how could the USSR afford the luxury of giving official support to such false theories and their inevitable, practical failure? The answer is quite simple.

When Khrushchev announced his objective of 'catching up with the United States in the *per capita* production of meat, butter and milk', as an essential step in his plan to bury the West, he knew perfectly well that this object would hardly be achieved by means of Lysenko's 'clump sowing' or his 'wonder cows'. Something much more solid was needed.

Khrushchev had already ordered his specialists to study efficient American methods prior to a drastic reformation of Socialist agriculture and the introduction of stock-breeding on American lines.

Before the First World War, Lenin had recommended 'the American way' in agriculture, and had laid down that the new Russia would follow this rather than the 'Prussian way'. Just as Stalin's Five Year Plans in the 1920's and 1930's copied America's ultra-modern agricultural machinery, just as Mikoyan in 1936 was sent with a team of experts to study farming methods in the United States and find out whether Russian food production could be increased on American lines, so Khrushchev's agents now had the job of bringing Russia's imitation of American methods up to date.

In the spring of 1955 an American newspaper, the *Des Moines Register*, proposed an exchange of agricultural experts. This came at just the right time for Khrushchev, and he responded vigorously. By July two agricultural delegations had left the USSR, one for England with Benediktov as its head, the other for the United States.

It was essential that Russian stock-breeding be reformed on American lines, for the figures were catastrophic. In 1953 the number of cattle per hundred inhabitants was a mere 27, as against 76 in 1928. American methods of maize cultivation were also to be adopted.

Hybrid maize, a typical product of the officially condemned and allegedly backward 'Mendelian-Morganism' of Western genetics, was now to be used for cattle-fodder and harvest yields. The United States and Europe supplied Russia with valuable seed and selected breeds of cattle.

Once again the 'corrupt West' lost no time in pumping new life into the backward 'progressive Socialist agronomy', and in putting it on a firm footing.

21 The Bomb

LATE IN AUGUST 1949, an American B.29 aircraft was flying a lone course on the edge of the stratosphere. There were no bombs on board, for this was not a military exercise. The B.29 was equipped as a 'flying laboratory', and its function was to make meteorological observations and measure cosmic rays.

When the results of these measurements were checked after landing, a discovery was made which caused a sensation. The photographic plates showed strange lines, not observed on any previous flight. They differed significantly from the familiar, very fine streaks which cosmic ray particles leave on the hyper-sensitive surface of such photographic plates. What had the plates recorded?

The phenomenon appeared so unusual that headquarters were informed immediately. A coded message was radioed to Washington. A few hours later teleprinters tapped out an order to special units of the U.S. Air Force, stationed all over the world. Within minutes special machines were taking off, R.D. aircraft, equipped with super-sensitive instruments to pick up all traces of radioactivity. These 'flying detectors' made vapour tests at cloud level, then climbed higher still to the edge of the stratosphere to collect diminutive particles of ash and dust in very fine filters. Such particles are driven upwards by violent atmospheric disturbances close to the earth's surface.

Rapid investigation of the material and data brought back by the R.D. aircraft led to an alarming conclusion—which, combined with the information supplied by the B.29, became almost a certainty. A mighty atomic explosion had taken place in Soviet Asia. The analysed dust particles and drops of water were strongly radioactive.

At first only a small group of experts in the United States knew of these tests, which were treated as 'top secret'. It was essential to be absolutely certain, after rechecking every detail which pointed to this appalling conclusion, before the sensational news was made public.

A secret conference was held, with Vannevar Bush presiding. As head of the Research and Development Bureau he was one of the men who had carried the American atomic-bomb project through to a successful conclusion. The atomic physicist Robert Oppenheimer was also present. Since 1943 he had been in charge of atomic-bomb production at Los Alamos.

Expert opinions on every aspect of what had happened finally dispelled the last vestige of doubt. From the material collected by the 'flying detectors' of the U.S. Air Force a fact emerged which could no longer be kept hidden from the rest of the world. Russia possessed the atom-bomb. The experts were even able to make approximate calculations of the explosive force of the Russian bomb.

It was now time to inform President Truman and the government. This was done, and on 23rd September 1949, the President made a brief statement at the White House. The next day all the newspapers all over the world announced in banner headlines that the first Russian atom-bomb had been let off in the Soviet Union.

And now, in the atmosphere of extreme disquiet engendered throughout the free world by this news, a disconcerting question arose. How had it happened? How could the Soviets have achieved this amazing feat a mere four years after the end of the war? One fact was clear, even to the layman. The production of such a bomb pre-supposed a high degree of scientific knowledge and technical ability.

Among the specialists, especially the nuclear physicists in America and England, this was a complete mystery. All that was known of Russian atomic physics excluded the possibility that the Soviet Union was then able to produce an atom-bomb.

The memory was still fresh of the Red 'inquisition' carried out a year earlier—on Stalin's orders—against the biologists and geneticists, with Lysenko as Grand Inquisitor. The scientists of the West had observed this ruthless suppression of free scientific research. And what happened to the biologists could be presumed to have happened in the other sciences. Was not modern physics also detested by the Bolsheviks? The Quantum theory of Max Planck, and Albert Einstein's theory of relativity, which had ushered in the 'Atomic Age', had been condemned by the Bolshevik authorities on the sole ground that they did not fit in with Marxist ideology, with dialectical materialism.

The West knew that during the 1930's Soviet physicists had made some progress, despite Bolshevik ideology. No Russian, however, had achieved anything really spectacular. The tremendous development of atomic and nuclear physics during the 1920's and 1930's was promoted almost exclusively by free Western research. Men of genius had been at work in Europe and America.

There were very few well-known atomic physicists in the USSR before 1939. There was D. D. Ivanenko, who contributed to the theory of nuclear development, I. Y. Tamm with his researches into nuclear energy, and D. V. Skobeltsyn with his work on cosmic rays. But vastly superior to all these Russians was Peter Leonidovich Kapitza, who worked in the West. In 1921 he was a student of the world-famous British physicist, Lord Rutherford, was appointed assistant head of the Cavendish Institute of Magnetic Research, and in 1933 he took over the Mond Laboratory at Cambridge, named after its founder, Sir Alfred Moritz Mond, which was indeed built especially for him. This Russian, doing scientific work without political restrictions, had by his researches in the field of magnetism proved himself to be a great authority on sub-zero temperatures and nuclear physics.

Stalin used Peter Kapitza as an example of how a scientist could be 'won' for Socialist construction. Kapitza was not a political refugee and could therefore travel freely between England and the Soviet Union. He took part in a scientific conference in Russia in April 1935, never to return. For the Kremlin refused him an exit permit, and to all questions from England the Soviet Ambassador gave the laconic reply: 'As a result of the extraordinary development of people's science in the USSR, we no longer have sufficient scientists.' For this reason this highly qualified Russian, with fourteen years' work in the free West behind him, was being detained in the 'fatherland of the Proletariat'. Kapitza was locked in a gilded cage, and exhibited from time to time as the 'star of Soviet science'.

While Kapitza was still at Cambridge two colleagues of his and also Rutherford's students, named Cockcroft and Walton, had succeeded in splitting and therefore transforming atomic nuclei by bombarding them with artificially accelerated hydrogen nuclei (protons). And in 1938 a successful experiment in the Kaiser Wilhelm Institute of Chemistry in Dahlem, Berlin, paved the way for the harnessing of atomic energy and the manufacture of the atom-bomb. Professor Otto Hahn and his colleague Fritz Strassmann split the uranium atom. It was soon realized that the splitting of atoms in this way would release an enormous amount of energy which would, moreover, be automatically multiplied beyond calculation by 'chain reaction'.

With the publication of Otto Hahn's discovery in January 1939, the great atomic race started. Realizing the fundamental future importance of this discovery, a fact that had filtered through from the West, the Soviet government urged Russian scientists to devote all their energies to atomic research.

In 1939 the Minister of Education, Kaftanov, on a visit to Berlin, demanded insistently that he and the colleagues who were with him should visit Professor Hahn's famous laboratory. At Dahlem, Kaftanov was given precise information on all the experiments. In April 1940, the Soviet Academy of Sciences announced the setting up of a 'Commission to study the uranium problem', and in *Izvestia* of 31st December 1940, the dean of Soviet physicists, A. F. Joffe, wrote under the heading *Uranium 235*, 'Mankind is about to release a new source of energy, which will be a million times greater than any hitherto known. . . . Man's power is entering a new phase. . . . The uranium problem now faces us.'

When the Germans invaded, Soviet atomic research came to a standstill. The most important institutes were soon in the front line. The two in Leningrad, the Radium Institute and the Technical and Physical Institute, were under artillery fire; those in Moscow, the Lebedev Institute and the

Institute of Physics, had to be evacuated. At the Kharkov Institute it was only with great difficulty that the most important apparatus was moved out before the entry of the German troops.

Thus in Russia research facilities were lacking. Also there were obviously not nearly enough experts to undertake this colossal task. The Russians just did not have the scientists of the requisite calibre. This was all taken into account by the scientists of the West, and particularly the Americans, during those autumn days of 1949, as they reviewed all the known facts. They could find no solution to the problem. The question of how the Soviets had been able to produce an atomic bomb remained unanswered. But three months later, on 27th January 1950, the answer began to appear.

On this date an incident occurred in London. A theoretical physicist, Klaus Fuchs, then working at the atomic research establishment at Harwell, travelled to London by train. At Paddington he was met by Detective-Inspector James William Skardon. A car drove them both to the War Office in Whitehall. There they entered an office, alone, and Skardon asked Fuchs a question: 'Are you prepared to make a statement?' Klaus Fuchs nodded, and then and there began to confess to the weirdest and perhaps most important act of treachery in all history. Skardon took down Fuchs's statement.

He began factually enough: 'I am a scientist, officially in charge of research at the atomic institute at Harwell. I was born on December 29th, 1911, in Rüsselsheim. My father was a clergyman, and I had a happy childhood . . .'

And then Fuchs calmly dictated to the inspector the following fantastic statement: 'At first I believed that I need do no more than inform the Russian authorities that the atom-bomb was being manufactured. . . . But later, especially at Los Alamos, I did something which I regard as the most shameful of all my deeds. I gave them reports on the principle of the design of the plutonium bomb. . . . I last supplied a report in February or March 1949.'

A European, a citizen of the free West, had betrayed to Russia the most strictly guarded secret of all, the secret of the atomic bomb. This could mean the complete ruin of the free world.

The United States government were informed, and Washington was stunned by the news. For years, since early 1942, this man Fuchs had been supplying the Soviets with every scrap of secret atomic information available to him.

Fuchs had belonged to the very small group of experts engaged in making the first atom-bomb. But how much had he actually known beyond his own work? A question put to the Atomic Energy Commission produced the shattering reply that Fuchs was not only familiar with the newest, improved uranium bomb, but also had taken part in discussions concerning the 'super-bomb', the projected hydrogen-bomb.

The Fourth Winter Palace, Leningrad, built by Bartolomeo Rastrelli, rebuilt by Count Kleinmichel after a fire in 1837. In the middle of the square the 130-foot column of Alexander by Monferrand. In the foreground on the right a "Moskvich", a replica of the "Opel Cadet", made in the ZIS Works, the Opel branch works transported to Moscow from Brandenburg.

A typical example of development in the East through the West: a BVG bus from Berlin sent to Moscow still displays the Berlin bear. It is passing the Kamenny bridge near the Kremlin. In the foreground on the left a typical Lombard wall of the Kremlin with the water tower (Vodovoznaya Banya) built by Antonio Fryazin in 1488. Behind, the Great Kremlin palace of K. v. Thon, the bell tower Ivan Veliky, designed by Italians, and Arkhangelsky Sobor, built by Alevisio Novi.

T. D. Lysenko, the founder of "progressive Soviet biology", with his "miracle corn".

Roswell Garst (right) showing Khrushchev over his farm at Corn Rapids, Iowa, the most up-to-date maize farm in the world. The Soviets hope to increase the output of their still backward agriculture with the aid of the hybrid maize grown in the USA and the plantation methods and harvest implements developed by Garst.

The news of Fuchs's treachery hit the United States like a bombshell. By the surrender of the free world's most vital secrets this traitor had increased the power of the Soviet dictatorship to a terrifying extent.

'When did it all start?' Inspector Skardon asked. 'About the middle of 1942,' replied Fuchs. Seven years ago, a period covering the entire development of the bomb, from the initial designs, through the construction and the first tests, right up to the latest model.

Cold as ice, Skardon took down Fuchs's statement. What Skardon did not yet know, what nobody in the West then realized, was that Fuchs was only one among many. Nobody guessed how widely the Soviet espionage net had been spread over England, the United States and Canada. Today we know at least the main facts. What follows is the history of the great betrayal.

In the spring of 1941 Professor Rudolf Peierls wrote from Birmingham University to Klaus Fuchs, then working in Edinburgh, inquiring whether he was interested in taking part in a special project. Peierls was then working on secret atomic research, and urgently needed an assistant capable of carrying out exceptionally complicated calculations. Fuchs, known as a brilliant mathematician, accepted and was merely told that he would be working on a very important and secret armament project. In May 1941, he signed a declaration under the Official Secrets Act, and began to work in Birmingham.

Six months later, 'Tube Alloys'—a cover-name—was set up. Its function was to co-ordinate the results of the work done by scientists in the different research establishments. Each month all the experts in Britain sent in their reports. The headquarters in Birmingham was then concerned with the problem of separating the different uranium isotopes; in England, as in America, this had only reached the experimental stage. Fuchs enthusiastically undertook the work assigned to him. That he might be admitted to certain secret establishments, the authorities at 'Tube Alloys' seconded Fuchs's proposal that he be granted British citizenship. For Fuchs, who had emigrated to England from Germany in 1934, was stateless.

On 7th August 1942, Fuchs became a British subject. By then he was already in regular secret communication with a Soviet agent. Fuchs himself had made the first overtures, as soon as he knew what his work was all about.

'When I realized what the objective was, I determined to inform Russia, and established contact through a member of the Communist Party,' Fuchs stated in 1949. 'Since then I have always kept in touch with certain people personally unknown to me. I only knew that they would pass on all the information which they acquired from me to the Russian authorities. . . . I did not hesitate to hand over all the information I had.'

The transcripts which Fuchs had made of his monthly reports were handed over by him in London to an agent known as Simon Kremer. He met him at least four times. Towards the end of 1942 Kremer disappeared and a woman received the material from then on.

Reports on the work of hundreds of expert scientists, the results of top secret experiments, were passed direct to Russia. They included the method of producing the essential Uranium 235 for uranium reactors and atom-bombs, and on how this was to be used in A-bombs. Certain calculations made by Fuchs on the required quantity of Uranium 235 and on its explosive potential were also included.

In November 1943, Professor Peierls and Fuchs went to the United States, together with other experts. The Allies had agreed that an atom-bomb should be built in the USA. A distinguished 'Brains Trust' was assembled, containing most of the world's greatest physicists, chemists and mathematicians, and from then on they worked at top pressure. It would be impossible to list the names and qualifications of all the specialists who co-operated on this mammoth task. Besides Americans and British, there were physicists from Germany, driven out by Hitler or refugees from Nazism, from Italy, and from the countries occupied by Hitler's troops, Hungary, Czechoslovakia, Poland and Denmark.

Among these specialists were the Nobel prize-winners Enrico Fermi and Niels Bohr, the first an Italian, the second a Dane. There were the Hungarians Leo Szilard, Eugen Paul Wigner, Edward Teller, the Germans, Hans Albrecht Bethe, Lothar Nordheim, Otto Frisch, Rudolf Peierls, Herbert Skinner, Rolf Landshoff. There was Bruno Pontecorvo from Italy, a talented pupil of Fermi. And many, many more research scientists of distinction and reputation contributed all their knowledge and all their skill to the realization of this project.

When Fuchs accompanied Peierls to the United States, research, development and production were concentrated in four places: New York, Chicago, Berkeley and Los Alamos.

From 7th December 1943, Fuchs took part in a series of conferences, at which nuclear physicists exchanged their ideas and discussed their further work. In this way he was able to form an accurate picture of the state of development of the atomic-bomb project and of how the bomb would be detonated—a picture available to very few people at that time. For Fuchs was entrusted with the most complicated mathematical calculations, and worked first with the New York group, at Columbia University and the Kellex Corporation.

Five days before the first conference which Fuchs attended, on 2nd December 1943, Fermi, in Chicago, succeeded in releasing the first controlled chain-reaction. 'CPI', the first uranium reactor, was in existence. The problem now was how to adapt the chain reaction of the uranium nuclei in the production of a weapon which the American Smyth Report said would 'exceed man's wildest nightmares in its potential destructive power'.

Whether it would ever be possible to produce such a bomb was still a matter of conjecture. But every effort was made to achieve this objective. Fuchs, thanks to his unusual talents, was well qualified to make a fundamental contribution.

All that Fuchs learnt he handed over to the Soviets. His contact man, the chemist Harry Gold, passed him directly the questions that Moscow wanted answered. The traitor answered them punctually and precisely. He reported all the successes and failures of the calculations and experiments. Soon he knew everything worth knowing about the top secret installations in the 'Manhattan Engineering District' of Oak Ridge, and was sending clearly drafted reports to Moscow.

On at least five occasions in New York Fuchs met Harry Gold, agent of Yakovlev, a Soviet Russian. In June 1944, he handed over to the Communist agent, in broad daylight, the plans for the production of the uranium bomb.

The most detailed information from Oak Ridge thus found its way to Russia. Fuchs punctiliously and accurately informed the Soviets about each new stage of development and about the time schedules of the whole vast programme.

Klaus Fuchs, though the most important, was only one of many spying for Russia. The Soviets had collaborators, agents and informers at all key points of the project. A stream of information poured steadily into Russia, from strictly guarded research centres and experimental establishments, from secret conferences and the meetings of specialists.

From early 1943 Fermi's pupil, Bruno Pontecorvo, had been working in the Canadian research centre at Chalk River. He travelled frequently to the United States and visited laboratories and factories where work on the atom-bomb project was in progress. He too was in possession of invaluable information, and he too committed treason against the West by spying for Moscow, where he finally fled in 1950.

In April 1942, the Canadian experimental physicist Allan Nunn May was brought to England to collaborate on the 'Tube Alloys Project'. When the time came to co-ordinate the British and Canadian results, he was chosen as head of the British group sent to Montreal. This Nunn May was another of the Kremlin's spies. At Chalk River a large series of experiments using heavy water had just been started. Nunn May kept the Soviet Ambassador regularly informed on all Canadian secret developments. He visited Chicago many times and had ample opportunity to look round the Argonne Laboratory, one of the four centres of the atom-bomb project. 'During this period May spent more time in Argonne and picked up more information there than any other British physicist', according to the subsequent statement of General Leslie Grove, the military commander of the Atomic Bomb Commission in the United States.

The Soviets had other 'delegates' installed in the key centre of Chicago. What one of their observers failed to do, another managed to achieve. But no single agent was allowed to know anything about the others.

Arthur Adams was in charge of the Chicago group of agents. He lived in a hotel as the accredited representative of a Canadian firm. The chemist Clarence Hiskey worked for him. Hiskey led a team which was working on atomic research in Columbia University, New York. In 1943 he had himself installed in the Metallurgical Laboratory in Chicago, exactly at the time when preparations were starting for the mass production of plutonium for the atom-bomb. When Hiskey was finally suspected, and removed, he had others ready to take his place, among them the chemist, John Hitchcock Chapin. And so the espionage went on.

Soviet agents did not neglect the laboratory for radiation research in the University of California, at Berkeley, where very important research work was in progress. The physicist Joseph Weinberg, a member of the Communist cell there, proved to be a most efficient spy.

In the United States, 200,000 people were working feverishly on this huge project. Every problem solved produced a hundred new ones. But gradually they began to approach their objective. 200,000 people worked day and night, billions of dollars were spent on the undertaking, and Russia reaped the benefit. Mountains of reports, drawings, blueprints, and photostats were piling up in Moscow. For besides Fuchs, Nunn May, Hiskey, Chapin and Weinberg, there were other specialists working for the Soviets on the atom-bomb project, Sidney Weinbaum and Sandford Simons, Franklin Reno and Fox Lomanitz, Tsien Hsue-shen, Ethel and Julius Rosenberg, and many more. The number was so large that a vast Soviet staff was occupied solely with checking and evaluating the reports collected by the agents and delivered in Moscow.

What use was all this knowledge, so far as the actual manufacture of the bomb in Russia went? Russia lacked everything needed to catch up with the West in this particular field. The long list of deficiencies began with the most important raw material, uranium ore, and ended with the numerous complicated items of equipment and apparatus which could only be made in the Soviet Union with the greatest difficulty.

Did the USSR possess any uranium deposits of its own? Uranium ore was prospected for, and found, in parts of Central Asia, in the deserts of Southern Kirghiz and Tadzhikistan, near the Afghan frontier, in the mineral-rich soil of the Altai mountains, and in small deposits in Svaneti and the Ossetian autonomous areas in the Caucasus. But all these workings were in thinly populated or in frontier districts, where construction work and transport would, in wartime, be fraught with difficulties. Communication with the Caucasus was cut off for some time by the German advance.

So an order went out from the Kremlin to the Soviet Purchasing Commission in the United States. 'Buy uranium ore!'

This was more difficult than stealing the most carefully guarded secret blueprints from a safe in the War Department. The quantity of ore needed to obtain pure uranium could hardly be transported, despite the lack of supervision at the airfields and ports. Whole train-loads and ship-loads of ore were required.

First, the Soviets attempted to 'do it legally'. The Bolshevik trade representatives explained that they needed the ore 'for army medical purposes'. When this did not work, they tried trickery. They put down uranium on a long list of chemical requirements, buried among other and unimportant items. They also tried official channels once again. In February 1943, General Belyayev handed in a request for sixteen tons of uranium to the U.S. War Department. This was refused. When General Rudenko, head of the Soviet Purchasing Commission, once again asked for sixteen tons of uranium ore and twelve kilograms of pure uranium metal, Secretary for War Stimson refused.

However, the Russians were not entirely unsuccessful. The U.S. government, still under the impression that Russia knew nothing of the atom-bomb project, feared that complete refusal of all Soviet requests would arouse suspicion and lead to investigations into the reasons behind it. So with naïve optimism Washington decided that the Russians would be given permission to buy small quantities of uranium, while great care was to be taken that the Russians did not exceed their quota. All major American firms were told to sell uranium to nobody except the American government. Thus 190 kilos of uranium ore went to the Soviet Union, through official channels, and finally four further licences were granted for the export of three hundred and twenty kilograms of uranium oxide, the same amount of uranium nitrite, twelve kilos of uranium metal and a thousand grams of heavy water.

Washington, naturally, had no conception that the Soviets had meanwhile been removing large quantities of uranium from the American continent. The Bolshevik Commission had bought thousands of kilograms of ore in Canada, where there was no embargo, and had transported it across the frontier into the United States. The destination given on the packing-cases from Canada was Great Falls. From there this very valuable cargo was flown by American lend-lease aircraft to the Soviet Union. The requisite quantities of heavy water also reached Russia by this route.

By mid-1944 the work of the 200,000 people involved in the 'Manhattan Project' had progressed so far that it was moving very rapidly towards its completion. One place now began to assume supreme importance, a name almost unknown even in the United States: Los Alamos, in New Mexico.

At an altitude of six and a half thousand feet on a mountain plateau in the middle of the Jemez Mountains, was 'Point Y'. Thirty-odd miles from this desolate spot, with its fragrant pine-woods encased by canyons cut deep in the rock, was the romantic town of Santa Fé, once the residence of the Governor of New Mexico.

Early in 1943 the peace of this landscape had been shattered by a vast building scheme. Laboratories, workshops, experimental installations and testing stations appeared. A whole town sprang from the ground, protected in every way from observation by unauthorized persons. So, at least, the authorities thought. But a traitor was already installed. In the middle of 1944, when work was in full swing at Los Alamos, the 'human calculating machine' arrived, Klaus Fuchs. Thus Moscow's most valuable agent was on the spot, at the place where the final act of the drama was to be played out, where the first atom-bomb was to be detonated. But even Fuchs himself did not realize that there was at least one other man working for the Russians in Los Alamos, the American scientist David Greenglass.

For six months Fuchs belonged to the innermost circle of top-grade scientists which Robert J. Oppenheimer had assembled at Los Alamos. For six months he collected and collated the information so easily available to him. At the end of this period he went on short leave. He visited his sister, Christel Heinemann, who lived with her family near Boston. During this leave, Fuchs wrote down all he knew.

On a busy Boston street Harry Gold took his report from him. It was of the greatest possible interest and importance to Moscow. For Fuchs had given all the details of the new plutonium bomb, including designs and methods of manufacture, noting also that plutonium was produced at Hanford, in the State of Washington. And he supplied the latest secret of the new super-weapon—the 'implosion device'—a detonator which exploded inwards, and was to be developed especially for the plutonium bomb.

Before Fuchs and Gold parted the next meeting was arranged. The rendezvous was to be Castillo Bridge in Santa Fé, on the first Saturday in June 1945, at 4 p.m.

The intervening six months gave Fuchs adequate time to collect still further information of incalculable value to the Soviets. On 2nd June Harry Gold received from Fuchs a large bundle of papers. Fuchs was able to tell him that the vital experiment was about to take place. In the course of the next month the first atomic bomb was to be set off.

On 16th July 1945, an atomic explosion blasted across the wastes of Alamogordo. Even before the giant mushroom which meant total destruction rose against the sky, the major part of the world conflict was over. With the fall of Berlin and the unconditional surrender of 8th May 1945, the Second World War in Europe had ended. Only in the Far East did the struggle continue against Japan.

In war-scarred Potsdam, the victors met. During their talks President Truman made certain discreet suggestions. He told Stalin—and he watched the Red dictator very closely as he spoke—that American and British scientists had together developed a new bomb of incomparably greater destructive power than any used hitherto. Truman also informed Stalin that it was to be used against Japan, if she did not surrender. Stalin, at that moment much better informed about the bomb than Truman, said nothing. Having already secretly acquired all the necessary information on the subject, Stalin simulated polite interest and, incidentally, expressed the hope that the bomb would be used.

From Stalin's reaction Truman drew only one conclusion; Russia knew nothing about the bomb at all.

Neither at Yalta nor at Potsdam did the Western Allies realize what had been stolen from them by their 'ally', nor what vast stores of knowledge had been secretly taken to Russia. And they could not know that Russia would soon turn against the West, armed with all that she had appropriated. So the Western leaders considered themselves obliged to award colossal reparations to their Red allies, and the countries of Eastern and South-eastern Europe were abandoned to enslavement.

The West had been warned. On 10th November 1945, three months after Hiroshima and Nagasaki, Truman received a distinguished visitor from Canada.

Prime Minister Mackenzie King, who was also the Canadian Foreign Minister, had come for secret top-level talks with the President of the United States. What was actually said we do not know. But we do know what it was that the two most important men of the Western Hemisphere discussed: Soviet espionage. And the background to those talks is as follows.

On the evening of 5th September 1945, Igor Gouzenko, a cipher clerk at the Soviet Embassy in Ottawa, extracted from the Embassy safe a sheaf of messages exchanged between Moscow and the Embassy, which he had deciphered for the military attaché, Colonel Sabotin.

Alan Moorehead has written, in his book, *The Traitors*: 'Gouzenko, then aged twenty-six, was of the generation which has been born and brought up in Soviet Russia, and he had been just two years in Canada. But in those two years he had marvelled at the goods that were sold in the shops, at the freedom and friendliness with which the Canadians went about their daily lives, and he had grown to detest the way in which these people were being cheated and spied on when their only desire had been to help Russia in the winning of the war. And now that his term abroad was over and he was due to return to Russia he had decided to put all his past life behind him and cross over to the Canadian side.'

About eight o'clock Gouzenko left the Soviet Embassy and went to the editorial offices of the *Ottawa Journal*. For a whole hour the young Russian remained there. He took telegram after telegram from his pocket, showed them document after document. But it was no use. Nobody believed his story. Not one of the editorial staff took him seriously.

There was nothing else for the poor man to do but return home to his wife and his small son. After a sleepless night, Gouzenko tried again next morning. This time his wife carried the dangerous documents in her hand-bag. At the offices of the *Ottawa Journal*, where he failed once more to convince the journalists, he was advised to go to the police.

Gouzenko, now in a state approaching terror, was sent from government office to government office. When Mackenzie King was told about this strange visitor, his personal advice was that Gouzenko should take himself and his documents back to the Soviet Embassy, if that was where he really came from.

Now Gouzenko feared the worst. His absence from duty and the loss of the papers must by now have been noticed at the Embassy. He and his wife went home once again. Where else could they go? As soon as they arrived there he noticed sinister figures in the street both in front of his house and behind it. He was being watched. Gouzenko slipped into the next-door house by the rear balcony, and told a young Canadian sergeant there the story of his fantastic predicament. The sergeant sent for the police. Gouzenko repeated his story to a police officer and the police promised to keep a watch on the house.

Shortly before midnight four men walked towards Gouzenko's house. The police heard a crash, and found that the door of Gouzenko's house had been broken down. Four Russians were inside rummaging through drawers and cupboards. One of them was Vitaly Pavlov, counsellor and second secretary at the Russian Embassy, and, as it later turned out, head of the Russian Secret Service in Canada. He was going through the clothes-cupboard. A second man in uniform, Lieutenant Rogov, was busy with another cupboard. The other two were a cipher expert and a lieutenant on Sabotin's staff.

On being asked by the Canadian police officer what they were doing, Pavlov replied: 'These men are Russians, and are looking for some papers belonging to the Embassy. The owner of the house has left the city and is now in Toronto. He has given us permission to enter his house and take what we want. . . .' (The report of the Canadian Royal Commission.)

A Canadian police inspector now appeared, and the Russians departed. Gouzenko, his family and his house were put under police protection. On the morning of 7th September, after the Russians had again attempted to break into the house, Gouzenko was finally taken, with his documents, to the headquarters of the Royal Canadian Mounted Police.

It was the Russians' attempt to get Gouzenko and retrieve their papers which finally convinced the Canadian government that he was telling the truth. And now they examined the documents. Their contents were truly terrifying. The full report, which was immediately placed before Prime Minister Mackenzie King, contained conclusive proof that a Soviet spy-ring had been operating successfully throughout the length and breadth of Canada for years.

It was in the summer of 1943 that the Soviet Military Attaché, Colonel Nikolai Sabotin, with his staff and his cipher experts, had arrived in Ottawa. Before leaving Moscow, Malenkov himself had given him detailed instructions on the work he was to do in Canada. In early 1943 Pontecorvo had begun working on the atomic-bomb project in Canada, and was sending in reports. By late 1944 Sabotin already had a group of about twenty Canadian 'collaborators' working for him, among them the British physicist, Allan Nunn May. Sabotin had thus been receiving the latest information on the progress of the atom-bomb project since May 1943. In July 1945, Nunn May handed over to the Russians stolen reports of laboratory tests on Uranium 235 and Uranium 225. These were so urgently wanted in Moscow that Sabotin's deputy, Colonel Motinov, immediately took them there by plane. Among the coded telegrams which Gouzenko now produced was the cable Sabotin had sent to Moscow the day after Hiroshima. 'To: Director. From: Alek'—this was Nunn May's code-name—'facts communicated . . . Bomb let off in Japan was built with uranium 235 . . . The amount of uranium 235 produced by the separator at Clinton is 400 grams daily. . . .'

This was what Mackenzie King told President Truman on 10th November 1945, in the White House. They decided that the Gouzenko affair should not be immediately made public. Mackenzie King suggested he fly to London and discuss the matter in confidence with the British Prime Minister, Attlee. He even had the idea of going on to see Stalin and informing him. For he thought it inconceivable that the Soviet government could know of this, and seriously believed it was a 'unique criminal act'. He imagined that a subordinate Soviet department had set up its own spy-ring, and that such disloyalty towards an ally would never have been tolerated by Moscow. This gentlemanly point of view, at a time when the Western Allies had been steadily plundered of their scientific state secret for years, now seems both depressing and foolish. Yet Mackenzie King's attitude was typical of the time, and this attitude alone explains how such large-scale treason could happen. The West judged Russia by its own standards. Months afterwards Mackenzie King addressed Parliament in these words: 'According to what I know of Marshal Stalin and what I have heard about him, I am certain that Russia's leader would neither permit nor excuse such conduct on the part of his country's diplomatic representatives.'

О П И С Ь

материалов отправленных в адрес Директора

8 Января (5) 1944 года.

№№ п.п. 1.	Источник 2	Откуда и при каких об- стоят. материал добыт. 3	Название мате- риала. 4	Дата и № 5	Кол-во листов 6	Гриф 7
105	Грэй	Из Департ. вооружения и снабж. арм. инж. отдел.	Чертеж	3.11.44	1	б-гр
106	"	"	"	б.д.	1	" "
107	"	Р у к о п и с ь.	Заметки к "	б.д.	2	"
108	Дебоув	З а п и с и.	Беседа с профес. рен. секр. сессии, парламента.	б.д.	1	"
109	Элли	К о п и я.	Письмо Уилгресса Кингу.	№-286 от 3.11.44	2	Секр
110	"	Сокращенная копия.	"	№-351 от 1.10.44	1	Секр
111	Фостер	Р у к о п и с ь.	Канадско-Британ- ския отношения.	4.ХII.44	3	б.гр
112	" ,	"	Продукция Сам.	Окт. 1944	2	-
113	Фостер	Р у к о п и с ь.	Продукция кораб.	" 1944	5	б.гр
114	"	К о п и я.	Телегр. №-2151	29.11.44	5	-
115	"	Документ.	Арм. комис. заказ.	20.ХI.44	9	Секр
116	"	"	Доклад.	30.11.44	4	"
117	"	К о п и я.	Переп. с компан.	29.11.44	4	б.гр
118	"	"	Исправления.	20.11.44	3	-
119	"	Департ. воор. и снабж.	Контракты.	21 11.44	2	-
120	"	"	Копр. контрактов.	Ноябр. 44	13	-
121	"	К о п и я.	Замеч. к контр.	28.11.44	1	Зар.
122	"	-	Переп. с компан.	24.11.44	9	б.гр
123	"	Деп. воорух. и снабжения	"	15.11.44	2	"

The Gouzenko case: Photo copy of an original list of secret documents, compiled by Soviet agents in Canada, which Colonel Sabotin, the military attaché at the Soviet Embassy in Ottawa, sent to the MVD director in Moscow. (From the report of the Canadian Royal Commission.) Opposite: literal translation of the Russian text.

LIST
of material sent to the director
on the 5th January 1944

No.	Source	From where and how the material was acquired	Nature of the material	Date	Page	Classification
1	2	3	4	5	6	7
105	Green	from the munitions and supply dept. of the technical division	plan	3.11.44	1	none
106	Green	from the munitions and supply dept. of the technical division	plan	no date	1	none
107	Green	in writing	notes across plans	no date	2	none
108	Debouz	notes	conversation about decisions in secret session of Parliament	no date	1	none
109	Ellie	copy	letter from Wilgress to King No. 386	3.11.44	2	secret
110	Ellie	shortened copy	letter from Wilgress to King No. 351	11.10.44	1	secret
111	Foster	in writing	Canadian–British relations	4.12.44	3	none
112	Foster	in writing	aircraft construction	Oct. 44.	2	—
113	Foster	in writing	ship building	Oct. 44.	5	none
114	Foster	copy	Telegram No. 2151	29.11.44	5	—
115	Foster	document	order from military Commission	20.11.44	4	secret
116	Foster	document	report	30.11.44	4	secret
117	Foster	copies	correspondence with company	29.11.44	4	—
118	Foster	copies	corrections	20.11.44	3	—
119	Foster	munitions and supply dept.	contracts	21.11.44	2	—
120	Foster	munitions and supply dept.	corrections of contracts	Nov. 44.	13	—
121	Foster	copy	footnotes to contracts	28.11.44	1	—
122	Foster		correspondence with company	24.11.44	9	none
123	Foster	munitions and supply dept.	correspondence	15.11.44	1	none

In the same month that the Gouzenko case broke in Canada, the final act of the Soviet atomic spy drama was going according to schedule in the United States, a thousand miles or more to the south.

On 19th September 1945, at 6 p.m., Klaus Fuchs and Harry Gold met once more, as arranged, in a street in Santa Fé. Near a church Fuchs handed the Soviet agent a large bundle of papers. Everything in the way of information on the atomic bomb which the Russians still lacked was in them—the size of the bomb, its load, details of its construction and how it was detonated.

With his brief-case bulging, Gold now travelled sixty miles by bus to Albuquerque, where a second meeting had been arranged for this same day.

Another contact man from Los Alamos was awaiting him, David Green-glass, brother of Ethel Rosenberg, who, with her husband, Julius Rosen-berg, also belonged to the Soviet spy-ring. Another thick bundle of plans and reports found its way into Gold's brief-case. Among these papers were con-structional drawings of the complicated 'implosion device', which the Soviets were awaiting with particular interest. They had already received through Harry Gold a preliminary description of this detonator from Klaus Fuchs. Thus the last of the secrets was handed over. Now the Soviets knew all they needed to know. Moscow was in a position to order the construction of 'its own' atom-bomb.

Several months now passed. In London Mackenzie King talked with Attlee, but the matter of their talks was not publicly revealed. The Moscow Conference of the Foreign Ministers of the United States, Great Britain and the USSR was pending, and it was hoped, in direct contact with Stalin, to influence the rigid attitude of the Soviets towards all the problems arising from the end of hostilities. Revelations about Soviet espionage in Canada could only be prejudicial to the atmosphere of the conference.

The Moscow Conference produced a few results, such as a proposal to the United Nations that atomic weapons be scrapped by all nations, but the tension between East and West remained. Meanwhile Colonel Sabotin had long ago disappeared from Canada. And on 15th February 1946, Mackenzie King finally gave the signal. The British and Canadian police acted simul-taneously. Fifteen arrests took place in Canada. In London Allan Nunn May, now working at the atomic research centre at Harwell, was interro-gated by the police.

The Soviets launched a counter-offensive, so formidable that it almost seemed as though it were the Canadian government which was on trial. 'The Canadian government, which leads the anti-Soviet campaign, is trying to cause political damage to the Soviet Union'—thus *Pravda*. 'Mackenzie King's attitude is not consistent with the conduct customary between countries enjoying normal relations with one another. . . .' And in an official statement by the Soviets, it was arrogantly stated: 'It has been established that owing to the superior technical standards of the USSR, the technical information obtained was not, in fact, of any use.'

At that time there were people not without influence in the United States and in England who openly maintained that the Soviets were entitled to use espionage. In a leading article in the *New York Herald Tribune* of 22nd February 1946, a foreign affairs expert stated: 'It would be as well to accept the facts of espionage and counter-espionage, and to carry out the two-way process as painlessly as possible.' Joseph E. Davis, at one time American Ambassador in Moscow, explained in *The Times* of 4th March 1946 that: 'In self-defence, Russia has an absolute moral right to obtain atomic secrets by military espionage . . .' And in England a Labour M.P., L. J. Solley, expressed the opinion that the counter-espionage investigations then taking place in Canada were endangering scientific progress.

The Nunn May trial, which ended in a sentence of ten years' imprisonment, made little impression on the public. The first of a series still to come, it resembled a rehearsal in an empty theatre for a tragedy of whose impact the West had as yet no conception.

The sentencing of Nunn May produced in one quarter repercussions which seem inconceivable to us today.

Soon after the trial an Association of Scientists in Britain published a manifesto in which criticism of the 'unusually harsh sentence' was advanced, on the grounds that it bore 'no relation to what had happened'. In 1947 this society made a further and similar protest; their spokesman was Professor Harold Laski.

Many scientists held this point of view. Some of these men, preoccupied with theoretical problems, research and abstract calculations far removed from ordinary human activities, lived in an ivory tower. Those who, in the world of science, had taken part in the recent scientific 'revaluation of all values', could not or would not understand that with the birth of the Soviet Union, old-established political values had also been 'revalued' long ago. Just as in the field of nuclear physics the laws of causality, regarded for hundreds of years as unshakeable, had become irrelevant, so twentieth-century totalitarianism had annulled the laws which had long prevailed between nations. Such scientists believed they could dismiss Lenin's maxim: 'The foundation of Communist morality is the struggle for the establishment and perfection of Communism,' as mere propaganda. It is, however, the basis of all Soviet policy.

So the Western scientists still dreamed of 'international science', and did not grasp the inevitable consequences of giving the Russians access to the atomic secrets. Russia assumed the role of a super-power which possession of this super-weapon conferred. And it was Moscow's declared objective to compel the entire world, including the United States, to bow beneath the yoke of totalitarian Communism.

It was a tragic situation. Well-intentioned and honourable scientists in the United States were crusading against the atom-bomb, and their crusade was wrecked by the Soviet Union. They had confidently expected that the Russians would at least give some consideration to the American atomic control project worked out by Robert Oppenheimer. The categorical refusal given by Andrei Gromyko on 24th July 1946 was a hard blow to them.

While the Soviet Union worked feverishly to produce an atom-bomb, the West was quite satisfied to rest on its laurels. In 1945 further atomic research was discontinued. The enormous team was broken up, and the scientists returned to their institutes and universities. The gigantic 'brains trust' which had been assembled in the United States disintegrated. Even among the top scientists, the opposition to further atomic projects was growing stronger every day.

Only one of the experts, Edward Teller, gave a clear warning against the abandonment of the stupendous and obviously successful weapon. When he was offered the second most important job supervising the work of Los Alamos, Teller said: 'I shall make one condition—either work must start at full pressure on the thermo-nuclear bomb (the hydrogen-bomb), or else at least a dozen uranium bomb tests must be carried out each year.' Both these conditions were refused.

So Los Alamos was abandoned by the great scientists. One year later David Lilienthal found that the buildings in which the unremitting efforts of two hundred thousand people had been concentrated were already in a state of decay.

But once again, in 1946, some thirty physicists gathered at Los Alamos. The subject of the conference was 'the Super-Weapon'—i.e. the hydrogen-bomb. Most of those taking part were of the opinion that its production would be a long and complicated business. Teller and several others estimated that the H-bomb could be completed inside two years. The 'Final Conference on the Super' ended without any decision having been reached. Fuchs was among the thirty physicists present and from him Moscow received up-to-date information about all the details of the conference. A résumé of Teller's views was naturally of particular value to them.

Teller did everything he could to get people to listen to him. He summoned an 'Emergency Committee of Atomic Scientists', to consider the production of the H-bomb. Einstein, who was in the chair, was against the idea. Teller, remembering the world situation during the period 1939 to 1941, considered Einstein's refusal quite illogical. Was it not the great scientist himself who, seven years earlier—because of the threat to the free world of Hitler's dictatorship—had recommended the making of the atom-bomb in a personal letter to President Roosevelt? How could Einstein be of a different opinion now, when the West was no less seriously threatened by the Soviet Union? It could only mean that he considered Stalin to be less of a menace than Hitler.

In fact Einstein was merely expressing the views of most American scientists at that time, views which were once again aired at the conference. The moral prestige of the United States would be damaged if they produced the H-bomb.

So after 1945 all was quiet in the West. In the United States, the strongest Western power, not only had work stopped on the uranium and plutonium bombs, but the 'super-weapon' was shelved and all rocket development suspended. This in spite of the fact that German V1 and V2 experts had been brought to America and the most highly qualified specialists were thus available. But America believed in peace and in disarmament. It was not long before this belief was shown to be a delusion, and it was realized with horror what appalling consequences post-war optimism had produced.

When these decisions were made no one in the West had any idea of what was happening in Russia. Moscow was 'catching up' fast. They were working doggedly, building uranium bombs, and even H-bombs.

While at Potsdam Stalin feigned ignorance for Truman's benefit, all the preparations were secretly under way for bringing the Soviet Union, then far behind in the field of nuclear physics, into the forefront. Immediately after the end of the war feverish activity had started, as laboratories, institutes and experimental establishments were built.

A colossal task lay ahead. But the Russian scientists and technicians had everything they needed, from theoretical calculations down to detailed drawings of the most intricate precision instruments and the most complicated equipment. The spies and traitors had done their work well.

If the Soviet Union had had to produce the atom-bomb on its own, if the Russians had had to repeat all that had been done in the West in the way of highly complicated research and of expensive development work, it would have taken them ten years at least to arrive at the stage reached by the United States in 1945. But the basic work had been done for them. They only needed to copy on a vast scale. Dallin has said in his *Soviet Espionage*:

'In addition to the scientific output of her own laboratories, Russian research had the help of another kind of laboratory, that situated at 19 Znamenski Street in Moscow—the GRU. An unprecedented enforced collaboration of science and espionage that continued throughout the war marked Soviet progress in the atomic field. The Soviet A-bomb has been the product of the combined efforts of Russian scientists and British, Canadian, German, Hungarian, Italian, and American Communists.'

The GRU centre in Znamenski Street was the 'Fourth Department' of the Red Army General Staff, the Intelligence Department.

It was very systematically done. On 11th October 1944, Tannu Tuva, which once belonged to China as part of Mongolia, and had been an independent republic since 1921, was 'incorporated into' the Soviet Union, or rather annexed by it. This meant that the essential raw material was available, for the mountains of this 'autonomous territory' contained rich deposits of uranium ore. After the end of the war the workings at St Joachimsthal in Czechoslovakia and those in Eastern Germany, in the Erzgebirge in Saxony and the Mansfeld copper-belt, were taken over for the Soviet atom-bomb project. In 1947 there was a complete reorganization of the atomic project. Kapitza, the one really top-grade scientist, was removed from his important job. Henceforth he was to work only as a scientist and not as an administrator, and would get his orders directly from a special committee set up to supervise atom-bomb and hydrogen-bomb research and production. This committee consisted of Nikolai Bulganin, Georgi Malenkov and Lavrenty Berya.

Gaps in the Soviet atomic programme were to be filled by the tremendous looting campaign of 1945. The booty did not only consist of dismantled factories, research laboratories, libraries and patents. It also included men. Two hundred German scientists and engineers were deported and forced to work in the Soviet atomic laboratories and research establishments. Among these were Dr Gustav Hertz, the Nobel Prize-winner, and Manfred Baron von Ardenne. The latter was appointed by the Soviets to work on the detonator for the hydrogen-bomb. It is his ability that the Soviets have to thank for the fact that they managed to construct an efficient H-bomb.

When the Fuchs case showed the West the extent of this large-scale treason and appropriation of Western knowledge, Moscow was quick to deny everything. The Soviet Union attempted in all seriousness, as they had done at the time of the Gouzenko affair, to convince the world that such 'technical hand-outs' were not necessary to them, in view of the 'advanced standards of technology in the USSR'. As David Dallin says: 'The Soviet Government has never acknowledged the legal and illegal, willing and forced, contribution of other countries to its atomic achievements. It has tried to represent the Soviet A-bomb as a product of purely Russian efforts, and has emphatically and quite unconvincingly denied having engaged in any kind of atomic espionage.' Characteristically, the Soviet news agency, Tass, disputed the fact that information on atomic research had been passed to Russian agents, even after the Klaus Fuchs trial. This accusation was, as Tass put it, 'pure fabrication, for Fuchs is not known to the Soviet government, and no representative of the Soviet government has ever been in contact with him'. (*Pravda*, 8th March 1950.)

It was nearer the truth when Molotov said, in 1947, long after the stolen information had been given to Russia, 'for some time now the atom-bomb has ceased to be secret'.

Though the truth about the Soviets' activities was finally recognized in the West, and the Bolshevik tissue of lies torn apart, the admiration felt by the Russian masses for the 'tremendous achievements of advanced socialist science and technology' knew no bounds. The millions behind the Iron Curtain had heard nothing of the Gouzenko affair, and had not read about Klaus Fuchs. For espionage, according to the *Soviet Political Dictionary* of 1940, 'is one of the main weapons used by capitalist countries, particularly in their war against the USSR. . . . Foreign espionage in our country is closely connected with disorganization and sabotage, and it aims at the undermining of Soviet military and industrial power.'

The Fuchs case gave the West, or at any rate the United States, the incentive to end delay. On 31st January 1950, Truman gave the order: the hydrogen-bomb was to be built.

Klaus Fuchs (left) at a confidential conference at Harwell, 1948, with Sir John Cockcroft (right).

The four-engined Ju-287, the first jet bomber in the world. Its designer, Dr B. Baade, fell into Russian hands. Dr Baade, head of development group I in Podberezye near Moscow, developed the Soviet jet bomber called the Tupolev, copied from the Ju-287.

Copy of the American Super-fortress, the B-29—the Soviet Tu-4 bomber—a "creation" of Tupolev. (Korea, 1951.)

Deported technicians from Junkers in the USSR: members of the "German Chess Club" in Podberezye (settlement for aircraft specialists near Moscow) after their winter tournament, 1949–50.

Winterturnier 1949/50 von 30.9.49–11.5.50 Gruppe 3		Deutscher Schachklub Podberesje																						Punkte		
		1 Durchgang											2 Durchgang											1.Durchg.	2.Durchg.	insgesamt
		1	2	3	4	5	6	7	8	9	10	11	1	2	3	4	5	6	7	8	9	10	11			
1	Brandl		o	1	1	1	1	1	0	0	0	0		1	o	1	1	1	1	o	1	o	1	5	7	12
2	Fr.Emmer	1		o	½	1	1	0	0	0	1	1	o		1	1	1	o	1	1	0	0	1	5½	6	11½
3	Heisig	o	1		o	o	1	½	1	o	1	1	1	o		o	1	o	1	1	1	o	1	5½	6	11½
4	Schumann	o	½	1		o	o	o	1	1	o	1	o	o	1		1	o	1	1	1	1	1	4½	7	11½
5	Kahofer	o	o	1	1		o	1	o	1	1	1	o	o	o	o		1	1	o	1	1	1	6	5	11
6	Michel	o	o	o	1	1		o	1	1	1	o	o	1	1	1	o		1	o	o	1	1	5	6	11
7	Rockstroh	o	1	½	1	o	1		1	½	1	o	o	o	o	o	o	o		1	1	½	1	6	3½	9½
8	Reuß	1	1	o	o	1	o	o		½	o	o	1	o	o	o	1	1	o		½	1	1	3½	5½	9
9	Antoni	1	1	1	o	o	o	½	½		1	o	o	1	o	o	o	1	o	½		1	o	5	3½	8½
10	Nötzold	1	o	o	1	o	o	o	1	o		o	1	1	1	o	o	o	½	o	o		1	3	4½	7½
11	Sattler	1	o	o	o	o	1	1	1	1	1		o	o	o	o	o	o	o	o	1	o		6	1	7

Eight years had passed during which the 'Super' project had been shelved, because ethical considerations had opposed all work on this weapon. The Soviets had gained valuable time. Was it not already too late?

In the United States work began again in earnest. The mathematicians, the theoretical and practical experts who had been scattered far and wide, were reassembled. They were divided into two groups. The first used the 'electronic brain', or ENIAC, for the incredibly complicated calculations, while the second worked with ordinary computers. The figures supplied by the theorists and the calculating machines were realized by the practical scientists. And in May 1951, on the Marshall Islands, the first test of 'thermo-nuclear' fusion was carried out, the decisive preliminary before detonating a hydrogen-bomb.

On 19th June 1951, the 'high-ups' all met at Princeton, '. . . all the people who had anything to say,' as Gordon Dean, president of the Atomic Energy Commission put it, '. . . Johnny von Neumann from Princeton . . . Dr Teller, Dr Bethe, Dr Fermi, Johnny Wheeler, Dr Nordheim from Los Alamos, and the principal scientists from all the laboratories met at this Conference. It went on for two days.'

This group of experts sub-divided their gigantic task in a remarkably short time. The superior quality of Western scientists was revealed once again.

Time was short, if the Russians were not to win the race and produce the ultimate weapon before the U.S. The Hungarian-born mathematical genius, Johann von Neumann, now constructed a 'Super' electronic brain for the H-bomb calculations, the giant MANIAC computer. It was capable of storing forty thousand computations at a time and of producing automatically any of them as required. The most difficult calculations, which would have taken three mathematicians working day and night three months to carry out, were done by MANIAC in ten hours.

In the autumn of 1952 the construction of the first hydrogen-bomb was nearly completed. A monster weighing sixty-five tons was built. It could not be used as a weapon.

The test took place in the South Pacific, on the Eniwetok Atoll. On 1st November 1952, there occurred the first enormous explosion produced by nuclear fusion. The fire-ball produced by the first 'Super' leaped convulsively upwards, at a temperature of millions of degrees, as hot as the sun. Then it disappeared beneath a gigantic mushroom cloud, and at point zero the island of Elugaleb sank beneath the boiling waves. The energy released, equal to that of five million tons of TNT, the most powerful conventional explosive, left a crater in the bed of the Pacific a mile long and one hundred and fifty feet deep.

Ten months later, on 8th August 1953, Malenkov announced: 'The United States no longer has a monopoly of the hydrogen-bomb.' Four days later the proof was available in the laboratories of the West. Tests carried out in the air by the 'radiation detector' planes of the U.S. Air Force showed that the Soviets had detonated a 'dry' H-bomb. While the United States were still working to fine down their colossal 'Super' into a bomb which could be carried by aircraft, the Russians had already achieved this.

The advantage which the West, thanks to its vast reserves of ability and technical knowledge and the millions spent on research and development, had reached in 1945 was reduced, by 1953, to nil. All the important advances had taken place in the West, the bold, creative theories and discoveries of Planck and Einstein, of Rutherford and Hahn, as well as the stupendous constructional achievements of the vast teams of expert technologists. Yet Russia possessed the terrible end-product of the West's titanic struggles, thanks to treason and espionage.

22   Wings from the West

In the year that Moscow staged its melancholy, medieval inquisition directed against scientific freedom, and hundreds of Russian scientists were forced to submit to the dogma of dialectical materialism, Russia gave the West another severe shock.

Only three years had passed since the end of the war. The nations wished to work for the peace they now hoped to enjoy. But behind the Iron Curtain rearmament was in full swing. Military attachés of the former Allies were the first to see with their own eyes a completely new Red Air Force.

On 'Red Air Force Day' in 1948 the Kremlin presented its first long-range bomber, the existence of which was unknown in the West. This inaugurated a series of demonstrations of new aircraft. Russia was threatening the West with the West's own inventions, exactly as Peter the Great had once threatened Europe with cannon forged by Swedes, Italians and Germans, and with European-trained troops.

The West realized, too late, what had happened. In 1948 Russia began to reap where others had sown. The colossal loot from Germany, the armament secrets stolen from the United States and England, were now about to bear fruit, a bitter fruit for the free world.

In the years after 1922 Professor Junkers laid the foundations for a modern air force and air transport system in Russia. Everything that had then been done voluntarily was repeated twenty-five years later under compulsion. Large numbers of German engineers and constructors were kidnapped by the Soviets and compelled to create a Red Air Force and air transport system out of nothing. Within a few years this Red Air Force compared favourably with the leading air forces of the West.

The story of the spectacular rise of Soviet air power can now be told. It began shortly after that October day in 1946 when the long trains started to roll into Russia from the Russian Zone of Germany, loaded with aircraft, machinery, turbines, jet propulsion units and, of course, the necessary aviation experts.

One of their destinations was a place ninety miles north of Moscow, Podberezhye, on Lake Moscow, an artificial lake fed by the Volga.

To house the German aircraft, machinery and equipment, the Russians had built huge factory installations. Living-quarters for the deported specialists had been rapidly run up, since these men would now have to work for years for the Soviets. There were barracks, wooden houses for the men and their families, and stone blocks of three-room flats. The barracks were reserved for skilled workers and engine-fitters, the three-room flats for engineers, the separate houses for the 'high-ups'. There are rigid class distinctions in the Soviet Union.

The quest for German specialists had proved more productive than Moscow had dreamed, and the accommodation was quite inadequate. Contrary to the promises made by the Russians, there was only one room available for each family of four. The furniture they had brought with them had to be 'sold', the best pieces finding their way into the homes of the Russian supervisors and the officers of the guard. Payment was promised for the furniture, but none was ever received.

Gradually the factory buildings were filled to capacity, like the living-quarters, with the loot from the Junkers and Siebel Works, the Heinkel Works from Oranienburg and the Messerschmidt Works from Wiener-Neustadt. Columns of heavy lorries, supplied by the Americans under lend-lease, carried the machinery, models and equipment, the contents of entire laboratories and drawing-offices. German-built aircraft were there, from jet-fighters and rocket planes to the newest heavy bombers. Apart from the models and prototypes already being developed, there were also the 'aircraft of tomorrow'.

For even by 1945, as the German aviation expert Professor Willy Messerschmidt has stated, machines had been developed which could fly at six hundred miles per hour, had a range of over seven thousand miles, and could climb to an altitude of thirty thousand feet in two minutes. 'My own designers had already developed a jet-propelled aircraft', Professor Messerschmidt explained, 'which could travel from Frankfurt to New York in six hours.'

The building of a technically up-to-date air force in Russia could now start. Moscow had chosen Podberezhye to be the centre for the foreigners working on Soviet aviation development.

A Russian general was in charge, as 'Director-General'. He assigned the Germans to their various jobs. The specialists were astonished by the way the Russians had assembled everything. Engineers and draughtsmen found the same desks lying ready for them which they had used in Dessau, Oranienburg, Halle or Leipzig. They were able to find their old drawings and tracings, technical notes and reports, neatly tied up with labels bearing Cyrillic lettering.

Other groups were installed at Kuibyshev on the Volga. This was to be the first great production-centre for the Red Air Force. The complete contents of all the factories and assembly-shops of the Junkers Motor Works at Bernburg on the Saale arrived on an endless procession of goods trains. No less important was the highly efficient machinery from the BMW factory at Eisenbach, which had also fallen into Russian hands. Elsewhere in Russia, almost at the same time, the dismantled factories of other important aircraft firms were being reassembled, of Arado from Babelsberg, Dornier from Wismar, Henschel from Berlin and Erfurt, Messerschmidt from Wiener-Neustadt and Heinkel from Rostock-Warnemünde.

'Two-thirds of the entire German aircraft industry', according to Professor Messerschmidt, 'was in the hands of the Russians.' With this vast potential now on Russian soil, the Soviet Union could be quite certain of catching up with the West within a few years. After 1945 the *Nyemetskaya Sloboda*, the 'German Quarter', was performing the same pioneer service for Russia as it had done in the days of Ivan IV. But now Podberezhye was no longer called *Nyemetskaya Sloboda* but *Malaya Germanya*, or 'Little Germany'.

In the circumstances, there was nothing for the deported Germans to do at Podberezhye, Kuibyshev and the other places, but to make a virtue of necessity. Hard work might help them to forget their circumstances.

Tremendous activity soon started in the drawing-offices and assembly-shops. There was plenty of work, too, for the Junkers test pilots, Dülgen and Hoffmann. They had to fly the new German types of aircraft, teach the Russian engineers, and train Russian pilots.

Captain Wolfgang Ziese, former chief test pilot of the Siebel Works, was given an entirely new job: he had to practise piloting an aircraft in a prone position. He practised this in converted German glider planes of the 'Kranich' and 'Grunau IIB' types. These were necessary preliminaries before testing the most advanced and secret aircraft, the supersonic experimental machine DFS-346, from the Siebel factory. This plane, designed by the German Research Institute for Glider Aircraft (*Deutsche Forschungsanstalt für Segelflug*) and built by Professor Alexander Lippisch, was of revolutionary design, with swept-back wings. The DFS-346 had to be controlled by a pilot lying prone, for only thus could he withstand the pressures of supersonic flight. Rauschen and Motsch, the chief test pilots, carried out the test flights from the airfield of Toplistan, five miles from Moscow.

There was one important gap in the Red Air Force development project. The Soviets, in October 1946, had not managed to kidnap any fighter plane experts. And Russia badly needed an up-to-date fighter, to counteract the American strategic bombers.

The Russians managed to rectify this. Some months after the deportation of the six thousand experts, the Soviets got hold of two German designers who guaranteed that within three years the Soviet Union would be able to send the fastest fighter planes in the world against the Americans.

The news went around like wildfire at Podberezhye. Dr Siegfried Günther and Professor Benz had come to 'Little Germany', under the 'close escort' of Soviet officers, as 'guests of the Soviet Union'. The Germans realized at once what this would mean to Russia, for they knew something of the achievements of these experts.

To the initiated, the memory of Professor Benz's last piece of construction-work was still quite vivid. He was the pioneer of the German jet-fighter, the He.162, or *Volksjäger*, completed within four weeks and in mass-production within a further six. This machine flew beautifully and even in 1944 could do 500 m.p.h., propelled by a single turbo-jet.

Dr Siegfried Günther, together with his brother, who was killed in a motor accident, was for many years chief designer at Heinkel's. Not for nothing was he considered one of the most brilliant aircraft designers Germany possessed. Before 1939, Dr Günther was working on the development of the first jet aircraft in the world, the He.178. On 27th August 1939, the machine was successfully tested in the air. This was two years before the British jet aircraft, the Gloster E.28/39, with a jet-propulsion system constructed by Frank Whittle, was completed.

After 1945 Günther got a job in an American office at Landsberg. He applied for work in his own field in vain, and in vain he submitted the plans of his latest project. The Americans politely refused. Ludicrous though it sounds, the senior officers of the U.S. Army of Occupation would not believe his identity. They said he was a fake.

After this disillusioning experience, Dr Günther decided to go to the Russian Zone. His family were living in East Berlin—and he knew that there he would at least have a roof over his head. The brilliant engineer found himself a job in a motor-repair workshop which belonged to his parents-in-law. He had no idea that his stay in Eastern Germany was only to last a week.

The Soviet secret service was better informed than the American Army. Günther had not been home forty-eight hours before the Russians tracked him down. In the middle of the night they knocked on his door, and Russian soldiers hauled him and his wife out of the house, exactly as had happened with the six thousand.

Dr Günther suddenly found himself in a Russian office, with Professor Benz. He, too, had been awoken in the middle of the night by the Soviets' 'invitation'. The two experts were offered fantastic contracts. The Soviets gave them no time to decide, for they were taken, under guard, to the East Berlin airport of Schönefeld. In a machine which Benz and Günther recognized at once as a Soviet copy of the American DC-3, they flew eastwards. In the evening they landed at Moscow and were immediately taken to Podberezhye.

There was no time wasted. The next morning, very early, the Russian 'Director-General' of Podberezhye summoned Günther to his villa, and after a brief, polite chat he was shown everything which had been brought to Russia, for assembly and further development.

Dr Günther could not believe his eyes as he went through the drawing-offices and the assembly-shops and examined the models. This was a super-firm, born of years of German aviation research and industrial achievement.

Slung beneath a stolen Superfortress, Russia's first supersonic aircraft, the German DFS-346, makes its test flight with Ziese, a German, at the controls.

The Soviets immediately appointed Günther chief designer at the factory building fighter aircraft. For Dr Günther, totally absorbed in his work, unwanted by the Western powers and condemned to inactivity, this seemed the chance of a lifetime.

Just as his colleagues had done, all those old friends and acquaintances whom he now met again at Podberezhye, he threw himself into his work— for Russia.

The hot summer months of 1947 flew past. The German aviation experts pored over their calculations and worked out formulas for improved designs. On the drawing-boards, the formulas began to take shape. Fuselages and wings were made in enormous quantities in the assembly-shops, first wooden parts glued together, then metal. Soon the first models were ready for their test flights. They were moved on barges down the Volga canal to the airfield at Toplistan. The improved German DFS-346 proved aerodynamically successful when towed without an engine. The time then came to test Russia's first supersonic aircraft.

The Junkers engines arrived from Kuibyshev, also the precision instruments made by the former Berlin firm of Askania. The supersonic machine, DFS-346, built at Podberezhye, was assembled and completed in the hangars at Toplistan.

The airfield was closed to all other planes; the German engineers were therefore astonished one morning to see an American 'Superfortress' coming in to land. The great test flight was scheduled for that day. But this B-29 had been appropriated by Russia from her Allies when it made a forced landing near Vladivostok in 1944.

The captured bomber was of use at Toplistan in the development of the new Red Air Force. It was used for launching smaller planes. The German-Russian supersonic DFS-346 was suspended beneath its enormous fuselage, and looked tiny compared with the B-29. Captain Ziese crawled into the pilot's seat. The pilot lay on his stomach. Every detail of these final preparations was being minutely observed and registered by the Germans, watched by the Soviet experts.

The B-29 roared down the runway. It rose to an altitude of thirty thousand feet and was almost out of sight, when it turned for the run over. Below on the airfield the engineers crouched over their control-panels, measuring distances and altitudes.

A radio signal indicated the beginning of the test-flight. Ziese had cut his machine loose, and at the same time turned on one of the two Walter rocket-engines. In the blue Russian sky, above the Kremlin, the first flight through the sound-barrier took place.

The speedometer needle crept up the gauge: 800 . . . 900 . . . 1,000 kilometres an hour. Ziese felt as though his 'bird' was heavy as a plank. At 1,100 k.p.h. he felt an almost imperceptible vibration in the body of the aircraft. A few minutes later he brought the test-flight to an end, lost altitude and landed on a single wide ski. Dr Günther had fitted this to the fuselage as a temporary arrangement.

A few days later Ziese was asked to go and see the 'Director-General' of Podberezhye. For his daring test-flight he was given the sum of twenty thousand roubles, as a special award.

The success of the test flight caused the Soviets to demand an acceleration of the Germans' efforts. The wonder aircraft DFS-346 was only one item of a vast and ambitious programme which the Soviets had entrusted to the deported aviation experts. In Podberezhye alone not only were supersonic fighter aircraft and other advanced types being developed, but also designs for heavy bombers and large transport planes. The Russians were determined to take the West by surprise.

The full scope of the programme only trickled through very slowly to the men who had to implement it. The Soviets, suspicious as always, had skilfully arranged that none of the Germans was able to get an accurate, overall picture of what was happening at Podberezhye.

Each department was sealed off from the others. Each specialist was only allowed to know about his own particular job. Even the designers worked under permanent guard and were firmly kept apart. No man might set foot in any department other than his own. No Heinkel engineer might enter the Junkers section, or Siebel or Messerschmidt. Such arrangements ensured that each working group was an isolated unit which could be dispensed with when no longer needed.

Even then the Soviets were also attempting to reach their objective without German aid. They considered themselves almost ready to 'spread their wings' and were preparing to carry on alone, on the basis of the plans, calculations and data already available at Podberezhye.

Soviet engineers set about copying the supersonic DFS-346, so as to carry out test-flights on their own. They wished to show that Russians could fly faster than sound without Western help. Somewhere on the outskirts of Moscow there began to emerge, in conditions of the strictest secrecy, exact copies of the aircraft on which the Germans had been working for so long, before 1945 at Halle on the Saale, and after 1946 at Podberezhye.

But the Russians did not manage to test either of their machines produced in this way. The planes were dashed to bits while being launched from the carrier-aircraft, the captured B-29. The Soviet engineers had used a different mechanism for suspending the DFS-346 and it was a complete failure. One of the Russian test pilots was killed when his machine rammed the B-29 immediately after launching. At the second attempt this happened again, but the pilot managed to save himself by parachute.

The Soviets were thus brutally reminded that aircraft production in Russia could not yet stand on its own feet. They still had to be guided by foreign experts who had already done so much for the Soviet Union.

In late 1947, just one year after the kidnapping, the Germans built an ultra-modern fighter plane. One of the Kremlin's principal targets was within sight. They would soon have a defence against the American bombers.

At Podberezhye the new supersonic jet-fighter for the Red Air Force began to take shape. A group of German and Austrian engineers at Kuibyshev were building jet-engines, quite unknown in the Soviet Union before 1945.

The Russians had begun by copying the jet-propulsion mechanism of the Junkers-004 and the BMW-003, which had been brought to Kuibyshev together with the 'Otto Mader' development project. As the deported engineer Ferdinand Brandner reported in the Munich technical journal, *Der Flieger*, this was regarded more as a sort of training operation for the Russians, so that they might familiarize themselves with jets. 'The object was to enable the Soviets to start designing, building and testing on their own, an objective which was to some extent achieved.' Several hundred Soviet technicians and engineers were detailed to watch every phase of the work at Kuibyshev.

Western Engines in the USSR			
Manufacturer	*Type*	*Russian copy (at Kuibyshev)*	*Use*
Junkers	Jumo 004	RD-10	MiG-9, Yak-17
Junkers	Jumo 012	—	—
Bavarian Motor Works (BMW)	BMW 003	RD-20	
Rolls-Royce	Nene	RD-45^f	MiG-15, H-28
Rolls-Royce	Derwent	RD-500	Yak-23

The work began in circumstances of great discomfort and difficulty, in the winter of 1946–47. 'German workers, in a temperature of twenty-five degrees of frost, without suitable clothing, had to put up the wooden barracks with the four testing-rooms where we worked day and night for five years on the valuable machines.'

The jet-engines which were being copied were given the Russian designation RD—*Reaktivny Dvigatel*. The copy of the Jumo-004 became RD-10, which was fitted in the MiG-9s and Yak-17s, while that of the BMW-003 became RD-20.

The production of what was then the most powerful German gas turbine, the Jumo 004, was under way, when the Russians learned that an important technical advance had been made in the English Rolls-Royce factory. They immediately determined to obtain a model of the British jet-engine.

It was no problem. Russian trade still attracted the Western businessmen, and Moscow could always buy what she wanted from capitalists anxious to sell their goods. The directors of the famous British firm were delighted to accept the Soviet order, and by Christmas fifty-five Rolls-Royce turbines, twenty-five of the 'Nene' type and thirty of the 'Derwent' type, had arrived in Kuibyshev. The Russians soon saw the colossal thrust of which they were capable.

From then on every effort was made to reproduce the new jet-engines. The British turbine, with a few minor improvements, became the standard engine of the 'wonder fighter' of the Red Air Force, which taught the Americans such a bitter lesson in Korea. In 1948, from Toplistan and later from the other experimental airfield near Moscow, Nikolovaskoye, the first of the 'wonder fighters', these small, easily manœuvrable and extremely fast jet-planes, took off, with German pilots at the controls. With this fighter, Dr Siegfried Günther and his colleagues had produced a masterpiece.

Hardly were the tests completed before the machines were removed from Podberezhye and Nikolovaskoye. It was rumoured among the Germans that Moscow had ordered mass production of the aircraft. It seemed odd that the Russian engineers, technicians and skilled workers, who had almost lived in the drawing-office and the assembly-shops watching every phase of the fighter's development, were no longer to be seen.

Only a small circle of Russian experts knew the reason. The aircraft created by Western engineers was now to become a Russian plane, the 'MiG'. The Russian engineers Mikoyan and Gurevich were named as the creators of the Red Air Force's first jet-fighter. Mikoyan was awarded the Stalin Prize.

The presentation of this masterpiece of Russian 'socialist technology' in the countries beyond the Iron Curtain was very carefully planned. Rumours were circulated, hints dropped, until at last the American pilots met the wonder fighter in action.

In the year 1948 foreigners were allowed to see the very fast jet-fighters for the first time. Shortly afterwards a few machines turned up during the blockade of West Berlin, on the edge of the airlift, as it were. The foreign military attachés in Moscow saw the plane for themselves on 1st May 1949.

As the Kremlin bells rang out for the biggest military display since 1945, a group of MiGs in formation roared over the Red Square, flying low and very fast. The fighters were already out of sight before any of the Western guests on the platform could take photographs. There was no doubt, however, that they were MiGs—about fifty of them. They were already being mass-produced.

The Air Staffs of the United States and England were now informed and forewarned. It was not until 1st November 1950 that Moscow delivered its long-awaited blow to the American public.

When American fighter squadrons flying over Korea neared the Yalu River, the pilots were suddenly appalled to meet aircraft faster than their own, tearing through their formations with all guns blazing. On their swept-back wing-tips were Russian markings.

The next day America and the world knew that the North Koreans were using a Russian jet-fighter, the MiG-15, built in the Soviet Union.

The Americans were alarmed. These MiGs were superior to the American F-84s and F-80 'Shooting Stars'.

The U.S. Chief of Air Staff immediately ordered a new type of aircraft sent to the Korean front. A week later a group of F-86 Sabre Jets arrived, under Colonel Smith. These machines had travelled from the United States to Korea in forty hours.

On 17th December the Soviet MiG-15s and the American F-86 Sabre Jets met and fought over the Yalu River. Lieut.-Colonel Bruce H. Hinton 'made flying history by shooting down the first MiG-15', according to the American report. 'Five days later the Americans shot down six in air combat—all confirmed.'

It was soon apparent that the American fighter-pilots were superior to their Red opposite numbers. This was due more to their flying skill than to the F-86. At high altitudes where the 'dog-fights' usually took place, the MiG could escape the F-86 by climbing higher still. 'The MiG machines produce greater propulsion at high altitudes,' the American report stated.

There was another curious fact about these machines. The MiGs looked so like the newest U.S. fighters as to be almost indistinguishable from them. More than once the American pilots mistook the Red fighters for their own machines.

'Waggle your wings, boys!' soon became a standing order among the U.S. Air Force crews in Korea. All aircraft which did not waggle their wings on receipt of this signal were MiGs. Life Magazine published an interesting article which goes some way to explain this extraordinary resemblance. Frank Campion's article appeared on 25th February 1952: 'In the summer of 1945 two particularly interesting objects, sent by air force intelligence, arrived at the North American Aviation Co.'s Los Angeles plant. One was a wing of the latest German jet-fighter, a Messerschmidt 262, and its batlike design was startling to the company's engineers who had never seen anything like it on a plane before. The other, of even greater interest, was a secret record of German wind-tunnel experiments on the aerodynamic behaviour of radically swept-back wings. Conclusive and exhaustively thorough, the data (which the Russians also lifted from the files of the Luftwaffe) saved North America three laborious years of research in designing the Air Force's fastest fighter now in operation, the F-86 Sabre jet.'

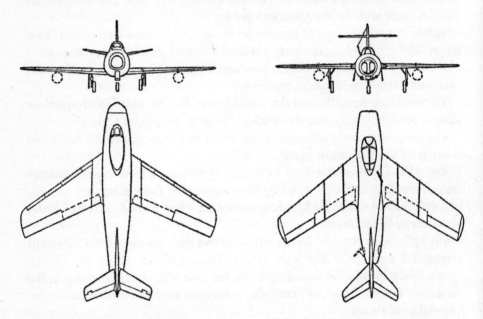

Opponents over Korea: The Soviet MiG-15 (right) constructed by Dr Günther, and the American F-86-A Sabre (left). The MiG-15 has the typical high-set tail-plane of the German DFS-346.

Hence the resemblance between the MiG-15 and the F-86. Both were descended from a model constructed and tested in Germany. The American public was astonished, for the true story of how the Soviets had produced their MiGs was still withheld from them.

This made it easier for Moscow to circulate its version of how the wonder fighter came into existence. An American technical journal, *Aero-Digest*, published an article by the 'Comrade Engineer and Inventor Gurevich', proudly entitled, *How I built the MiG 15*.

Gurevich naturally does not breathe a word about the German origins of his 'wonder machine'. His story was taken up by the world press and studied with great interest, even his final paragraph, in which he says ambiguously: 'In conclusion, I should like to repeat that the role I played was an insignificant one, and that there are many others who deserve credit. We are now concentrating our attentions on further problems in the building of new aircraft with which to confirm the supremacy of the USSR and do honour to the achievements of the great Stalin.'

When Professor Ernst Heinkel was shown the first photograph of the MiG, he declared without hesitation: 'That is Günther's aircraft, which we discussed in my office in the early weeks of 1945. Had I been able to continue production, the machine would certainly have been built by me. The Soviet engineer Mikoyan has as little to do with this as that other Soviet engineer Tupolev had to do with TU-70—which is nothing but an exact copy of the B-29 Superfortress, the American long-range bomber. . . .'

Since the beginning of the Korean War, American Superfortresses had been subjecting North Korean territory to extensive and systematic bombing; they had destroyed bridges, factories, airfields and railway stations. With the deployment of squadrons of MiGs, however, this had come to an end. The American propeller-driven heavy bombers were hopelessly outclassed by the Red fighters, travelling almost at the speed of sound, and daylight raids had to be discontinued. The effectiveness of the heavy bomber as a weapon of attack was called into question for the first time.

Nevertheless General Hoyt S. Vandenberg, then U.S. Air Force Chief of Staff, did his best to reassure the American public. He continued to maintain that the 'strategic bomber' would be America's decisive weapon in the event of a Third World War.

In all arguments about American defence strategy, the Chief of Air Staff had one answer which became almost a dogma in the United States. The Strategic Air Command could win any war, and was therefore the decisive deterrent against the Russians.

Writing in the *Saturday Evening Post* on 17th February 1951, General Vandenberg said: 'Our stockpile of A-bombs is not the sole deterrent to aggression. It is our ability to deliver the bomb anywhere in the world. . . . The muscle of our strategic arm is the B-36, which has more speed, range, armament, and carries a heavier bomb load than any big plane the Moscow régime can get into mass production in the next few years.'

This argument was dangerously wrong; it showed that even the military experts of the great powers did not know what was going on in Russia. While the United States enjoyed a false self-confidence owing to a belief that America had a huge technological supremacy over the Soviet Union, Vandenberg's statement was being rendered untrue by events then taking place behind the Iron Curtain.

Having broken through with a very fast fighter plane, the Kremlin now set about building a Red bomber fleet to equal that of the United States. The great expert, with whose help they hoped to achieve this ambitious target, had been brought to Russia by the Soviets in the mass deportation from Germany on 22nd October 1946.

In Dr Baade, chief constructor at the Junkers works, Moscow had acquired an outstanding engineer. Baade, who first earned a world fame with his Ju-52, had a vast international experience. Before the war he had worked in American aircraft firms. At Podberezhye, the Russians put Dr Baade in charge of their No. 1 Construction Department.

From the moment he took over, a new and revolutionary aircraft design began to appear. It was steadily improved upon. The design incorporated an arrow-shaped wing formation. Swept-back wings were chosen for all large Soviet aircraft such as the long-range bombers, 'Bison' and 'Bear', which caused a sensation abroad, and the civil aircraft, Tu-104 and Tu-114, the largest transport plane in the world.

The Soviet engineer A. N. Tupolev, whose name these new aircraft bear, was not responsible for the revolutionary swept-back wing design, any more than for all-metal airframe construction though this is also credited to him in Soviet aeronautical literature.

Was it pure coincidence that Tupolev, undeniably a competent engineer, had twenty-five years earlier been put in charge of another foreign development project in Russia? When Junkers built the first large Russian aircraft factory at Fili, in 1922, the Germans brought to Russia what was then the most important innovation in the aircraft industry, all-metal construction, first used in the F-13. Exactly two years later, in 1924, Tupolev completed work on his Ant-2, the first Russian aircraft to be built entirely of metal. 'Tupolev was strongly influenced by Junkers' construction methods,' the Frenchman J. Marmain tells us, in *Aviation Magazine*. The Russian also copied Junkers' propeller-driven sledges and propeller-driven boats, which were then presented as Soviet inventions.

Tupolev's TS AGI ANT-5, a copy of the Junkers propeller-driven sledge.

Tupolev was among the few gifted Soviet aviation engineers who had had direct contact with foreign firms. Before the Second World War he had been to France and had inspected the Caudron aircraft factory. Marcel Riffard, who took him round, 'was somewhat surprised to see Tupolev, during his tour of inspection, suddenly open a drawer or a cupboard—much to the astonishment of the workmen and factory staff.' He was faithfully following the example set by Peter the Great.

The Soviets' first efficient heavy bomber after 1945 was, indeed, Tupolev's 'creation'. It was based on a theft.

Before the end of the war, the Russians came into unlawful possession of three valuable pieces of loot, which belonged to their American allies. When a Boeing B-29 Superfortress made a forced landing near Vladivostok, after an attack on Tokyo, Moscow immediately impounded the machine. Two more B-29s experienced the same fate. Stalin let the surviving members of the bomber crews go home, but despite strong protests from Washington he did not hand over the aircraft.

These brand-new heavy bombers, the products of American aviation skill, on the development of which millions of dollars had been spent, were invaluable objects of study to the Russians. The Soviet engineers were so impressed by the American 'Super-Fortress' that they determined to copy the B-29.

This job was given to Tupolev. The Soviet copy of the B-29 eventually left the assembly-lines as the Red Tu-4 bomber. Its equivalent in the branch of civil aircraft became the Tu-70. Both were mass-produced by the Soviets.

When America learnt in 1949, the year in which the first Soviet atomic explosion took place, that the Russians possessed this long-range bomber, there was great alarm. For the first time the United States was within range of Soviet atom-bombers.

'Russian aircraft', according to U.S. News and World Report of 7th October 1949, '. . . could drop atom-bombs on the greater part of our country.'

But in addition to copying the B-29, the Soviets had already started work on Dr Baade's revolutionary new construction project, the long-range jet-bomber.

Baade had at his disposal the complete contents of his old office in Dessau when he took charge of No. 1 Construction Department at Podberezhye. On his desk were his constructional drawings and all the calculations used in his last project. And when the Soviet Director General showed him one of the hangars, he saw there the prototype of his latest plane, the Ju-287, with its strange, swept-back wing formation.

Just before the end of the war, Baade had started on the Vo-series of jet-bombers, the first in the world, and these were ready to be flown at Brandis, near Leipzig. One of these Ju 287s fell intact into the hands of the Red Army and was transported to the USSR.

Under Russian eyes Dr Baade sent up his Ju-287, the first 'Russian' jet-bomber. His chief test pilot, Captain Dülgen, showed Soviet engineers, on breath-taking test-flights over the airfield of Nikolovaskoye, the colossal power of the improved Ju-287. This Ju-287 was already far ahead of all similar developments in other countries.

The Soviets had realized at once that the continuation of work on this model would put them in possession of the first heavy bomber with jet propulsion. They issued orders accordingly.

Working under pressure, Baade and his compatriots set about the job. They modified the wing structure. The wings of the Ju-287, which in the V-1 model had been 'negative', i.e. with tapering wing-tips inclined forwards, were made 'positive', i.e. wing-tips inclined backwards. Thus the jet aircraft reached a speed of well over six hundred miles per hour.

As reward for his successful construction work, Dr Brunolf Baade was given a professorship by the Soviet Institute of Aviation Research. But his name was not divulged in Russia in connection with his achievements. It was not until 1959 that an aircraft was designated with the initials of Brunolf Baade. The jet passenger aircraft, which the East German aircraft industry built for the East Zone Lufthansa, was called the BB-152. Baade himself has never been permitted to leave Soviet territory.

While work continued feverishly at Podberezhye, other deported specialists at Kuibyshev on the Volga were developing new propulsion units of immense power for the new models. We have to thank the Austrian engineer, Ferdinand Brandner, for this information. He is one of the few who so far have had the courage to talk openly about these vast projects in the USSR.

'In 1948, after some time spent in prison and prisoner-of-war camps, and working in the Urals, I was ordered to join my former Junkers colleagues as head of the construction department at Kuibyshev. From the Air Ministry in Moscow, I received instructions to build a turbo-propeller, with promises that I should be sent home when my work was finished. It was on this promise that we built our hopes of seeing our homes again. We did this and other jobs too besides some constructional development based on the war booty captured by the Russians from Junkers and BMW. But the Soviet Union only kept their promise after long years of procrastination.

'With the energy of men who still had hope, we set to work on our principal assignment. The turbo-propeller was to be of 6,000 h.p. . . . The single-minded determination with which we set about carrying out the Ministry's orders is perhaps comprehensible only to us—we were fighting for our freedom and for permission to return home . . . We completed the job within two years. In September 1950, the first consignment of German specialists was sent home . . . It was then that we really began to suffer, and our torment reached a climax, when, by 1952, we had still not got home. Professor Klimov's development work—on exactly the same lines as ours—was going on in Leningrad at the same time.'

From the summer of 1950, the Soviets had taken special security measures. The Germans were no longer allowed to fly the new aircraft. Moscow obviously feared that some foolhardy foreigner might take one of the 'Russian' planes beyond the Iron Curtain. In cases where the Russians could not dispense with foreign pilots for test-flights, the tanks contained only enough fuel for a short flight.

'After a further job, the construction of twin-engines', Brandner goes on, 'we were compelled to do our last one, the production of a 12,000 h.p. model, to be completed in the shortest possible time. It took us three months to build. Within three months, from first plans to final construction, and with about a hundred men working on it, this model was completed. I very much doubt whether anyone in Western Europe would believe such a time schedule possible; it could only be done under the special circumstances which prevailed.'

Of the eight hundred German and Austrian engineers forced to work at Kuibyshev, twenty-five died, five committed suicide and two went mad. The rest returned home in the summer of 1954, eight years after their deportation.

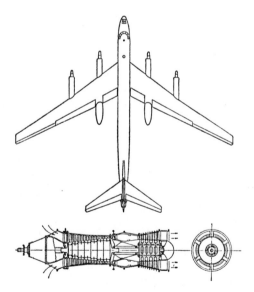

The Tu-114, 'Rossiya', seating 220, the largest passenger aircraft in the world, is the commercial version of the long-range bomber and A-bomb carrier, the USSR's Tu-20, known to the West as the 'Bear'. It is driven by 4 turbo-prop jets of 12,000 h.p. each. A group of deported engineers in Kuibyshev, headed by the Austrian F. Brandner, developed the powerful Type K turbine, on orders from Moscow.

In July 1955, at the aircraft works at Tushino, near Moscow, the Soviet long-range bomber appeared for the first time—the 'Bear', as the Americans called it. It was fitted with four of the turbo-prop engines developed by Brandner at Kuibyshev, each of 12,000 h.p.

Three years later the Soviet Union astounded other nations with what was the largest passenger aircraft in the world, the Tu-114, the *Rossiya*. This Tu-114, however, is none other than the converted atom-bomber, the Tu-20. It can carry two hundred and twenty passengers and has a maximum range of twelve thousand miles.

23   The Birth of the Sputnik

IN THE AUTUMN OF 1957, the Soviet Union announced that it had succeeded in sending the first artificial satellites into space, Sputniks I and II. This news was completely unexpected. Europe was astonished, America overwhelmed.

How had the Soviet Union achieved such a brilliant technical success, ahead of the Americans?

Early on the morning of 11th April 1945 the Sherman tanks of 'Combat Command B', Third United States Armoured Division, passed through the small town of Nordhausen, at the southern edge of the Harz Mountains, on their way to the Elbe, where the junction with the Red Army was to take place.

Four miles from Nordhausen, a group of men came running towards the tanks, waving excitedly. They wore striped pyjama-like garments, the regulation Nazi concentration-camp dress. Colonel Welborn, who led the leading squadron, learned from these men that the Germans had been working nearby on 'something quite fantastic'. The word 'V2' was mentioned. The nearest village was Niedersachswerfen.

Colonel Welborn ordered a halt. A few minutes later he was standing with Colonel William B. Loveday outside a tunnel that led into a hillside. A wide cement path disappeared into the darkness. A little way down it they found a store of giant rockets—the V2s. For the first time, the Americans saw the famous 'super-weapon' for themselves.

Welborn immediately sent a radio message to the commander of the Third Division. He also informed his Intelligence Officer, Colonel Castille, who hurried to the place. Cautiously the American officers entered the tunnel and found the huge underground installations. They soon realized that this was the very heart of the V2 programme, the so-called 'Mittelwerke'.

'It was like being in a magician's cave', Castille later described the vast, subterranean munitions factory. Bright and gleaming, 'like the Lincoln Tunnel in New York', it was an endless series of machine shops and laboratories, carved out of the rock. And beneath the vaulted roof of a vast assembly-shop, the Americans found rows of the great rockets.

It was all undamaged. It looked as though the screw-spanners and measuring instruments, not to mention the production-lines carrying the half-finished rockets, had been abandoned only a few hours before. Indeed, 'Mittelwerke' had only ceased producing shortly before the Americans arrived.

But the top German rocket experts—Professor Wernher von Braun and his colleagues—had vanished from the Nordhausen district.

In January 1945 they had moved from the rocket experimental establishment at Peenemünde on the Baltic, where the V2s had been produced, to the town of Bleicherode in the district of Nordhausen, for the Red Army was then only sixty miles from Peenemünde. Bleicherode-Ost became their new headquarters.

Here they impatiently awaited the end of the war and the arrival of the American Army.

Before this happened, the SS took over. Four hundred of the most important men working on the German V-weapon project were forcibly moved to the Allgäu Alps.

Castille knew nothing of all this. He only knew that he had found a unique munitions plant intact. On his orders the military police sealed off the whole area.

Two days later Major I. P. Hamille of the technical Special Branch arrived there from General Patton's headquarters, with jeeps filled with experts. He had been waiting impatiently for this. But now that he saw the vast underground factory, his rage was such that he nearly blew up. And with good reason.

His orders were explicit. He was to secure the entire installation intact. It was known in the United States that this particular booty was worth millions of dollars.

But later instructions had cancelled his original ones. And now his hands were tied. 'The orders I received', Hamille later reported, 'were that Nordhausen was part of the Russian Zone and that all documents and equipment were to be left for the Soviets. This order came from very high up.'

General Eisenhower had signed an order to the effect that 'All factories, installations, works, research institutes, laboratories, patents, plans, drawings and inventions must be placed, intact and in good condition, at the disposal of the Allied representatives'.

Hamille knew what this meant. This new order was one of the results of the Yalta Conference. In February 1945, Stalin had asked Roosevelt and Churchill for 80 per cent of German industry as reparations. There was no acceptance in writing of Stalin's claims, but he nevertheless regarded this as a firm agreement.

In the final weeks of the war there were disagreements between the Allies. The Russians sent the Western Allies unfriendly notes and exerted maximum pressure to obtain the largest possible area of Germany. The Americans, counting on Russia's help against Japan, were anxious to avoid a serious breach with Stalin.

As a result of all this there could be no question of dismantling the rocket installations. All Major Hamille could do, with certain high-ranking officers of the U.S. Army turning a blind eye, was to take matters into his own hands.

He left everything as it was in the workshops, but hurriedly removed the hundred almost completed V2 rockets and a number of valuable documents from the underground arsenal. He ordered a freight-train, consisting of numerous tank wagons containing rocket-fuel, sent off to Antwerp under very close guard, for shipment to the United States.

What Major Hamille now sent to America formed the basis of the U.S. Army's rocket range at Huntsville, where Wernher von Braun subsequently worked.

In June 1945, another group of American Intelligence Officers arrived at Nordhausen from Garmisch. They had acquired some vital information from prisoners formerly at Peenemünde. They secured the secret plans and designs for future improvements to the V2 from a hiding-place in a salt-mine, where they also found five boxes filled with plans drawn up by Lieutenant-General Dr Dornberger, the Commandant of Peenemünde. For the German scientists at the Baltic rocket research establishment had been working on larger rockets than the V2. Among these was the A-9/A-10 project, a long-range rocket with which to bomb New York from a distance of two and a half thousand miles. Its eventual use as a carrier rocket for satellites was also envisaged.

'With our large rocket engines and using multi-stage rockets, we would be able to build space-ships which could circle the earth, like moons, at an altitude of three thousand miles and a speed of 15,000 m.p.h.,' Dr Dornberger explained, years before the first Sputnik.

The American Intelligence Officers only stayed for twenty-four hours. They had just time to evacuate the remaining scientists and their families before they abandoned Nordhausen to the Russians.

The next man to arrive and stare incredulously down the tunnel at Niedersachswerfen, a few days after the Americans had evacuated Thuringia, was Major Hamille's opposite number, the Soviet 'Special Branch' officer, Vladimir Shabinsky.

In 1947, after his escape to the West, this Russian made the following statement: 'I was at that time a Lieutenant-Colonel in the Red Army and was working in Berlin for a Special Branch of the Soviet Government, which was concerned with seizing factories, manufactured goods, raw materials, cattle, agricultural machinery, manures, crops, laboratories, libraries, museums, scientific documents and engineers and scientists from all over Europe. This branch was formed in 1944 and Georgi Malenkov was its head.'

The first detailed inspection of the V2 factory by a Soviet special commission took place next day. The installations, the Commission established, had two parallel main tunnels, each about three-quarters of a mile long. Thirty-six smaller tunnels radiated from and linked the main ones. A series of galleries ran to three or four stories. In one of the main tunnels the production of V1s was carried out, in the other V2s, with a monthly output of six hundred rockets.

Shabinsky counted 'over 1,000 machine tools for the production of rockets. The storage space was filled with rocket spare parts, with extra-hard steel, copper plate and the most intricate remote control equipment.' As Dr Dornberger has said, they found among the machine tools at 'Mittelwerke' many new types.

At first the Russians could not believe that it had all been left intact for them. A Soviet colonel laughed aloud, and according to Shabinsky remarked: 'The Americans have given us all this! In ten years they'll regret it! Imagine—our rockets firing across the ocean!'

Almost ten years later to the day, this prophetic utterance, made in what was then the most advanced rocket installation in the world, was fulfilled. In 1955, Soviet scientists attending the Astronautical Congress at Copenhagen announced that during the projected Geophysical Year the Soviet Union would put satellites into orbit around the earth.

While taking over 'Mittelwerke', Soviet military police cordoned off the whole area. Combing through the tunnel installations and the deserted underground vaults, the Soviets seized mountains of papers, all stamped 'Top Secret'.

A few days later, NKVD Major Yegorov, in charge of the operation, personally escorted the transport of the documents from Nordhausen to Berlin, under close guard.

At Marshal Zhukov's headquarters, he handed it all over to Colonel Shostok. Even a cursory inspection revealed that one of the boxes contained technical scientific information of the greatest importance, the complete blueprints for the future developments of the V2, and the complete plans for putting satellites into space. The full significance of these documents falling into Soviet hands was not then realized in the West.

'The Russians have made use of our experience in the building of long-range rockets and have taken over all our Peenemünde ideas', Dr Dornberger declared, when he went to work for the Americans. 'They adopted our plans for the conquest of space, worked out by us in 1942. Satellites are only the first stage.'

This 'space plan', originally worked out by Dornberger, von Braun and their colleagues, consisted of a ten-point programme for rockets and for space travel.

(1) Unmanned single-stage rockets, long-range, type V2.
(2) Unmanned rocket-propelled stratospheric projectiles, long-range.

(3) Manned projectiles, very long-range.
(4) Unmanned multi-stage rockets.
(5) Manned stratospheric projectiles.
(6) Unmanned satellites.
(7) Manned carrier rockets for putting satellites into orbit.
(8) Manned satellites.
(9) Unmanned space-stations.
(10) Manned space-stations.

The plans which then fell into Russian hands made one fact abundantly clear. The first nation to build artificial satellites and a space-station, would rule the world.

Only after the spectacular launching of the Sputnik in the autumn of 1957 did thirty-six scientists of the American Rand Corporation (which in the United States acts as a sort of civilian General Staff) come to the bitter conclusion that: 'The Soviets have succeeded brilliantly in their long-term planning and in their exploitation of other people's work. Furthermore, they are extremely competent scientists and it is easy to imagine the enthusiasm with which they took over the Peenemünde plan and adapted it for their own purposes. It is not known to what extent they have actually followed the Peenemünde plan, but we do know that they have already carried out points (1), (4) and (6), and have gone a long way towards achieving the others.'

When Shabinsky returned from Nordhausen to Berlin, he took part in an army celebration dinner. Despite the security measures, a certain amount had filtered through about the colossal haul at Nordhausen. 'We drank to the taking over of the V2 factory. And a Lieutenant Colonel named Tarakanov shouted: "What fools these Americans are!" '

Since July a secret department of the Red Army, installed in the outskirts of ruined Berlin, had been engaged upon a feverish search. After the discoveries at 'Mittelwerke' the Soviets had concentrated on getting hold of as much data on rocket development as possible, together with all the scientific brains in Germany, all plans and projects, all equipment and special machinery.

The names of manufacturers were collected and listed from the documents of the firms supplying materials, the names of scientists and technicians from plans, and from pay-sheets the particulars of former employees in the V-weapon factories. Colonel Shostok had a file containing the names of all these people whom the Soviets wished to get hold of.

The hunt was relentless. Many more experts were rounded up than was at first hoped.

When the American troops evacuated Thuringia the majority of rocket specialists from Nordhausen and other Thuringian V-weapon installations went with them to the West. A group of some eighty men was moved by the U.S. Army to Witzenhausen. Having got hold of Wernher von Braun and some one hundred and thirty of his colleagues without any difficulty, the Americans apparently lost interest. Many of the research scientists and engineers who worked at Peenemünde, 'Mittelwerke' and the other establishments, were soon allowed to leave the places to which they had been moved by the Americans. Some wished to go home, and therefore crossed over into the Russian Zone.

Among those who went back from Witzenhausen to Russian-occupied Germany was Helmut Gröttrup, the expert on rocket guidance, who had been working at Peenemünde since 1939. No sooner had he reached Soviet territory than he was put under close arrest, as was his wife, Irmgard. He was pressed to accept a very special assignment. He was to start V2 production once again, for the Russians now, with a full team of scientists and technicians.

Since many of the leading specialists had gone to America, Gröttrup had to replace them with new men. Slowly, using as bait the large sums of money placed at his disposal, he built up his team, which included not only former colleagues from the V-weapon project at Peenemünde, 'Mittelwerke' and the factories, but also experts from the universities and institutes, including those in Western Germany. The Soviets offered every inducement to attract the 'brains behind the rockets'. Gröttrup and his staff were well treated at Nordhausen, and comfortable accommodation assigned to them. In addition, there were perquisites of all kinds, otherwise unobtainable in Germany so soon after the end of the war.

Gröttrup set to work to bring 'Mittelwerke' (now called 'Zentralwerke') back to its wartime efficiency with a monthly output of six hundred V2 rockets. It employed some five thousand men, the best available experts from the German Physico-Technical Institute, from the Arado Works, from Krupp's and from the German Institute of Aviation Research. Many brilliant men who had worked for years in this field were once again employed here.

On Soviet orders, the V2 was further developed, and new projects undertaken. For a whole year, from October 1945 to October 1946, all went smoothly. Then the Soviets went on to their next carefully calculated move, the dismantling of 'Zentralwerke', and the transportation of all the staff to the Soviet Union.

With Gröttrup now 'Director-General', the Russian Military Police escorted two hundred specialists from the rocket factory to Russia. Long railway trains filled with machinery, laboratory equipment, testing and measuring apparatus, complete wind-tunnel installations and experimental equipment for the testing of rocket engines rolled eastwards. Nothing needed for the 'Soviet' rocket project was left behind. And in closely guarded special transports, locked and sealed, went the captured plans, technical calculations, constructional drawings, models and designs, among them the complete file of secret documents from the safe at the Air Ministry in Berlin, captured intact.

Once behind the Iron Curtain the Russians distributed their gigantic booty of captured manpower and machinery throughout the country.

In small groups, the Germans went sent to places whose names they had never heard of—to Nitishi and Kimri, Zagorsk and Podberezhye, Sovrino and Obiralovka.

The Russians only assembled large numbers of men in two places, in two 'Specialist Collectives', as they were called. On Gorodomlya Island, in a lake north of Moscow, all the propulsion experts were brought together. The specialists in rocket-guidance and recording equipment were installed in the village of Monino, near Moscow, where a reproduction of the Zeiss Works at Jena was already in existence.

Whether or not the Soviets would reach their ambitious target depended largely on the results achieved by these two 'collectives'. They were the backbone of the vast programme upon which the USSR now embarked. For in 1946 the Russians neither possessed liquid fuel rockets nor understood how to control them. This was up to the Germans.

At Monino, the Russians had at their disposal three experts on the highly complicated problem of remote control: Dr Eitzenberger, Dr Buschbeck and Dr Faulstich. In the person of Buschbeck and Eitzenberger the Russians enjoyed the benefit of the sum total of German experience regarding radio-controlled recording gear and remote control.

For years a Jena physicist, Professor Abraham Esau, had experimented successfully with very-high-frequency apparatus and towards the end of the war the Germans led the world in this field. Radio-controlled recording and measuring techniques, in an advanced stage in the West, were still in their infancy in the Soviet Union.

The mastery of such an unusually complicated technique as the guiding by remote control of space bodies or large rockets to a small target area, or the guiding of a satellite in orbit round the earth, was something which the USSR had not even contemplated.

At the Gorodomlya 'collective', Gröttrup was in charge of the propulsion section. In the rocket centre on the island special departments for rocket fuels, chemistry, ballistics and aerodynamics were set up. Among Gröttrup's distinguished colleagues were the engineers and constructors Dr Albring, Dr Rösch and Dr Umpfenbach. The chemist Siegmund, who specialized in the highly important hydrogen-super-oxide dissolvent for the V2's pump engines, was also a member of the group. Special sections contained the pump construction technicians and the testing personnel.

In offices and construction departments, all carefully segregated from one another, work went on with the captured plans, drawings and models. The Russians were trying, first of all, to get a precise overall picture, for they were mere beginners. Large numbers of Russian engineers, scientists and military experts surrounded the Germans at Gorodomlya and Monino. The Russians thirsted for knowledge. They asked endless questions and, as soon became obvious, they were men of exceptional ability. They kept urging the Germans to greater speed. Theories, calculations and plans were not enough. The production of rockets must be started at once.

In the newly built testing-rooms work began, and after a year of intensive effort on the part of the Germans, the long, slim bodies of the new V-rockets left their launching-pads and shot up into the Russian sky.

Shortly before this, the same impressive drama had been played out on the other side of the world. In the United States, the 'Peenemünde Group', working under General Donald L. Putt as part of 'Operation Paperclip', had assembled one of the shining silver rockets salvaged the previous year from 'Mittelwerke'.

But the V2 project in America was carried out in vastly different circumstances, and for quite a different purpose. Rockets were not something completely unknown to the Americans. The first tests took place on the White Sands Proving Grounds, where the American physicist, Robert Hutchins Goddard, had carried out his series of experiments with liquid-fuel rockets ten years before. As early as 1935, these had risen to a height of six thousand feet and attained a speed of five hundred miles per hour. And when the V2 arrived at White Sands in May 1946, the American research rocket, type Wac-Corporal, was already nearing completion. On 26th September of this same year, this rocket reached a height of over forty miles.

Now the press saw a V2 being tested and learned how far ahead German rocket technique was of American. 'Height of sixty-six miles reached,' the loud-speakers announced. 'Wonderful, these German birds!' The Americans did not hide their admiration. These big rockets, it was agreed, would be perfect for research in the stratosphere. The V2s would be used for scientific purposes, to carry recording instruments into space, but for nothing else.

The Peenemünde V2 represented the first stage in the conquest of space. It was only a short step from this to the intercontinental rocket. Plans for further development were available, and it only remained to put them into practice. This, however, did not interest the responsible authorities in America, even though Wernher von Braun in a report drew attention most forcibly to the immediate importance of a multi-stage rocket as a carrier for an 'artificial moon'. He was also responsible for the preliminary work on the big stage-rockets A-9/A-10. Braun's project was put away in the secret safe. No money was available for its construction.

Only once after 1945 did developments in the United States appear to be advancing towards a satellite project. In December 1948, the Defence Secretary, James V. Forrestal, told Congress about a futuristic 'Satellite Vehicle Program'. This necessitated concentrated research in one particular field and Forrestal outlined the already realistic possibility of putting artificial satellites in orbit round the earth by means of multi-stage rockets. In conditions of the strictest secrecy the American aviation industry, represented by Douglas North American Aerojet and Martin, worked out the plans for the Forrestal programme. These included the design of large stage-rockets, actually larger than those in the later satellite projects 'MOUSE' and 'Vanguard'.

Congress refused to consider the programme. They regarded the 'Forrestal project' as utopian and unpractical. Its originator died tragically soon afterwards. Forrestal threw himself out of a seventeenth-storey apartment window. His cry: 'The Russians are coming!' were the last words he spoke.

Had Forrestal made a brilliant guess about what was going on behind the Iron Curtain, or had he secret information? We do not know the answer to this question. We only know that his warning words went unheeded.

While the United States marked time and despite the enormous possibilities open to them did nothing, Russia made the most of the loot which had fallen into her hands. The decision had already been taken in the USSR. Ten years later the Soviets were to produce the first satellite. The 'Sputnik' was to be an unparalleled piece of propaganda for 'progressive Socialist co-operative development'.

Above the entrance to a giant block of flats in Moscow, the words, 'Ministry for Machine Construction' were inscribed. Behind this innocuous name-plate, in this one Ministry, the Soviet Union concentrated all its work of research and development, testing and perfecting in the field of rockets and long-range missiles. The Red General Staff, who, according to Swiss sources, have at their disposal over one-third of the entire Soviet gold and dollar reserves, valued at fourteen thousand million dollars, used this sum for the project. For the final objective of all Soviet endeavours was, and remains, world revolution. This is a question of power. Nothing could give them more power than rockets capable of being fired at any target anywhere in the world.

A mere handful of experts, a small group consisting of members of the Academy of Sciences and staff officers, directed the vast rocket development project which started in Russia immediately after 1945. Not a word of this filtered through the Iron Curtain to the outside world. Not even the names of the men responsible were disclosed.

At sealed experimental establishments rapidly set up by the Red Army on the Caspian Sea and in the far north, thousands of Russians were trained by the deported specialists. German experts instructed the Russians in how to build the V2, which was already being mass-produced, and how it should be fuelled and launched. The Russians were taught how to use the recording and measuring instruments. On Soviet orders, Russian engineers and technical officers of the Red Army were trained. The old game was played once again, the game which had worked so well during the NEP period and the first Five Year Plan, when Western engineers crammed the Russians with the principles of machinery, motor-car and tractor construction. Under German instructors, the first generation of Russian rocket experts was trained within a few years.

But the Russians wanted more. Their ambition was to go ever further along the lines indicated by the captured plans and blueprints. Their aim was to possess a new long-range weapon which could be directed at any point on the earth's surface, to possess rockets which could carry a bomb-load of several tons towards a target many thousands of miles away. This was the perfect way to compensate for their lack of a modern air force and of a modern long-range bomber.

From the beginning, the Soviets concentrated on the greatest possible range. The V2 with its range of less than two hundred miles was only a beginning.

Gröttrup accordingly received instructions to treble the performance of the V2. The time allotted was unusually short, for the Russians were in a hurry. The 'R-10' appeared on the Germans' drawing-boards at Gorodomlya. In shape and form it resembled the V2. But the Russians had already made demands in which their pronounced tendency towards simplification and their typical regard for fundamentals were apparent. They wanted a new power unit, bigger than that of the V2, and a new guidance system.

The Germans soon realized that apart from Gorodomlya and Podlipki, where their deported compatriots were working in another rocket collective, there was feverish activity going on in other places as well. And eventually the German scientists and engineers learned the truth. The Russians knew about the 'Sänger project', a secret plan for a rocket-propelled aircraft, designed in detail by the research scientists Eugen and Irene Sänger. In two hours this rocket-propelled aircraft could circle the earth in undulating orbit, penetrating the thinnest layers of the atmosphere.

A Soviet Lieutenant Colonel Grigory Tokayev, who later fled to the West, described the reaction of the Kremlin to the discovery of the 'Sänger project'. Stalin, when he was told about it, immediately ordered a secret conference. Molotov, Malenkov, Berya, Vosnessensky, Voroshilov, Stalin's son Vassily, and Colonel Serov were present to hear Tokayev's report on the project.

'If we can build this "Sänger-aircraft" we shall rule the world', Stalin declared. He ordered that every effort be made to track down Dr Sänger and bring him to Russia. Two days later, Tokayev, Serov and Stalin's son Vassily were in Berlin to start the search. They were disappointed to learn that Dr Sänger was safely out of reach, working with French colleagues in Paris.

The 'Sänger project' came to nothing, so the 'R' programme was accelerated. In spite of the very short time allotted, 'R-10' was finished on schedule. A range of 570 miles had been reached, with a target deviation of only one in a thousand—that is to say, at 570 miles a deviation of just over half a mile.

The 'R-10' was a success. But the Soviets knew that there was more to be got out of these Germans. And fresh instructions were already lying on Gröttrup's desk at Gorodomlya. A rocket was to be produced which would carry an effective load of one ton to a target fifteen hundred miles away.

This rocket would have to travel eight times as far as the V2. Would it be possible to construct such a 'super V2'?

On receipt of these instructions, Gröttrup spent even more time than usual with his colleagues. From the first discussions to the designs, drawings and endless calculations, the new project began to take shape remarkably quickly. The prototype 'R-12' was designed and built in record time in 1948 and judging by the tests it promised to be another resounding success.

The Russians attended all the conferences and left no one in doubt as to their aims in connection with the development of 'R-12'. They wanted large power units and above all a simpler, and therefore tougher and more effective, construction. They stuck to the same principle of simplification as with the MiGs. When the Germans built the first Soviet jet-fighters, the Russians ruthlessly eliminated everything which they considered super-fluous, with the result that the MiG-15, when it was sent up over Korea, flew faster and at higher altitudes than the more technically perfect American machines. For these were almost 'flying laboratories', and with their highly complicated instruments and special fittings weighed almost twice as much as the Red fighters.

It was the Russian demands which produced the necessary impetus for that revolutionary change in rocket design that led to the Sputniks and Luniks and soon put the Soviet Union so far ahead. The classic rocket, as embodied in the V2, was basically altered to suit Russian specifications.

What was the secret behind this new design? No super-fuel capable of producing this hitherto inconceivable thrust then existed, and this was known in the West. The Soviet rockets also fired on the familiar liquid fuel. The new project depended on a process worked out with all the simplicity of genius.

In all constructions on the V2 principle, there was a limit of increase in the amount of fuel—for with a weight ratio of 66 per cent fuel, a 34 per cent 'casing' had to be lifted. The rocket worked out by the Germans in the Soviet Union enabled an increase in the fuel ratio by nearly 100 per cent. The ratio of contents to 'casing' was now 92 to 8.

In such a rocket, consisting almost entirely of fuel, the thrust would be considerably increased, and it would be capable of carrying the heaviest warhead. Since 1957, the Soviets have shown the world that while the Sputnik I weighed only 83·6 kg., the Sputnik III had a weight of 1,327 kilograms, and the 'Space Ship' launched on 15th May 1960 carried, in a cabin weighing 2·5 tons, an effective load of 1·5 tons, consisting of a dummy and numerous measuring and recording instruments.

In 1949 the order went out from the Ministry in Moscow, to which the designs and calculations for the 'rocketry revolution' were submitted, to build the first rocket in accordance with this new principle. The theory was to be tried out in practice.

All effort was now concentrated on this one point. Almost overnight research teams were moved to Gorodomlya, and the German experts who had been working at Podlipki arrived at the large rocket centre on the island. The Russians gave them their orders. A rocket was to be constructed immediately, capable of covering a distance of 1,875 miles and carrying a 3-ton warhead to hit a small target.

This job was carried out by the Germans in just one year.

Brilliant modifications reduced the weight of the rocket itself to a minimum. The whole body was reduced to one big fuel tank. In place of a solid casing, there was a thin covering of lead. The pressure-pumped fuel gave the body of the rocket the necessary stability. The heavy pumps of the V2 were dispensed with, and the fuel was pumped from the tank by a turbine powered by hot gases from the rocket combustion-chamber. Even the guiding fins were done away with, for the rocket combustion-chamber itself took over the guidance. This was suspended and rotatable.

By 1950 the new type was completed. The Soviet Union possessed the first super-rocket.

As soon as the 'R-14' was ready for firing, the Germans were taken off the work. They were not present at the launching. An order from on high forbade them from any further activity in rocketry. They were no longer allowed to visit their former places of work. For the Soviets now knew enough. They had learned all they needed to build artificial satellites and intercontinental rockets. Gröttrup's colleagues were put into a sort of 'quarantine'. Their brains must be numbed, they must forget. They were sent to Sukhumi, in Transcaucasia on the Caspian Sea. There they were left to wait interminably, sitting about with nothing to do. They hardly noticed as the months lengthened into one, two and finally three years. Again and again they were fobbed off with promises: they would go home soon, very soon. The 'progressive' Soviet Union kept their Western slaves for long enough to ensure that all direct contact with the results of their own researches was lost.

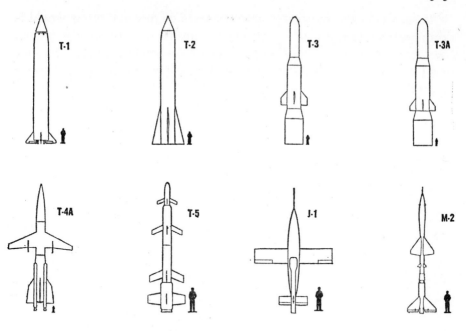

The 'secret' of the Soviet rockets

T-1 (M-101) (copy) First USSR rocket after 1945, almost exact replica of the V2.
Developed by the Gröttrup group in Gorodomlya. Steering
system of the V2.

T-2 (M-103) (copy) Two-part rocket following the German A-10 project in
Peenemünde (3,000 km. range). This rocket, in altered form,
became the second part of the rocket components of the 'Sputniks'
and the 'Mechta', forerunners of the 'Lunik'.

T-3 (M-104) (further development of the copy) Long-range rocket, 8,000 km.
range, three-part ballistic missile, carburetted–hydrogen–oxygen
drive. 2nd and 3rd stages essentially the same as T-1 and T-2.

T-3A (further developments of the copy) A further development of the T-3, with
even stronger thrust in first stage. 10,000 km. range. Defence
against the T-3A already solved by West. The satellite rockets
CH-9 and CH-10 for the 'Sputniks' and 'Lunik' came from the
T-3A.

T-4A (copy) An attempt by the Soviets to realize the Sänger-project (long-
range rocket bomber) from captured German plans and calculations.

T-5 (copy) Model from the German 'Rhine Herald'. Nuclear warhead, as with
American atomic artillery.

J-1 (copy) Guided missile for middle distances (after V1).

M-2 (copy) Two-part solid-fuel rocket, ground-air guided missile (after the
German 'Rhine Maiden').

The Germans only learned of their journey homewards a few hours before they were to leave. In late 1954 they were suddenly moved. Early in 1955 the rocket specialists were finally released by Moscow. It was from these men, who dared not say much, that the Western news agencies first learned how far the Russians had progressed in the field of guided missiles.

The Gröttrup group had just left Gorodomlya, when the Soviets set about a decisive reorganization. An Austrian, Dr Hans Hoch, became Gröttrup's successor as head of the collective. Work was now concentrated on complicated guidance techniques, which presented the Soviets with great problems, and on control while in flight.

Dr Hoch did much pioneer work for the Russians in this field. He developed an electronic computer with which to check every position of a rocket during flight, to a fraction of a second.

In February 1951, the Russians began assembling in Moscow all specialists on remote control. From the various collectives, from Kuibyshev, Monino, Gorodomlya, a commission of German experts was selected and brought to the capital at the request of the Ministry of Defence. Their new place of work was a settlement on the outskirts of the city, surrounded by barbed wire and closely guarded.

In charge of this project was a son of Berya, the much-feared Chief of the Soviet Secret Police. The foreign specialists were directly under the Soviet government, a fact of which they only learned in a roundabout way. In charge was the Defence Minister, Ustinov. Dr Hoch and his highly qualified staff were also summoned to Moscow. He learned that his successor at Gorodomlya was already installed. The Russians had appointed Waldemar Wolff as the new head of the collective. Dr Wolff was formerly the leading ballistics expert at Krupp's.

In record time the Russians assembled an *élite* of scientists and engineers to solve the problems of remote control and rocket guidance, which the Russians had not yet mastered. This problem was even more urgent than before. Work would go on for twelve hours or more a day. Berya's son and the Minister, Ustinov, were both about, and the pressure was relentless.

Under this pressure, constantly worried by a very tight time schedule and the threat of being accused of sabotage, they finally succeeded in completing an achievement which was to astonish the West, the remote control of Sputniks and Luniks. Dr Faulstich, with a staff of experts on radio recording equipment, worked out the problems of rocket guidance.

Dr Eitzenberger and Dr Buschbeck, the 'big guns' of this technique, were brought to Moscow and also put to work under great pressure. On Russian orders, they constructed a very small television transmitter which could be built into the warhead of the missile. This apparatus transmitted pictures continuously to the ground station. From there, the operator, following the flight of the rocket on the screen, could radio instructions to the missile, guiding it over enormous distances to the target, as surely as though there were a pilot on board.

The idea behind this had originated in England. Before D-day, the RAF had guided pilotless bombers from the south coast of England to the German V1 launching-sites in Northern France, with the help of the cathode-ray tube.

The Eitzenberger group also evolved detectors, sensitive to light, for rockets which were to be used against floating targets. These electronic eyes reacted to the refractions of light produced by the wake of a fast-moving ship. A ship could not pull away from an attack by these 'seeing-eye' rockets, which were automatically guided to the most vulnerable part of the vessel, the rudder and screw installations in the stern.

For the production of this and other intricate and highly complicated detector and remote-control equipment, the Russians, who had been so far behind in this field, used the Zeiss factory from Jena, now installed at Monino, and the transplanted Siemens and Schuckert works. The Askania Works, from West Berlin, a leading firm in the manufacture of precision instruments, also helped to make good any Russian deficiencies, as legal proceedings later revealed.

In a vast, comprehensive programme, centrally controlled from the 'Top Secret Ministry', the work of numerous Russian research and experimental establishments was co-ordinated by Moscow with that of the specialist collectives. For the solving of individual problems, there were also, according to scientists who fled to the West, various electronic institutes installed in the technical colleges in the Russian Zone of Germany.

For four years, which seemed an eternity, the Germans worked in Moscow. Then they too were suddenly 'disposed of'. The Russians used the same unpleasant technique as they had employed previously with the propulsion and rocket experts. The long period of 'quarantine' now began for the men who had given of their best, year after year, for 'Socialist development'.

In the summer of 1955 the Germans arrived in the Crimea, whence their compatriots had been finally released only a few months before.

That same year of 1955, in which the work of the German remote-control experts was completed, and rocket specialists were for the first time among those returning home from Russia, American radar picked up rocket launchings in the USSR. The rockets covered distances of nine hundred miles.

At that time the United States had no official satellite programme. It is true that the Americans had been filling their magazines and illustrated papers with imaginative stories about rockets and satellites, flights to the moon and manned space-stations. It is also true that, while the Soviet Union

was shrouded in silence, the projects of well-known scientists and experts
were publicized in the United States, among others Professor Singer's
'MOUSE' project for satellites, and Wernher von Braun's comprehensive programme for space travel, which already included an expedition to Mars,
worked out to the last detail. So there was a general impression that the
Americans already had one foot in space. In fact, nothing had been done,
not even preliminary development work. No money had been forthcoming
for the 'Peenemünde people' who had come back with the U.S. Army to
carry out any of the numerous rocket projects which they submitted to the
Pentagon. The army was actually prohibited, on the orders of Defence
Secretary Wilson, from producing rockets with a range of more than two
hundred miles. Until the International Geophysical Year of 1957, for which
the Soviets had announced the launching of their satellites two years before,
the USSR had the field to itself.

The Americans, however, had a surprising success in 1958 with their
'Explorers' and 'Vanguards', which followed closely on the heels of the
Sputniks. At the first attempt the discovery of the 'Van Allen Radiation
Belt' was made. These satellites, built so very rapidly, showed what the
Americans, thanks to their superior technique and industry, were capable of
doing, so long as they concentrated on a specific target. Such concentration
of effort would decide how soon America could catch up with the Soviets.
Meanwhile it was thanks to their German and Austrian scientist-prisoners
that the Russians were the first to send a rocket to the moon and the first
to build a manned space-ship.

The Soviets improved and perfected principles of construction taken over
from the West. The basic design of the rockets did not differ much from
those of German or American origin. The Russians neither discovered a
'wonder' fuel nor was the discharge velocity of the gases released unusually
high. Even using propulsion units with a short combustion time, they never
exceeded a velocity of 3,000 metres per second. This fact must not be forgotten when speaking of the fabulous 'wonder rockets' of the Soviet Union.

Sputniks and Luniks are certainly notable technical achievements, in that
they show the capacity of a totalitarian régime to concentrate all its brain-
power and material resources (not to mention all available inventions and
advances from abroad and, of course, foreign experts) on a limited number
of specialized projects. It was exactly as Alexis de Tocqueville had pre-
dicted, a century before, when he wrote: 'I would not deny that a centralized public administration would be in a position to achieve great things,
at a given time and in a specific direction.'

The results of this total concentration of resources, man-power and material, in spite of the impression it managed to produce, should not be
allowed to conceal one vital fact. The results achieved do not represent any
genuine progress either in science or in industrial technique.

'We are not interested in empty shells!' Dr Leonid Sedov, head of the Astronautical Commission of the Soviet Academy of Sciences told American rocket engineers, referring scornfully to the mere 14 kilograms of the Explorer I. The Americans were polite enough not to mention the fact that all the instruments carried by the Sputnik were evolved in the West. And, in fact, the Americans' small Explorer I was responsible, at its first attempt, for the first scientific discovery of the International Geophysical Year. The Explorer I went into orbit around the earth and found the Van Allen Radiation Belt. The Soviet satellites were able to give out radio signals for a longer period—from Sputnik III onwards (for Sputnik II gave no signals after seven days)—only when copies of the solar batteries invented in America had been built into them!

ON 26TH APRIL 1956, the main lecture hall at Harwell, the British atomic research establishment, was packed to capacity. A lecture had been announced which caused surprise and considerable interest among the British scientists. They were to be addressed by a Russian colleague. The feeling of anticipation was increased by the fact that this coincided with the Khrushchev and Bulganin state visit.

Professor Igor Kurchatov, member of the Soviet Academy of Sciences, referred, to the astonishment of the British scientists, to a subject which in the West counted as the most secret project in the entire field of nuclear physics, the 'harnessing of the hydrogen-bomb' for peaceful purposes. The production of energy by nuclear fusion, would, if successful, be a technical achievement of epoch-making importance, giving mankind an inexhaustible source of power. For the basic raw material required, heavy water, is available in almost unlimited quantities.

The Englishmen listened intently to the words of Professor Kurchatov, which an interpreter translated, sentence by sentence. As if he were referring to the most normal thing in the world, Kurchatov spoke of the 'possibility of producing a thermo-nuclear reaction in a discharge of gases', and described the method by which, without recourse to atom-bombs, the temperatures of millions of degrees required for a nuclear fusion reaction could be achieved. When Kurchatov had finished his lecture, the walls of Harwell reverberated to an unprecedented storm of applause.

A careful study of the stenographer's text of this lecture reveals that Professor Kurchatov did not suggest anything new. He had described experiments in the most advanced field of nuclear research, then known only to a very few specialists in Britain and America and classified top secret.

Nevertheless, the Russian's lecture caused a sensation, and received much publicity. An article in the magazine *Discovery* referred to Kurchatov's address at the atomic research establishment as 'a most unusual and unexpected occasion'.

What happened at Harwell was soon repeated elsewhere and in other contexts. Since then there have been frequent articles in the press and in technical journals expressing astonishment and wonder at the knowledge and ability of the Soviet scientists and technicians. Perhaps because Russian professors had begun to attend scientific congresses, or perhaps because Soviet delegations had been keeping an eye on the leading European and American industries, it was becoming apparent that Russia possessed all the necessary information about what was being done in the West.

'The Soviet delegations which come to the United States are unusually well informed', an American newspaper has said. 'Russian technicians concentrate on observing specialized processes, and they make no bones about it. They manage to visit even the most secret installations.'

And Walter R. Hibbard, Jr., of the American Institute of Mining and Petroleum Engineers and Metallurgists stated, with astonishment: 'Their detailed knowledge of American technical literature is phenomenal.'

This knowledge on the part of the Russians occasionally leads to strange results. At the Geneva Conference in the autumn of 1958, when permission was suddenly and sensationally given by Washington to reveal the existence of new top secret equipment at the conference, American scientists working on similar problems at leading nuclear research institutes in California and New Mexico, Princeton and Chicago, made no attempt to disguise their astonishment.

They were seeing some of this apparatus and equipment from their own country for the first time. The fact did not escape shrewd observers that the Russian delegates, in contrast to their American colleagues, did not appear to be looking at something completely new. And the very pertinent questions which they put in connection with the apparatus made one fact clear. This 'top secret' equipment from the United States was not unknown to them.

In the same year Dr Dennis Carnay, head of United Steel's Duquesne Works, on his return from a scientific trip to the USSR, reported an almost incredible fact. Students at the Moscow Steel Institute 'have at their disposal the results of original American research which have not been even mentioned in technical journals in the United States'.

How does it come about that the Soviets possess such detailed knowledge? How could they be so promptly and accurately informed of the latest results of Western research?

The answer is to be found in a plan, first discussed in England by the Royal Society and which the Soviets got hold of and put into practice.

A person passing by the four-storied building with the sign *Institut Nauchnoi Informatsii* (Institute of Scientific Information) on the outskirts of Moscow would scarcely guess that a gigantic machine is operating day and night within these walls. The building houses a unique apparatus, the only one of its kind in the world, the most modern 'super brain', which supplies complete information in all branches of science and technology.

No comparable institute in any other country can boast such a volume of correspondence. Each day some five hundred communications arrive, 'printed matter' from the United States and from India, from Japan and from England, publications from ninety-five countries in sixty-five different languages. The total in 1956 was nine thousand foreign technical journals. Since then the number has increased.

Most come by express post, many by air-mail. The Academy of Sciences, of which the Institute is a subsidiary establishment, gladly pays the postage. It is worth it . . .

In 1697 Prince Golitsyn, a contemporary of the Tsar Peter the Great, bought all the knowledge available at that time, and returned to Russia with a library of six thousand volumes. Today the world, and particularly the West, sends its intelligence direct to the Soviets by express post and air-mail for the negligible payment of subscription plus postage.

Like a giant radar system, the Institute maintains contact with all the universities, research establishments, laboratories and development centres throughout the world. Thus the 'intelligentsia', the scientists and engineers, are informed immediately of all new developments anywhere in the world that affect their own field of study. They are, in fact, informed more quickly than their 'colleagues' in the countries in which the new developments originate.

The Soviets have perfected this brilliant method of collecting international intelligence by an amazing feat of organization. Every available means known to modern technology has been put to use in the Institute.

A staff of nearly fifty thousand scientists, engineers, translators and librarians work on the evaluation of the piles of technical material, fourteen thousand of these being employed full-time in the Institute. The contents of thousands of articles are summarized, the most important pictures, drawings and diagrams reproduced, and synopses—especially concerning work being done in non-English-speaking countries—are printed in Russian. Two hundred thousand reports were written in 1955. In the first half of 1956 the number was a hundred and eighty-four thousand. The extent of the collected material rises in almost geometrical progression from year to year.

Thus the most up-to-date information from all over the world finds its way to the universities and institutes of the Soviet Union. These reports are classified according to subject: astronomy and geology, biology and bio-chemistry, geography, geology and geophysics, mathematics, mechanical engineering, metallurgy and mechanics, physics, chemistry and electronics.

Every research establishment, every industrial laboratory is on the receiving end of a vast distribution network. From Moscow's *Institut Nauchnoi Informatsii* an endless stream of abstracts and digests flows into every corner of the Soviet Union.

The Moscow Institute has organized a further 'time-saver', for vital information: express information. Three hundred selected Western publications are given priority, and summaries of their contents distributed each week by express post.

A comparison between the Soviet geographical bibliography and the *Bibliographie Géographique Internationale* published at the same time in Paris, reveals how much more intensive and up-to-date Soviet information is, even on obscure subjects, than that available in the West. In Paris the 1955 edition appeared first in 1957, and consisted of seven hundred pages. Its Soviet counterpart of 1957 consisted of over four thousand pages, with larger format and smaller type.

It is the same story in the all-important field of chemistry. In the Soviet *Khimiya*, about six thousand five hundred technical publications are noted. In 1957, the number of foreign papers noted was a hundred thousand, covering sixteen thousand pages. The American magazine, *Chemical Abstracts*—on which the *Khimiya* was modelled—published only sixty thousand notices referring to five thousand three hundred publications, although the American publication also concerned itself with subjects only distantly related to chemistry, e.g. geology and biology.

In order to sort out, evaluate and distribute global intelligence in record time, the Russians have installed in the Moscow Institute of Scientic Information the most up-to-date model of the 'electronic brain'.

In one room the 'mechanical interpreters' operate electronic machines which produce translations. With the aid of magnetic or electronic 'repositories', which act as a mechanical memory, English texts in particular are rendered into Russian. Even grammatical rules are observed by the machine.

A series of very intricate 'evaluation machines' are used for industrial and administrative information. They operate with index cards, on which thousands of facts are stored. 'On demand' these robots produce the most accurate information dealing with a multitude of special requirements in industry and administration. They immediately provide the most up-to-date and practical information on the equipment needed for various installations or on the necessary instruments required for fitting up a laboratory.

But it is the so-called rapid selectors that form the nucleus of this magic and lightning-quick evaluation of the flood of knowledge that flows in from all over the world.

Set according to a carefully calculated formula, film-strips with microfilms of texts, diagrams, constructional drawings and similar documents are stored inside the machine. In a single selector spool holding two thousand three hundred feet of film, there are microfilms of seventy thousand book pages. With this selector, the contents of whole technical libraries can be consulted in the shortest time. The photo-electric cells inside the machine record a hundred and eighty microfilms a second, when run at maximum speed. In an hour they can 'scrutinize' five hundred thousand documents and correctly sort out the required texts or diagrams.

When the desired document has been found, a light goes on, and the machine automatically copies and ejects it.

A journalist, Anton Zischka, who inspected the 'super-brain' and the rapid-selectors in 1954, wrote: 'It has been left to the Soviet Academy of

Sciences to organize this comprehensive sorting system. The West, on the other hand, is not at all well-informed about Russian work and progress. Quite the contrary. . . . The result is, that while we do not know what appears in Soviet technical publications, Soviet scientists are accurately informed about all our achievements, and do not need to repeat any experiment which has already been described in Europe or America. This extra knowledge puts them in the stronger position.'

Where did all these super-machines come from?

The rapid selector dates from 1949. It was developed and built according to the design of Vannevar Bush, wartime head of the American Office of Scientific Research and Development. When the machine was shown in Washington scientists were very optimistic. Here was a way of storing scientific and technical data with the quickest possible method of sorting it out. But the United States did not try very hard to meet the requirements of its 'eggheads'. In the West the position is still much as Dr Vannevar Bush described it fifteen years ago: 'We have to go after our information with a horse and buggy.' The Soviets, on the other hand, have copied the rapid selectors and made the best possible use of them. And the whole world is astonished, the Western experts most of all, at Russian progress.

The translating machines also originated in the West. The idea of 'training' modern computers to translate into foreign languages was first developed by the British mathematician, Andrew D. Booth, in 1947. His idea was that the 'memory' of the computer should be able to produce a 'dictionary' as it produces mathematical symbols and calculations.

The American electronic brain 'IBM 701' which supplied the first translations from Russian into English. The text (above) reads: 'Refining raises quality of petroleum.'

It was tried out in the following year. The famous firm, International Business Machines (IBM), built for Booth and a group of American scientists and engineers a computer called 'IBM 701'.

In the IBM building in New York a small group of specialists watched the trial run of the translating machine. The presence of the press made the test sensational. An English and—foretaste of things to come—a Russian vocabulary were fed into the machine's 'memory'.

Its first job was to produce a translation from Russian into English. Nine seconds after the Russian 'programmed' text was fed into the 'IBM 701', its automatic typewriter printed the sentence: 'International understanding constitutes an important factor in decision of political questions.'

A rapid development programme was started after this first demonstration, in the course of which Booth and Richens in England, and Oswald and Bull in the United States succeeded in producing the first 'interpreter machines', capable of mastering the most difficult texts.

It is the same story with the rapid selectors and translator computers as with all other machines operating in the *Institut Nauchnoi Informatsii*. None of these was invented or developed in the Soviet Union, neither the card-index and Hollerith machines, nor the magnetic 'brain', nor the electronic computer. But they have helped the Soviet Union save millions of dollars, and have made a decisive contribution to increasing the prestige of Russian scientists and technicians in the eyes of the world.

The sorting and checking of information is complemented by the appropriation of foreign knowledge by reproduction.

Whole technical journals from abroad are reprinted by the Soviets, and published in Russian in huge editions.

The American *Physical Review*, the most important publication in the world dealing with physics, is a case in point. It appears fortnightly and consists of several hundred pages of original articles on the latest research by American physicists. As the magazine does not pay its way, the contributors have themselves to contribute towards its printing costs.

Officially the Soviet Union only receives a few copies from America. When Professor Donald Hughes, one of America's leading nuclear physicists, was in Russia in 1957, he was somewhat surprised to find that the *Physical Review*—in Russian—was available in every institute. He discovered that every issue of the *Physical Review* is reproduced by the Soviets, in editions of ten or fifteen thousand copies, and without payment of copyright.

Dr Rolf Landshoff, in charge of the theoretical physics department for rockets and space research at the Lockheed Works, also made a recent and surprising discovery. He was shown a literal Russian translation of his new work, *Magneto-hydrodynamics*, which the Soviets had already made available in America before his own original version in English was published. The

Soviets had made another rather foolish mistake a short time before. A special report had arrived at Lockheed's from the USSR. This turned out to be a word-for-word translation of a research report which had originally come from the Lockheed Works.

Such Soviet piracy, for it can hardly be called anything else, is not limited to scientific publications. The Russians consider themselves entitled to all foreign literature without payment of royalties. How impossible it is to get money out of them was shown when a case was brought in a Soviet court of law.

In 1930 Arthur Conan Doyle, creator of Sherlock Holmes and of Dr Watson, died. The copyright of Conan Doyle's works passed to his son Adrian.

In due course Conan Doyle's son learned that his father's stories enjoyed great popularity behind the Iron Curtain. Hundreds of thousands of copies were being printed and sold in the Soviet Union. But not a single kopek was being paid in royalties.

Eventually Adrian Conan Doyle decided to bring an action against the publishers responsible in the USSR. As his legal adviser he chose a well-known professor of international civil law from Harvard University. But to quote the recognized international copyright laws existing in every civilized country was, as the plaintiff knew, quite useless.

For the Soviet Union has never recognized these laws nor, consequently, the laws of ownership governing original works, whether these be literary or artistic works, or patents of inventions. It regards everything of this sort as common property to be freely appropriated.

On the advice of the Harvard professor Adrian Doyle based his charge on one count—a violation of Article 399 of the Soviet constitution, which prohibits and penalizes the enrichment of one person at the expense of another.

As damages, Conan Doyle's son demanded from the Soviet publishers the sum of 2,033,700 roubles, that is to say 15 per cent of the profits which they had made, illegally, from the sale of his father's books.

In November 1958 the case was tried in Moscow, and the defendant publishers won. Doyle appealed to a superior court. He finally put his case before the Supreme Court of the USSR, on 17th August 1959, but the verdict was the same. His case was dismissed as unfounded.

The Moscow judges had no choice. Any other verdict would have unleashed a flood of litigation, thousand upon thousand of civil actions against the Soviet Union for violation of the copyright laws would have followed and claims for damages to the tune of many millions would have been filed for all the books and articles which had been pirated and sold in the country of 'progressive socialist co-operative organization' without permission and without the payment of royalties.

When the decision of the Soviet court was published in the West, A. J. Cronin, the novelist, wrote in the *Daily Telegraph*:

'Almost three million copies of my books have been illegally printed in the Soviet Union. During the last twenty years I have made repeated attempts to receive compensation in some form or other. . . . I began about 1936, in tones of righteous indignation. When that proved useless, I tried an appeal to their sense of justice, and a few years later I adopted a gentler tone and emphasized the expenses involved in supporting my children and countless other indigent relations. This did not soften Soviet hearts, however. . . .

'My next attempt, some time later, was of a more jocular kind. In case there were currency difficulties, I said that I would gladly accept a fur coat for my wife. . . .

'Three years ago, feeling that I should like to see the pictures in the Hermitage, before they were perhaps destroyed by a stray rocket from Cape Canaveral, I offered to accept a trip to Russia in place of my royalties. This suggestion was also ignored, although it was passed to various authorities over there.

'Finally, at the beginning of this year, I offered to regard the whole matter as settled in exchange for a small quantity of Beluga caviar. The caviar has not yet arrived.'

A few months after this letter of Cronin's, a large number of pirated and unauthorized works by Western writers arrived in London. At the 'Soviet Book Exhibition', which opened at the Royal Festival Hall on 6th February 1960, there were exhibited Russian editions of the works of sixty English authors, including Conan Doyle, Somerset Maugham, Joseph Conrad, A. J. Cronin and Graham Greene. A storm of protest in the British press at last forced the Soviets to discontinue such piracy, or at least to practise it less barefacedly.

The British gynaecologist, Dr Grantly Dick Read, had an even more bitter experience than his compatriots in the literary world. The Soviets attempted to take the credit for his life's work by claiming it as Russian.

While still a young doctor, Read had worked out a new and revolutionary method of painless childbirth, and his book *Natural Childbirth* appeared in 1933. This innovator, who had attacked the system of using anaesthetics during childbirth, met with the strongest opposition from his colleagues. There was no question of Dr Dick Read obtaining a professorship. He could not find the means to open a training clinic. In disillusionment he went to South Africa, and was offered a clinic in Cape Town.

Shortly before his return to Europe, in 1953, Dick Read heard that Russian scientists had evolved a sensational new method of painless childbirth—the so-called 'Pavlov Method'. It was so successful that the Russian Ministry of Health now officially sponsored it.

All over Europe people were talking about the 'Russian' method, developed by the great physiologist, Pavlov. In Paris the French gynaecologist, Dr Lamaze, opened the first clinic using the 'new' method. It was filled to capacity. Out of one thousand eight hundred and sixty-three confinements, Dr Lamaze wrote in the medical journals, only eighty-one cases were not painless. The French doctor had learned this method in the Soviet Union, where he had spent six months as the guest of a state organization for expectant mothers.

In March 1957, in Zürich, Dick Read commissioned a lawyer to fight for his rights. He gave the facts to his Swiss lawyer, showing that the Russians' 'Pavlov Method' was his own life's work.

'At the beginning of 1952', Dick Read has stated, 'the Soviet consul in Pretoria asked me to send all my work to a professor in Kiev. I complied with his request. The stuff went by diplomatic bag, and must obviously have got there. I never received any acknowledgement, nor a word of thanks. I can safely say that I know all there is to know about obstetrical techniques—and before 1951 nothing was published by authoritative Soviet doctors about the influence of controlled movement in childbirth.'

In every sphere the Russians proved themselves to be master copyists.

'One thing astonished me', Hans Scherer wrote. 'In Moscow and Leningrad I noticed how Russian artists copied famous paintings . . . the details were reproduced with minute accuracy, and the colours were amazingly faithful to the original. Their talent for reproduction goes so far that one could not tell the difference between the copy and the original, were it not that the rule of invariably altering the scale of the reproduction also applies here.'

A. Polovnikov, the Leningrad correspondent of the *Literaturnaya Gazeta*, tells us how successfully the Russians have made use of this talent in quite another field.

'A colour television apparatus made by Russian engineers was recently shown at the Television Research Institute in Leningrad. . . . Among those present was a large group of American, French and Dutch experts. At the beginning of the demonstration the head of the Institute, I. Rosselevich, informed the visitors that they would be shown three television sets. The electronic tubes in two of the sets were American, while the third contained one of Russian manufacture.

'A colour tube of Russian manufacture? This astonished the foreigners. Hitherto such tubes had only been produced in the United States.

' "Watch for yourselves and try to guess which set has the Russian tube", the director said jokingly.

'Practically everyone guessed wrong', the report ends. 'Only one man gave the right answer, but he admitted that this was pure chance.'

At the Brussels Exhibition in the same year, at which the Americans demonstrated their colour television equipment, the Russians did not produce 'their' tubes. They preferred to wait until they had the whole range of Western equipment, successfully copied and reproduced.

Only a few hundred yards from the American 'Cinerama', the world's first 3D cinema, a French invention bought and improved upon by the Americans, the Soviet Union displayed their own version, 'Kinopanorama'. 'This Kinopanorama', the American film authority, Thomas Quinn Curtiss, has stated, 'is exactly like Cinerama, in every detail.'

In the Soviet pavilion English experts discovered a 'product of the Leningrad engineers' identical with a piece of research equipment first used ten years before by the Royal Navy: a Soviet under-water television set.

'A new marvel of Soviet technology', it was proudly announced in the Soviet newspapers, 'has been produced by members of the Scientific Research Institute for Artificial Limbs in co-operation with the men of the Institute of Mechanical Engineers at the Academy of Sciences in the USSR.' This was exhibited in Brussels, under the name of the 'Biohand'. What was this new marvel of Soviet technology? An improved version of the famous 'Sauerbruch artificial hand', long ago made in Germany. In 1948 a group of Berlin doctors and electrical engineers announced the construction of an artificial hand, the gripping action of which was controlled by bio-electric impulses within the body itself. The secret of this German electrically-controlled artificial hand was that on the 'commands' of the brain, the movement impulses in the muscular stump were transformed by a small amplifier into power impulses, which worked a magnetic control device in the hand itself.

For experts of every sort a visit to the Soviet pavilion at the Brussels Exhibition meant a meeting with old friends, now bearing a Soviet trademark. Unfortunately none of the experts wrote a 'Baedeker' for Russian industry, explaining which Western originals the Soviets had copied. Everything the Russians displayed with such pride was either a direct copy (like the racing car built three years before in the United States, complete with tail-fins) or at best improvements on Western models. For example there was a dredger, the hydraulic machinery for which had been produced in Magdeburg, and a grading machine for road-building, the American word 'grader' being modified into the Russia form of 'greter'. 'They've got nothing new', an American commented. 'But they've everything we've got.'

What about their very large-scale expansion projects such as the 'Davidov Plan' and the 'Plan for the Transformation of Nature'?

The much-discussed projects of the Soviet hydraulic engineer, M. Davidov, involves the creation of a 'Siberian Lake'. Hot, dry winds from the Kirghiz Steppes, travelling as far as the Ukraine, have always endangered crops, particularly in the fertile 'black earth' district. Professor

Kurt Hiehle of Eisenach, who tackled this problem, drafted a plan for changing the climate of the whole area. 'Since 1945 I have been working on a project to draw water from the Black Sea into the Caspian. I would then evaporate over 150 cubic kilometres of water from the surface of the Caspian which would fall as rain on the areas bordering the Caspian depression and irrigate it.' The professor, who had meanwhile fled to the West, wrote this in 1950. He added, 'The idea of moving vast quantities of water into the Caspian depression has now been taken up on a grand scale by M. Davidov.'

Still faithful to the Russian passion for giant projects, Davidov has extended the German climatologist's concept into an even vaster plan. He has proposed the damming of the waters of the two Siberian rivers Ob and Yenisei to create a 'Siberian Lake', and a canal costing thirty thousand million dollars would carry water from this lake down to the Caspian depression.

The 'Plan for the Transformation of Nature', proclaimed in Stalin's time, was a large-scale project against drought. It was based on the basic biological research of the Academician Vassily Robertovich Vilyams, who died in 1939, and whose real name was Williams.

Williams, whose father came to Russia from America as a railway-engineer at the time when the Americans were laying the first railway lines for the Tsar, devoted a lifetime to research on this project. In long years of experimentation he had developed a complete agricultural system to protect the growing corn from damage by drought. It was known as the *Travopolnaya Sistema Semledyelya* or 'grass field system', and involved the planting of protective strips of woodland, intensive cultivation of the soil, rotation of crops with grass being put in every seventh year, irrigation and so on. The most important element of the Williams system was the planting of grass every seven years, as this has a favourable effect on the structure of the soil.

While the 'Siberian Sea' project remains a possibility for the future, the Williams plan has been tried and has failed catastrophically. Lysenko, the 'magician' of modern Soviet biology, insisted that his own bogus 'agro-biological' projects be incorporated into the Williams plan, and ordered his so-called 'clump sowing' when the strips of woodland were laid down. Lysenko seriously maintained that 'clump sown' acorns would 'combine with' the grain seeds and 'crush the common enemy', weeds.

Years later, when it was revealed that the failure was due to Lysenko, the Minister for Forestry, W. Koldanov, cautiously commented: 'These [Lysenko's] theories, attractive as they seemed, did not stand up to practical tests and must therefore be regarded as false.'

A number of other Russian 'pioneer achievements', proudly proclaimed by the Soviet press, leave no doubt as to their origin. The West is, unfortunately, much more familiar with its political history than with the history of its science and technology. And so our newspapers have simply reproduced every sensational Tass claim without bothering to check its originality.

Using the sun to generate power, for example, which the Soviets maintain they are the first to do, is a process with which the West has been familiar for a long time. In the French Pyrenees a giant solar reflector has been in use as a source of power for many years, and there are others in the United States.

It is the same story with tidal power plants, of which Soviet engineers claim to be the pioneers. This type of installation has been operating for a long time in France, at the mouth of the Rance, in the Gulf of St Malo. French hydraulic engineers, as early as 1918, were granted two hundred and eighteen patents for these installations, which make use of the water-power produced by the ebb and flow of the tide. And the first 'power-plant in the world to be operated by heat from the earth's centre', which the Soviets claim as their own, is actually the brilliant conception of Italian engineers who have been working at it since the 1940's at the famous Vulcan Works, Larderello, Tuscany.

'Science is international', the intellectuals of Europe and America declaim, as though the Iron Curtain did not exist. 'Science should be international', would perhaps be more accurate. Now, as always, the one-way stream of knowledge flows eastwards. For what new inventions or discoveries have the Soviets ever handed over to other countries?

A veil of mystery shrouds the famous Bogomoletz serum, for example. Bedell Smith in his book, *Moscow Mission, 1946* has described the sad sequel to official attempts to learn something more about this drug. Washington inquired, through the American Ambassador, whether this serum, in addition to its value in rejuvenation therapy, could be employed in the treatment of cancer. A rumour to this effect had circulated in the West soon after the end of the war. Since this had nothing to do with military secrets, and was a method of saving human life, two members of the U.S. Embassy staff went to see the Secretary of the Soviet Academy of Sciences, and requested the information desired by their government. The Secretary promised to make inquiries.

The Americans heard nothing more from the Academy. All further inquiries remained unanswered. It was only by chance that they subsequently learnt what had happened. The Secretary of the Academy had been accused of 'giving away Soviet scientific secrets' and been found guilty. Meanwhile the Soviets had already begun selling the Bogomoletz preparation in the West.

Ten years later an incident occurred in connection with this particular serum at the 'Gerontological Congress' at Merano, on 23rd July 1957. A report was read to the eminent scientists from thirty different countries by the Soviet Professor Marchuk, head of the Bogomoletz Institute at Kiev. In his address the Soviet scientist described some of the results of treatment with the serum, which, he maintained, were little short of miraculous. There were shouts of protest from his audience. Some of the scientists maintained that judging by their own experience with the serum, the results described by Marchuk were impossible.

What was Marchuk's reply? He explained that the only formula for the serum which the Soviet authorities would release to American and European scientists was less effective than the one used in the Soviet Union. The Russian professor added: 'I am not authorized to communicate the formula of this serum, not even to this distinguished gathering.' What he had said was the truth. The explanation which the Soviet professor let slip to silence his foreign colleagues' justified protests was only too well founded.

The law regarding 'betrayal of state secrets' hangs like a sword of Damocles over every Soviet scientist and engineer, although its existence is not generally known this side of the Iron Curtain. According to a supplementary law of 8th June 1947 to the Soviet Penal Code of 1927 'betrayal of state secrets' means 'the communication of information on scientifically, technically and sociologically important inventions, discoveries and finished products before this information is made public—even when this information is of no military importance. This also applies to the communication of information on all inventions, discoveries, finished products, scientific and experimental research in technical and other branches of the armaments industry.' Violations of this law are punishable by three to twenty years' forced labour, provided there is no question of espionage or high treason, which can only be tried by a military court.

This law, which recalls so vividly Peter the Great's Ukase of 1724 concerning 'things which must be kept secret', is still in force. It has not been amended by Khrushchev.

The Kremlin alone decides what can be released. It restricts the 'publication' of information to its famous 'shock tactics'.

'In the last analysis, everything depends on human beings living at peace with one another, in a state of mutual trust—based on good relations and on a reciprocal "give and take".' Such were the words of Einstein, written at Princeton. Since 1917 the Soviet Union has only been interested in the 'take'.

As always the West has made it easy for Russia. 'One of the conspicuous characteristics of modern industry and trade', the American, Frederick Lewis Allen, has said, 'is the free interchange of information, which is published and thus becomes available to everyone in industry. Almost all foreign businessmen are astonished at how little in America is secret.'

The years when the West disregarded large-scale copying, because Soviet development was considered as an experiment with uncertain results, are

Tunnel entrance to the " Mittelwerke " near Nordhausen, the underground V-1 and V-2 factories, which became the birthplace of modern Soviet rockets after having been moved to the East.

American officers in front of the rocket combustion chamber of a V-2 in the " Mittelwerke ", which the Americans handed over to the Russians intact.

These three Soviet " specialist hunters "—Kuchetnikov, Dyerkach, and a fuel expert (from left to right)—decided which German experts would be ordered to Russia.

*This is how the Soviet " rocket miracle "
started after 1945. A captured V-2 on its
ramp in the USSR shortly before taking off.
A rare pictorial document.*

*Copies of the West at Soviet parades: the T-2 (above), a copy of the A-10 project, the Peenemunde
" America rocket "; and the ground–air rocket M-2 (below), a copy of the German " Rhine
Maiden ". Both are being demonstrated at the 40th anniversary of the October revolution in Moscow.*

past history. The Soviet Union has already begun, thanks to the willing or unwilling co-operation of the West and the immeasurable gifts made to it by the strongest industrial power in the world, to demonstrate its industrial potential beyond the Iron Curtain. All that Russia has taken from Europe and America is now coming back like a boomerang.

The first signs are easily seen. Some time ago for instance. American pharmaceutical firms received information which seemed rather odd. Medical drugs of Russian, Chinese and Eastern European origin were appearing in increasing quantities in the world market, while the Americans found their orders diminishing. Careful analysis revealed that these products were identical with medical preparations which had been originally produced by the chemical industries of Western Europe and America. The preparations differed from the Western originals only in name.

Under the name 'biomyzin', the Soviet version of the antibiotic aureomycin, discovered at the American Lederle Laboratories, is being supplied to Asiatic and African countries. And dozens of other well-known preparations are copied and exported as part of the 'patent piracy', as the Americans call this stealing of ideas.

The Eastern European countries are cheaper sources of supply than those of the West. This is not surprising. Behind the Iron Curtain production is hampered neither by the high costs of research and development, nor by having to pay for licences or patents.

There is one other significant aspect of the Russian export drive.

'If we had known', a spokesman of the American Health Department stated recently, 'that the Soviet Union was interested in helping the Asian and African peoples in the sphere of medical welfare, we would have been the first to appreciate and support their offer. It looks, however, as though the Soviet Union is sending medical supplies as a further means of checking Western influence in the underdeveloped countries, and of promoting their own political ambitions.'

After the Sputnik demonstrations, Russia set out to impress the peoples of Asia and Africa with 'irrefutable evidence' in support of the 'progressive socialist' régime and its numerous advantages even in the sphere of medicine, health and hygiene. And it is exactly the same story with the 'industrial aid' which the Soviet Union now offers to the underdeveloped countries.

THE MUNICH SURGICAL CONGRESS of 1959 featured, among the many medical sensations described by the press, one special attraction. For the first time the Soviet surgeon Demikhov would demonstrate to Western doctors a process which had been the subject of many rumours concerning the 'miracles' performed by Soviet doctors.

Pictures had appeared in the daily newspapers and magazines of the West, which recalled the Chamber of Horrors. These were photographs supplied by Soviet news agencies of a dog with two heads. The accompanying text explained that the head and shoulders of a small terrier had been surgically grafted on to an Alsatian. The two-headed dog lived, performed its normal functions, and barked and ate with both its heads.

These Russian photographs were designed to awaken interest in the success of an epoch-making experiment, never performed before. The Russians had broken through the 'biological barrier' which forbade the grafting of entire organs.

Every medical student knew that it was possible to perform skin or bone grafts. Every large clinic in the West possessed its blood bank and its reserves of skin and bone for emergency operations. Corneal grafts were also being performed, the sound cornea being taken from a corpse and grafted on to the eye of a blind person, whose sight was thus restored. But skin, bones and cornea seemed to be the limit beyond which surgery could not go.

Only in a few exceptional cases involving identical twins had entire organs been transplanted. The grafting of organs can then be successful, for identical twins are produced from the same cell, and therefore the reactions with which the body resists the grafted tissue or organ are less violent.

Had the Russians achieved something entirely new? Reports about a second heart which Soviet surgeons had put into a dog, and which had functioned normally, lent foundation to the idea. After the shock of the Sputnik, public opinion was inclined to believe the Russians capable of anything.

The surgical demonstration by Demikhov in front of his critical audience of eminent specialists at the Munich Congress should enable a rational appraisal to be made of the sensational reports concerning Soviet 'surgical miracles'.

The Soviet surgeon did not, however, show his audience the actual grafting of a second head on to a dog.

Two dozen doctors stood round the operating-table at the Munich Clinic as their colleague from Russia removed the cervical arteries from an anaesthetized Alsation. He pulled them out carefully and severed the living blood-vessels with his scalpel. The life of the dog would now normally last, at the most, for five minutes.

In a mere fraction of this time Demikhov put the living blood-vessels to-gether again. For this he used a sort of surgical 'sewing-machine', which sutured together the edges of the incisions in the severed arteries, making them airtight. Seconds later blood flowed again through the arteries, and the dog lived.

The doctors present at the demonstration were enthusiastic. Their praise was not so much for the operation as such, for it was one familiar to every medical student, but for the instrument Demikhov had used, the 'suture-machine'. The Russian had demonstrated an instrument which was totally reliable, where the hand of the surgeon might fail, in joining together very fine blood-vessels. In the surgical treatment of casualties this Soviet dis-covery opened up new possibilities. It was a definite step forward. But it had little to do with a solution to the problem of organic grafting. The dog with two heads, and the one with two hearts, must have died within a few days, as a result of the resistance reactions of the 'host' body to the albumen in the graft.

Professor Übermuth had to be cautious in what he said, for he worked in the Russian Zone. It was in his surgical clinic in Leipzig that the Soviet sur-geon had grafted a second heart into a dog a year before. The dog had lived for seventeen days. Now the professor wrote in the *Münchener Medizinischer Wochenschrift* (1959: 529): 'Mature reflection on the subject leads to the con-clusion that Demikhov has achieved an amazing technical advance.'

It was an American, James Rand, who discovered the true background to this great Soviet achievement, during a visit to Russia. Rand, head of the largest private company that handles and develops new inventions (the Rand Development Corporation) visited the 'Surgical Instrument Research Institute' in Moscow. The 'suture-machine' is there.

The idea for this had originated with Professor Paul Androssov, surgeon-in-chief at the Moscow Casualty Clinic. In 1950 he had produced a primitive 'suturing apparatus'.

His invention was passed to the Moscow Institute to be perfected. The three hundred doctors, engineers and skilled mechanics employed there were, as Rand discovered to his surprise, exclusively engaged on the task of per-fecting technical inventions for the use of Soviet doctors.

The 'suturing apparatus' of Professor Androssov was much improved. After three years' work on it at the Institute, it had reached the stage at which it could be mass-produced. The doctors in the Soviet hospitals used the 'suture machine' so extensively that several dozen further models were designed in the Institute, especially constructed for use in vascular, pulmonary or abdominal operations, and in neuro-surgery.

James Rand offered the Russians fifty thousand dollars for a nine-month option on this machine and several other surgical instruments. He was prepared to pay the same sum for licences to produce the apparatus in America.

This figure did not seem excessive to the American. For Rand had estimated the enormous costs incurred by the Russians in the development of this apparatus. The three years' work of several hundred highly qualified scientists and engineers at the Moscow Institute, he calculated, corresponded to 'a capital expenditure of fifteen million dollars'.

With their 'suture machine' the Russians had produced an instrument which would be invaluable in saving lives but which in no way corresponded to the over-simplified Soviet propaganda stories. This apparatus was simply one more complex surgical instrument in a long series that began with the stethoscope and went on to the cystoscope, X-ray and anaesthesian apparatus, the electro-cardiograph and electro-encephalograph, the 'iron lung', the 'heart-and-lung machine' and the 'artificial kidney', to name only a few among many. The Russian contribution of the 'suture machine' is thus seen in its proper perspective.

Among the Soviet showpieces are their turbine drills for the petroleum industry.

A Polish engineer, W. Wolsky, first used a ram-driver drilling bit for underground motive power in 1900. A Russian engineer, Matvey Alkunovich Kapelyushnikov, proposed a hydraulic-driven turbine to send the drilling bit down to the bore.

Copying this construction, the German boring tool manufacturers, Alfred Wirth & Co., built a large number of these turbine drills for the Russian petroleum industry. Kapelyushnikov's invention turned out to be unsuccessful, for his turbine had a working time of only a few hours—'But in the course of the next ten years a group of engineers succeeded in making the turbine drills practicable', Professor Karl Krüger of the Berlin Technical College reported. 'In 1955 the Elektrowieff system was introduced, whereby the turbine drilling bit was coupled to an electric motor.' The Soviets also used 'the Roumanian invention of the double drilling string, whereby two bore-holes were used instead of one, and this accelerated the process'.

At a time when the rotary process was in use all over the world, including the USSR, the Russians thought that they had discovered something quite new with this 'underground drive'. American firms in 1958 acquired a licence for it. The contract with Dresser Industries of Texas was given worldwide publicity by Tass. 'They did not miss this rare opportunity', commented the *New York Times*, 'of showing that they had something new to offer, even to the United States.' The licence was granted by the Soviets in the expectation of 'acquiring supplies of up-to-date American petroleum distillation and dressing plants, as they had had no replacements since 1947'.

'When they have the ball at their feet they don't waste time, but shoot straight for the goal.' The American Dr Lyman has thus described the Soviet attitude to science. An impressive example of their tactics, of their general assault on specific, selected sectors of the scientific front, so as to take the West by surprise, was the Russians' 'Atomic giant' at Dubna, near Moscow.

On 1st July 1953, twelve countries (Belgium, Denmark, Western Germany, France, Greece, Great Britain, Holland, Italy, Yugoslavia, Norway, Sweden and Switzerland, Austria following in September 1959) signed the charter of the European Nuclear Research Organization, the CERN or 'Centre Européen pour la Recherche Nucléaire'.

For the purposes of combined nuclear research, a synchrotron (an apparatus for the acceleration of protons, that is to say the nuclei of hydrogen atoms) was built near Geneva. A similar apparatus was already in existence in Birmingham, England, as well as at Brookhaven and at Berkeley in America.

The Soviet Union's answer to CERN was to set up a 'Joint Nuclear Research Institute' for the Eastern Bloc. Its members were the Eastern European countries, China, Mongolia, North Korea and North Vietnam. While building began, quite openly, at Geneva in May 1954, the Soviets concentrated all their efforts on constructing a giant 'accelerator' secretly and in record time. Apart from dropping a few hints, they said nothing about this project, for they planned to disconcert the rest of the world by their achievement when the moment came. In 1956 the time was ripe. Once again Soviet propaganda was to be given a great boost.

In that year scientists from both East and West met for an atomic congress, the first to be held on Russian soil. The men attending the congress were taken to the village of Dubna, seventy-five miles from Moscow. Here their Soviet hosts showed their colleagues from the countries beyond the Iron Curtain the 'largest accelerator in the world'—the super-synchrotron. Permission was given by the Russians to take photographs.

What the Western scientists saw was in fact a very special piece of equipment. The cyclotron was built into a vast hall, and into this cyclotron the 'proton-circuit' had been fitted. The cyclotron had an outer circumference of twelve hundred feet, and weighed thirty-six thousand tons, four times the weight of the Eiffel Tower. It contained more steel than a battleship. 'We had to melt down the Iron Curtain to produce this great cyclotron', a Soviet Academician whispered to a Western colleague.

During the tour of the research centre at Dubna, where Bruno Pontecorvo, the Italian-born British physicist who in September 1950 fled to Moscow via Stockholm, was head of one department, and Professor Heinz Pose, formerly of the Max Planck Institute at Göttingen, of another, the visitors realized that this Soviet giant accelerator, which gave the protons rotating in the 'circuit' an energy of ten thousand million electron volts, put all previous synchrotrons in the shade. For the one at Birmingham produced a mere thousand million, Brookhaven three thousand million, and Berkeley six thousand million.

The Western scientists, on their return, now did exactly as Moscow had expected. They began, unwittingly, to circulate pro-Soviet propaganda. Enthusiastic reports by well-known experts appeared throughout Europe and America, as they described their 'astonishment at the technical efficiency of these unparalleled installations'. Photographs of the 'Dubna giant' were in every newspaper.

Strangely enough, after this first demonstration nothing more was heard about the Soviet synchrotron. When Dr Maurice M. Charipo of the Naval Research Laboratory returned from a second visit to the 10,000-million eV installation in 1959, he was able to give his colleagues the reason for this silence. Dubna, he maintained, was a 'white elephant'. After almost three years it had not yet fulfilled its promise.

'It's a very sick machine', commented Dr Louis Alvarez of the University of California, who was also there. 'And the doctors will have to take a lot of trouble to get it going again.'

Without such publicity, the proton synchrotron at Geneva was nearing completion. In comparison with its 'big brother' at Dubna, it was a very modest and, at a total cost of three hundred million Swiss francs, inexpensive affair. Its hundred cyclotron units for the 'proton-circuit' were not, like the Soviet installation, made of thirty-six thousand tons of steel, but a mere tenth of this, three thousand eight hundred tons. This combined effort of European science had given an impressive proof of Western ability.

The 'World records' achieved in this outwardly not very impressive re-search centre at Meyrin, near Geneva, on 24th November 1959 were given very little press publicity compared with that awarded to the Sputniks. But here at CERN great advances were being made at the very frontiers of nuclear research.

On the 24th November at 19.40 hours, when J. B. Adams switched on the synchrotron, symbolically named the 'Eurotron', it reached, at the first trial run, twenty-four billion electron volts—in the official language of nuclear physics, twenty-four thousand MeV or twenty-four GeV.

Thus, during its initial test, the Eurotron had achieved a world record. Later its capacity was increased to thirty billion electron volts (30 GeV).

After this demonstration J. B. Adams and a small group of European scientists uncorked a bottle of vodka, on the label of which was written in Russian: 'To be opened only after producing a kinetic energy of more than 10·1 billion electron volts!'

Russian scientists had given this bottle to J. B. Adams, the head of the Eurotron centre, when he attended the conference at Dubna.

The empty vodka bottle was sent from Geneva to Dubna as 'bottle post'. Instead of the vodka, it contained a photograph of the flash of light on the oscilloscope screen at the moment when the protons were accelerated into the vacuum chamber of the Eurotron 'circuit' with an energy of twenty-four billion electron volts. The photograph meant that at its trial run the Eurotron had reached two and a half times the alleged Dubna capacity.

The Russians had hoped to 'overtake' the West by a massive effort. In their unimaginative and wastefully extravagant way, the proved synchrotron principle evolved by the West was used for installations larger than any then in existence. They had made a mammoth out of an elephant, and it did not thrive.

The Europeans, however, built installations of enormous capacity at a fraction of the cost, using a new principle based on the brilliant discovery of the Greek, Nikolaos C. Christophilos.

And the Soviet Union's reply? In record time at Sepukhov, south of Moscow, a new synchrotron was begun, in which, needless to say, the basic principle of the Geneva installations was copied, and enlarged so as to surpass the Eurotron. Seventy billion electron volts (70 GeV) was to be the target. At the time of writing the project has been suspended.

They are now announcing a quite different type of construction with an even higher capacity, the 'Plasmatron' with a 'circuit' of only 6 metres' radius, an energy of 100 GeV. . . .

Soviet 'suture-machines', turbine drills, and the proton-synchrotron at Dubna are all characteristic of Russian progress in science, research and technology.

According to an expert on Russia, Dr Arnold Buchholz, the first Five Year Plan laid down in 1928 rigid 'organization and planning, in the scientific as well as other fields, which helped to create for Soviet science a characterestic unity between theory and practice'. At that time the 'military deployment of scientists at all focal points of the battle' was inaugurated.

The 'production' of engineers and scientists was undertaken, as the cornerstone of this 'planned' scientific development project.

When the Soviet Union first published the statistics of their 'mass production' of experts, the figures were alarming, and not without reason. They showed that a veritable army, millions of students, was in training, an unmistakable potential danger to the West.

What was the result of this mass-production of scientists?

As numerous investigations have established, Soviet science presents a double image, a mixture of great achievement and of backwardness. Spheres in which the Russians have succeeded in drawing level with the West are matched by other fields which can be described as completely neglected and undeveloped.

The most important advances which the Soviets can show have been in mathematics—for which the Russians have always had a particular aptitude

—in physics and in nuclear physics. In theoretical and experimental nuclear physics, such as the practical use of atomic energy, they have reached Western standards. As the American, Dr Van Vleck, has put it, they are as 'far ahead' as the United States. Revolutionary new discoveries, and the completely new methods resulting from them, have given the Russians something to show, just as in the past. But among the true pioneers, from Copernicus, Galileo, Kepler and Newton, to Einstein and Planck, Rutherford, Heisenberg, Schrödinger, Hahn and Fermi, to name only the greatest, there is not a single Russian. Their best work is second-hand.

In astronomy and chemistry the Soviets quickly caught up. In 1945 the largest telescope in the USSR—the 1·25 metres reflecting telescope in the Crimea—was part of the loot taken from Germany.

In practical medicine Russia possesses a few eminent men, especially surgeons. Medical research, however, lags far behind the tremendous achievements of the West, as a result of the dogmatic teachings of the Pavlov school. The average level of Russian medicine does not correspond to that prevailing in the West.

In geology, geophysics and oceanography, the Soviets have more to show in the quantity of scientific work done than have the Americans. In quality, however, the Soviets again lag far behind. There is no question of their overtaking the West in these fields, despite isolated successes. And in biology, genetics, biochemistry, biophysics and pharmacology Russian science remains as far behind as ever. These sciences are definitely underdeveloped.

As a criterion—albeit a rough one—figures of the Nobel Prize-winners between 1945 and 1959 can be used; the statistics for scientific awards are as follows: Out of twenty-four prizes for physics, three went to Soviet citizens; in chemistry, there was one Russian out of twenty-two Nobel Prize-winners; and in medicine and physiology, out of twenty-six none was Russian.

The proportion is not high for a country with a population of two hundred and fourteen millions.

When the Nobel Prize for physics was given in 1958 to three Russians, Tamm, Frank and Cherenkov, for their work on the 'Cherenkov Ray', French scientists issued a paper pointing out that the phenomenon known as the 'Cherenkov Ray' was first discovered as early as 1926 by Dr Lucien Mallet. This French electro-cardiograph expert had observed the 'blue light', as he called it, which appeared in transparent substances, including water, during the passage of gamma-rays. In a series of experiments he established its remarkable luminescent qualities and carried out analyses with a spectrograph. He submitted his report to the French Academy on 26th July 1926.

'It is regrettable', commented Francis Perrin, in charge of French atomic research, 'that neither the Nobel Prize jury nor the Soviet scientists should have acknowledged Dr Mallet's work, although it was recognized by the appropriate Academy of Sciences and was therefore available to every research scientist.'

The Russians' poor showing in the field of major creative achievement has made the Soviet Union all the more anxious to win prestige by accelerated, concentrated effort in specific directions. When Britain announced her intention of building an atomic power plant, Moscow immediately ordered a similar project to be started, as a rush job. It was in operation on 27th June 1954, some months before Calder Hall. From the point of view of propaganda, the Russians' target had been reached. 'The Soviet Union builds the first atomic power station in the world', Tass announced.

Research in the Soviet Union is carried out under conditions of urgency which usually exist in the West only in the wartime production of armaments. There is an abnormally large outlay in money, men and materials for science and technology. Starting in the primary schools, a very thorough specialist selection system has been organized, to exploit all available scientific and technical talent among two hundred million Soviet citizens.

In addition, the USSR appropriates the latest developments in pure and applied science from the free world, and stocks its laboratories with the most modern foreign apparatus and instruments.

Taking all this into account, the results achieved do not seem either exceptional or particularly impressive.

The steady progress of Soviet science, of which the USSR boasts and with which it threatens the West, has been impeded by one insurmountable natural obstacle. In every nation there is a limit to the amount of talent available. In Russia, this limit has already been reached.

'Indicative of the total national potential', writes Dr Arnold Buchholz, 'is the fact that 52 per cent of all Soviet students are women.'

The critical factor upon which the future well-being of the people depends is neither the quantity of raw materials and foodstuffs, nor the power potential, but solely the number of qualified experts. Such is the view put forward briefly in a report by the professors of the famous California Institute of Technology at Pasadena.

While general mobilization of all those with any talent has been going on for some time in Russia, the West has done little along these lines. The vast intellectual potential which Western Europe and North America have at their disposal among their five hundred million people is only used fractionally in research and development.

But even this small effort has sufficed to produce an enormous number of new discoveries and a good deal of steady progress in all branches of the pure and applied sciences. And this without compulsion, without a total concentration of effort, often with completely inadequate and, compared to Russia, ludicrously few material facilities.

Hitherto there has been no indication that the vital, inexhaustible source of creative power which has emanated for centuries from the Western countries is drying up. All that has happened in Europe and America during the last sixty years suggests quite the reverse.

The programme drafted by the chemist, Andrei N. Nesmeyanov, President of the Academy, on the Kremlin's orders, laid down: 'Our task is to bring all branches of Soviet science to the position of first place in the world.' This has remained mere wishful thinking.

Meanwhile Moscow, realizing how much it has undertaken, has already been compelled to cut down on large-scale development. The mass production of scientists and engineers has led to an acute shortage of qualified skilled workers, foremen and works managers in every field.

A nation must cut its coat according to its cloth. Many of the Academicians produced by this method of 'over-production' have been forced to accept subordinate positions in industry. At the same time the doors of the universities have been partly closed. The secondary schools, which formerly consisted of ten classes, have been replaced by secondary schools of eight classes. After leaving school all young people have to take jobs. It is only possible for them to get their leaving certificate when they have combined three to four years' study in evening classes with their normal employment. And even those who have taken their certificate, and are thus permitted to study at a university, do not go straight to college. They still have to work in industry, and are only given the chance of a higher education after three more years of evening classes and correspondence courses. This means that in future, students in the USSR will not leave the university at the age of twenty or twenty-one, but at twenty-eight or twenty-nine. Thus the chances of going to a university have decreased.

While the Western countries continue to be deceived by the Russian surplus of Academicians, and while Soviet propaganda vaunts the USSR as 'the first scientific state', the 'planned mass production' of scientists is, in fact, already a thing of the past.

RECENTLY, AND ESPECIALLY since the Sputniks, it has become a Western habit to magnify Russia's scientific and technical, and above all her economic, achievements. 'Intimidated by their own sensational headlines', Heinrich Kraft has commented in an economic review, 'and by the anxiety caused them by the military strength of the leading Communist power, publicists of all political persuasions talk only in terms of "world power", of "gigantic achievements", when discussing Russia. To hear them one would think that the Soviets' astonishing achievements eclipse everything that is happening, or is likely to happen, in the free world—with the possible exception of the United States.'

Its ceaseless propaganda boasting of ever-increasing productivity, its gigantomania evident in its huge industrial works, power-plants and canal construction, and its skilfully prepared 'inspections' by foreign scientists, have all been successfully combined by Moscow to deceive even Western specialists concerning the true potential of the USSR.

Small wonder, then, that the peoples of Asia and Africa believe the Soviet Union possesses the key to the door of an industrial paradise.

The fact that the Soviet Union, with its two hundred and fourteen million inhabitants, is now in second place to the world's greatest industrial power, with incidentally only one hundred and seventy-seven millions, makes it all too easy to forget how large the discrepancy between the production levels of the two countries is. According to reliable estimates, American production is two and a half to three times greater than the output of Soviet Russia.

In early 1960 important branches of Soviet production lagged far behind the output of similar goods in the United States, having then reached a stage that the Americans had passed many years before. They were nineteen years behind in steel production, thirty years in petroleum, sixteen years in electricity, thirty-six years in the production of heavy lorries and omnibuses, forty-nine years behind in motor vehicles, twenty-three years in boots and shoes, thirty years in radios, ten years in television sets, thirty-one years in refrigerators, nine years in meat production, and eighteen years in milk production.

Detailed study reveals that the allegedly 'unparalleled and unique' development of Soviet productivity is a myth. In fact, America has shown, over the last sixty years, an increase in its production of consumer goods per head and per working hour at the rate of 2·3 per cent per annum. The increase rate of the USSR on the other hand, has amounted to an average of 1·2 per cent per annum.

There is no need to cross the Atlantic for such statistics. The USSR, in many branches of industry, has been unable to equal, let alone surpass, the industrial output of Western Europe.

A comparison between Russian industry and that of the West German Federal Republic shows significantly what the position is in regard to the Soviet 'giant'. Western Germany in 1959 produced 29·4 million tons of steel, almost exactly half the corresponding production figure of the mighty Soviet Union.

In the production of capital and consumer goods the Soviet Union's output is not much ahead of West Germany's, and in a large number of important products Western Germany is ahead of the Soviet Union.

During 1959 West Germany produced 1,356,000 motor-cars, while the Russians turned out a total of only 124,800. In the total production of vehicles, private and commercial, Russia was still well behind, for in 1959 West Germany's output was 1,720,000, while that of the USSR was 629,000.

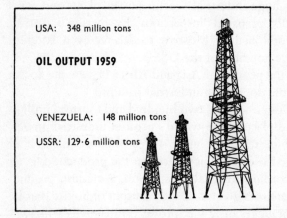

USA: 348 million tons

OIL OUTPUT 1959

VENEZUELA: 148 million tons

USSR: 129·6 million tons

A comparison with Western Europe shows very clearly how little truth there is in Russian propaganda about the allegedly vast industrial preponderance of the USSR. The Soviet Union's productivity still lags behind that of Great Britain, France and Germany. In 1959 these three countries produced 65·1 million tons of steel, the USSR only 60 millions. While the electric power generated in Britain, Germany and France amounted to 274,000 m. kilowatt hours, in the USSR only 264,000 m. kwH were generated.

In 1959, 5,591,000 motor-cars were produced in the United States, while Britain, France, Italy and Western Germany turned out a further 4,100,000. Against these 9,690,000 cars manufactured by the West, the 'progressive' Soviet Union produced only 124,800.

The 'critical' and 'self-critical' articles in the Soviet press about the shortages of consumer goods and the wretched quality of what is available

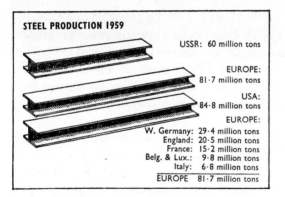

STEEL PRODUCTION 1959

USSR: 60 million tons

EUROPE:
81·7 million tons

USA:
84·8 million tons

EUROPE:
W. Germany: 29·4 million tons
England: 20·5 million tons
France: 15·2 million tons
Belg. & Lux.: 9·8 million tons
Italy: 6·8 million tons
EUROPE 81·7 million tons

give a fair picture of the productivity of the Soviet Union. Heinrich Kraft has spoken with truth of the disproportion between the hopelessly backward consumer goods industries and the basic heavy industries driven to bursting-point, when he said that Russia's economy today resembles a 'deformed cretin'.

The Soviet Union has failed to create a truly functioning industry, capable of supplying all the manifold human wants in a highly developed economy.

The position as regards their 'progressive agriculture' is much the same. Here, too, the USSR has succeeded in concealing the truth about its failures by means of deceptive propaganda such as the 'tractor miracle', the 'giant granaries' and the 'cultivation battle'.

At a meeting of the Central Committee in June 1959, Khrushchev announced that ensuring the people's bread supply is 'only a partial solution of the problem, and does not conceal the fact that now, as always, they need meat'.

The disparity between the bumper crops produced by model *kolkhozes* run on Potemkin lines for the benefit of the West, and the average yield of the vast mass of *kolkhozes* is still very evident. The Soviet Union, which includes the Ukraine, 'the granary of Europe', is no longer a leading agricultural export nation as was Tsarist Russia.

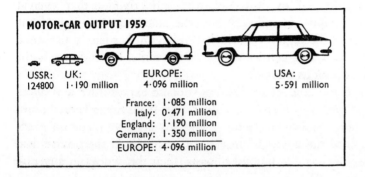

MOTOR-CAR OUTPUT 1959

USSR: UK: EUROPE:
124800   1·190 million   4·096 million

USA:
5·591 million

France: 1·085 million
Italy: 0·471 million
England: 1·190 million
Germany: 1·350 million
EUROPE: 4·096 million

Forced collectivization by the Soviets has now been carried out ruthlessly in the occupied countries of Eastern Europe. As a result of these 'progressive methods' the yield per acre in the Russian Zone of Germany and in Czecho-slovakia has sunk so low that it can no longer even meet the needs of the home market: in this same period the countries of Western Europe have raised their yield per acre by 30 per cent and their overall productivity to 60 per cent above the pre-war level.

A comparison with the United States really shows the grotesque extent to which agriculture lags behind in the USSR.

Even today almost 50 per cent of the working population of Russia is employed in agriculture. Yet it is still impossible to produce enough food for the people, and the USSR has to import. In the United States, the 8 per cent of the working population employed in agriculture produces more food than the home market can absorb. The figures speak for themselves: 52 million Russians were engaged in agriculture in the Soviet Union in 1959, as against only 5·8 million farmers in America.

And a further fact must be remembered when considering the poor performance of Soviet agriculture. It was European and American firms which first built the tractor-works and the chemical factories for the pro-duction of fertilizers, and they also supplied an enormous amount of up-to-date agricultural machinery. The Soviet Union imported seeds and breeds of cattle from the West, not to mention expert advice, which it still uses.

The 'progressive Communist system', to which numerous Asian and African peoples are looking hopefully today, is not capable, even though many still believe that it is, of filling the 'empty bellies of the masses'. The USSR has shown itself quite unable to create the ideal agricultural system.

Adlai Stevenson described his journey through the Soviet Union in 1958. 'We saw vast agricultural enterprises and enormous factories . . . we visited schools, universities, power-plants and building-sites. We were left with the impression of an immeasurably large, rich but underdeveloped country, where they are everywhere working for one object, that of quickly being able to challenge America's world supremacy.'

Professor Alexander Rüstov, however, was of the opinion that 'even if the productivity of Russian industry and the standard of living of the workers had reached the high level which Bolshevism has falsely promised for the last forty years, our verdict would be the same. For industry is the servant of mankind, not its master'.

The fact is that after the quite disproportionate expenditure and enor-mous sacrifices of these past forty years, the results from the industrial point of view are mediocre and unsatisfactory. The Soviets have made no parti-cular contribution to the industrial history of mankind. If the Soviets had succeeded, as Bolshevism continuously boasts, then this would in any case

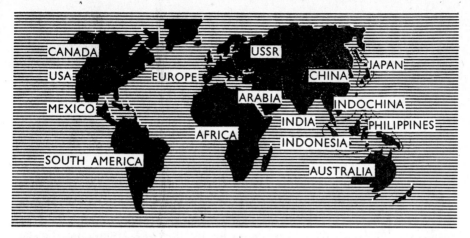

A map of the world showing geographical proportions.

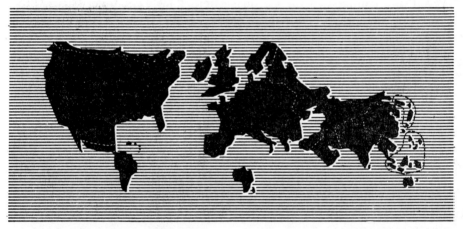

A map of the world in proportion to its production (dollar basis).

A map of the world in proportion to its population.

have been a triumph for international capitalism, which supplied the credit, the machinery, the designs, the patents, the engineers and the technicians, everything indeed of decisive importance, the whole capitalist production system in fact, for the Russians' use. And it is still being supplied.

Bolshevik-planned industry feeds on the industrial freedom of the rest of the world. It would long ago have died a natural death, had it not been for the repeated injections of fresh life-blood which are still being pumped into it.

Now Moscow has launched its new Seven Year Plan, with the ambitious target of reaching the production level of the United States. Will it be possible for the USSR to achieve this?

'When Mr Khrushchev announces his intention of giving the Russian people a standard of living equal to that of the West, by means of his Seven Year Plan', commented the German Minister for Economic Affairs, Professor Ludwig Erhard, 'we must not take him too literally. It is impossible for Soviet Russia to jack the standard of living of two hundred and fourteen million people up to our level and at the same time to find the enormous capital necessary for its armaments programme. Still less is it possible for Russia to develop her own economy, if she is to fulfil her promises of more and more help and interest-free loans to the underdeveloped countries. Russia cannot meet these commitments on so many fronts, and will have to retrench in one direction or another. . . . This is why Soviet Russia is interested in maintaining trade relations with the West, which will bring her certain advantages in improving the Russian standard of living.'

The Kremlin hoped that the West would 'help to dig its own grave' and from the moment of launching the Seven Year Plan, this hope has been promptly realized.

'Come to our country . . .' The invitation was issued to various groups of American economists, among them Professors Galbraith and Leontief of Harvard, Reynolds of Yale, and Lewin of the University of Pennsylvania. The Soviet planners consulted them, working out how further industrialization could be successfully carried out in the Soviet Union, using the methods advised by American economists and sociologists, and how the unwieldy Soviet planning machinery, then largely free-wheeling, could be put to work. Khrushchev himself said in Los Angeles, on 19th September 1959: 'I now read less Karl Marx and Lenin and more books and articles by American senators, scientists and journalists.'

Once again Moscow sent groups of agricultural experts to the United States to study the extremely productive American agricultural system, and to reorganize Soviet stock-breeding and cattle-feeding along American lines. For the same reason the highly mechanized maize farm at Corn Rapids was put, at his own suggestion, on Khrushchev's itinerary during his visit to the United States. The owner, Roswell Garst, stated that Khrushchev wanted to

The atom-giant Dubna: " The biggest acceleration plant in the world", 80 miles from Moscow—a
super-synchrotron for 10,000 million electron volts—turned out to be a flop (above). At Meyrin,
near Geneva, the much more modest proton-synchrotron (below), built by European co-operation,
achieved 24,000 million electron-volts at its trial run on the 24th November 1959.

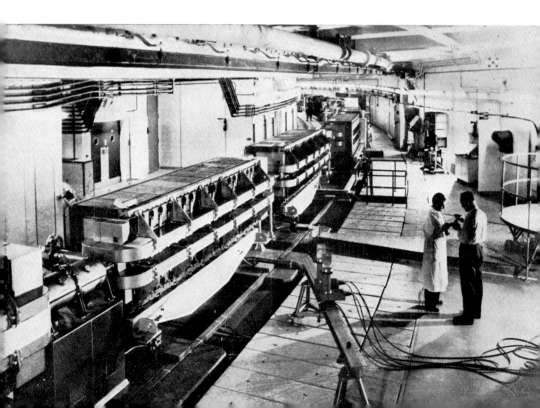

The giant power station at Kuibyshev. "With its 2.1 million kW capacity it is the most powerful in the world", according to its chief engineer, N. Razin, "and surpasses even the famous American hydro-electric station of Grand Coulee". Total USSR output in 1959 was only 264 thousand million kW, against 469 thousand million in Europe, 795 thousand million in the USA.

Building generators for the USSR's vaunted "Electrosila" power station, Leningrad. It is equipped with installations which were taken from the Siemens works in Berlin after the war.

Inside the Moscow small car factory—formerly the ZIS works, today the Likhachev works—where the "Moskvich" is made. (See picture, p. 313.)

see for himself 'why 8 per cent of the population of the United States could produce enough food with a high albumen content for the whole country, and why 50 per cent of the population of the Soviet Union was needed to raise foodstuffs containing far less albumen'.

Copying the American pattern in every detail, the Soviet Union ordered the cultivation of maize as a basic cattle-food. The special machinery for such maize cultivation was supplied by the United States. Khrushchev admitted without shame that the Soviet Purchasing Commission, Amtorg, had bought the machinery in order that it might be thoroughly studied, 'taken to bits' and then copied. And the seeds, the hybrid maize, cultivated according to practical theories based on the Mendelian-Morganist principles damned by Lysenko, was also supplied by the United States.

In order to acquire from the West all that they needed so urgently for their Seven Year Plan, the Soviets envisaged, as an inducement, the old and tried method of large-scale imports.

'In addition to chemicals, synthetic materials, synthetic fibres and machinery', reported the *New York Times* on 17th August 1959, 'Khrushchev expressed a wish for cooling and air-conditioning plant, machinery for cellulose, paper and wood processing, equipment for the manufacture of textiles, leather goods and foodstuff, packing machinery, pumps and compressors, mining equipment, cranes and other types of transporters, pipes for domestic gas installations, medical supplies and drugs.' The demands of the Seven Year Plan are colossal.

In Western Europe and America the purchase of steel tubes has begun. They are needed for the construction of new oil and gas pipe-lines. Soviet industry cannot supply enough of them.

There have been other supplies sent from the West which contribute directly or indirectly towards strengthening the Soviet potential, developing industry, and meeting the demand for consumer goods in Russia. A month after the Soviet Union announced its programme for enlarging its textile industry in order to catch up with the West, the firm of Intertex-International, New York, was commissioned to equip a new textile factory with fifty thousand spindles. For twenty million dollars American firms were to build at Kalinin, from their own plans, the world's 'largest and most comprehensive spinning and weaving installations'. At a cost of $22,400,000 the British firm of Vickers & Bookers Ltd was commissioned to erect two mechanized sugar beet factories, one near Moscow, the other in the Ukraine.

27   The Way of Courage

'JUST GIVE ME ONE example of a service you have rendered humanity! What do we owe you—you who have claimed our indulgence? You have contributed nothing, except threats and hostility. We gave you our knowledge, and in exchange you invaded our lands and showed us no quarter.

'You have stolen our scientific knowledge, our luxury goods, our modern methods of warfare. And you have shown your gratitude by driving your Cossacks' lances into our bodies. With all the advantages that the West has given you, you have become violent and brutal despots.'

In these words Frédéric Lacroix damned Tsarist Russia in 1845. They are equally applicable to the Soviet Union today.

All that the West stands for, all that it has achieved and is still achieving culturally, technically and scientifically, has been done without a single important contribution from the Russians. If the Russians had never existed at all, it would have made not an iota of difference to what the West has to offer all humanity.

The present position of Russia, had she not been taught, helped and supported by the West, would be unthinkable. Even at this moment Russia can only keep up by the continuous theft and exploitation of every new development in the free world.

The West still possesses the greatest reserve of talent in the world, and the most highly developed industrial power of all time.

If the confidence of the West in its own vastly superior potential is seriously shaken, if spectacular propaganda stunts by the Soviets succeed in producing real alarm, leading to an over-estimation of Russia's capabilities and potentialities, then the decisive reason for this is our ignorance of the true nature of Russian power.

How is a sound assessment of the capacities and capabilities of Russia possible, when even today the quality and quantity of this ceaseless importation from the West is unnoticed and unknown in Europe and America, and, consequently, in the rest of the world? The world should realize that the Russians are better acquainted with what we have to offer than we are ourselves, that the 'Russian copying technique' has been and still is quicker and more thorough in its practical application of Western knowledge, inventions, discoveries and general development than is the Western economy itself.

Whether Russia will actually overtake the free world or not will be decided by the West. The fate of the West, and of its future generations, lies in its own hands. The free peoples of the world have every advantage, a generally superior potential of cultural, scientific, technical, industrial—and, of course, moral—strength, and an abundance of creative talent.

After the painful experience of the post-war period, the West has at last recognized whither appeasement of the Russians must lead; and its governments appear willing now to draw the correct conclusions and to adopt an attitude towards the Soviet Union and its objectives justified by past experience of Russian behaviour. 'There is only one way of dealing with a power like Russia, and that is the way of courage', Karl Marx advised in the *New York Tribune* of 30th December 1853.

Everything depends on whether the people of the West, of Europe and America are willing to stand fast and strike a hard bargain as Tsarist Russia and the Soviet Union have always done.

Bibliography

Adelung, Friedrich von: *Siegmund Freiherr von Herberstein* (St Petersburg, 1818).
Alexandrov, Victor: *L'orso e la balena* (Milan, 1959).
American Federation of Labour: *Slave Labour in Russia* (1949).
Arne, T. J.: 'Les rapports de la Russie avec la Suède et l'Orient au temps des Vikings', in *Le Monde Slave* (Paris, 1925).
Ashby, Eric: *Scientist in Russia* (London, 1947).
  Article in *Discovery*, July 1951.
Baedeker's Guide to Russia (Leipzig, 1888).
Bärwolf, A.: *Da hilft nur beten* (Düsseldorf, 1956).
Bartz, Karl: *Peter der Grosse* (Berlin, 1941).
Basseches, Nikolaus: *The Unknown Army* (1943).
Beazley, C. R., N. Forbes, & G. A. Birkett: *Russia from the Varangians to the Bolsheviks* (Oxford, 1918).
Bernadski, V. N., & A. E. Suknovalov: *The Historic Past of Leningrad* (Leningrad, 1958). In Russian.
Bernhard, G.: *Armes reiches Russland* (Berlin, 1904).
Bessler, Hans: *Wirtschaftsgeschichte des Mittelalters* (Aarau, 1956).
Beus, I. G. de: *Die Zukunft des Abendlandes* (Frankfurt a.M., 1956).
Blum, K. L.: *Graf Jakob Johann v. Sievers und Russland zu dessen Zeit* (Leipzig, 1864).
Blunck, Richard: *Hugo Junkers* (Düsseldorf, 1951).
Bocheński, I. M.: *Der sowjetrussische dialektische Materialismus* (2nd ed., Berne, 1956).
Boltz, C. L., in *Discovery*, August 1951.
Borgese, G. A.: *Russland—Wesen und Werden* (Amsterdam, 1950).
Boustedt & Trietsch: *Das russische Reich in Europa und Asien* (Berlin, 1910).
Brändström, Elsa: *Among Prisoners of War in Russia and Siberia* (London, 1929).
Brandt, B.: *Foreign Capital: its influence on national economic development* (2 vols., St Petersburg, 1898, 1899). In Russian.
Browning, O.: *Peter the Great* (London, 1898).
Brückner, Alexander: *Kulturhistorische Studien: die Russen im Ausland, die Ausländer in Russland im 17. Jahrhundert* (Riga, 1878).
  Peter der Grosse (Berlin, 1879).
  Katharina die Zweite (Berlin, 1883).
  Die Europäisierung Russlands (Gotha, 1888).
  and C. Mettig: *Geschichte Russlands bis zum Ende des 18. Jahrhunderts* (2 vols., Gotha, 1896, 1913).
Brüggen, Ernst Freiherr v.d.: *Wie Russland europäisch wurde* (Leipzig, 1885).
Buchholz, Arnold: *Ideologie und Forschung in der sowjetischen Naturwissenschaft* (Stuttgart, 1953).
  Weltbild der Sowjetunion (Hamburg, 1956).
Cahen, G.: *Histoire des relations de Russie avec la Chine sous Pierre le Grand* (Paris, 1912).
Capello, G.: *Gli italiani in Russia nel 1812* (Città di Castello, 1912).
Chancelour, Richard: *The Book of the Great and Mighty Emperor of Russia and Duke of Moscovia* (1553).
Clarke, Daniel: *Travels in Various Countries of Europe, Asia and Africa. Part I: Russia, Tartary and Turkey* (London, 1810).
Clausewitz, Carl v.: *Der russische Feldzug von 1812* (Wiesbaden, 1953).
Collins, Dr Samuel: *The Present State of Russia* (London, 1671).
Congress for Cultural Freedom: *Science and Freedom* (London, 1955).
Contarini, Ambrogio: *The Travels of the Magnificent M. Ambrosio Contarini . . . in the Year 1473*.

Cookridge, E. H.: *Soviet Spy Net* (London, 1955).
Creators of the new technology (Moscow, 1957). In Russian.
Curtin, J.: *The Mongols in Russia* (Boston, 1908).
Custine, Marquis de: *La Russie en 1839* (Paris, 1846).
De Cyon, E. M.: *Witte et les finances russes* (Lausanne, 1895).
Dallin, David J.: *Soviet Espionage* (New Haven, 1955).
Danilewsky, N. J.: *Russland und Europa* (Stuttgart, 1920).
Dick, William E., in *Discovery*, December 1951.
Dobb, M.: *Soviet Economic Development Since 1917* (3rd ed., London, 1953).
Dornberger, Walter: *V2* (London, 1954).
Dostoevsky, F. M.: *The Diary of a Writer* (2 vols., London, 1949).
Ducrocq, Albert: *Destins industriels du monde* (Paris, 1951).
Dukmeyer, Friedrich: *Korbs Diarium itineris in Moscoviam* (2 vols., Berlin, 1909–10).
Ediger, T.: *Russlands älteste Beziehungen zu Deutschland, Frankreich und der römischen Kurie* (Inaugural dissertation, Halle a.S., 1911).
Ehret, J.: *Litauen in Vergangenheit, Gegenwart und Zukunft* (1919).
Ekblom, R.: 'Rus et Vareg dans les noms des lieux de la région de Novgorod', in *Archives d'études orientales* (Uppsala, 1915).
Encyclopaedia of the Social Sciences (New York, 1937).
Episodes from the history of Russian science and technology (Moscow, 1957). In Russian.
Evers, G.: *Vom Ursprung des russischen Staates* (1808).
Ewers, I. Ph.: *Das älteste Recht der Russen* (Dorpat, 1826).
Falkovski, N. I.: *Moscow in the History of Technology* (Moscow, 1950). In Russian.
Fechner, A. W.: *Chronik der evangelischen Gemeinden in Moskau* (2 vols., Moscow, 1876).
Florovski, A. V.: 'Die Anfänge des Buckdrucks bei den Ostslawen', in *Slawische Rundschau* (Prague, 1940), XII, 1–2.
Forscher und Wissenschaftler im heutigen Europa (2 vols., Oldenburg, 1955).
Forstreuter, Kurt: *Preussen und Russland von den Anfängen des Deutschen Ordens bis zu Peter dem Grossen* (Göttingen, 1955).
Frähn, C. M. J.: *Ibn Foszlan's und anderer Araber Berichte über die Russen älterer Zeit* (1823).
Friede, Dieter: *Das russische Perpetuum Mobile* (Würzburg, 1959).
Fritzler, K., 'Das russische Reich, eine Gründung der Franken', in *Slavia* III (1924).
Lo Gatto, Ettore: *Saggia sulla cultura russa* (Rome, 1935).
 Gli artisti italiani in Russia (Rome, 1943).
 Storia della letteratura russa (Florence, 1944).
 Storia della Russia (Florence, 1946).
 Storia del teatro russo (Florence, 2 vols., 1952).
Gerhard, Dietrich: *England und der Aufstieg Russlands* (Munich, 1933).
Goetz, L. K.: *Deutsch-russische Handelsverträge des Mittelalters* (Hamburg, 1916).
Golder, F. A. (ed.): *Bering's Voyages* (2 vols., 1922, 1925).
Golovachov, A. A.: *Geschichte des Eisenbahnwesens in Russland* (St Petersburg, 1881).
Graham, Stephen: *Ivan the Terrible* (New Haven, 1933).
Guagninus, Alexander: *Omnium regionum Moschoviae*, etc., in Marnius & Aubrius, *Rerum Moscoviticarum auctores varii* (1600).
Härberger, A.: 'Vikinghi svedesi nella Russia', in *Europea Orientale* X (1930).
Hafferberg, H.: *Petersburg in seiner Vergangenheit und Gegenwart* (St Petersburg, 1866).
Hanisch, Erdmann: *Geschichte Sowjetrusslands 1917–1941* (Freiburg, 1951).
Hanway, Jonas: *A Historical Account of the British Trade over the Caspian Sea* (London, 1753).
Harvest, Harry: *Massloses Russland* (Zurich, 1951).
Haumant, E.: *La culture française en Russie* (Paris, 1910).
Haxthausen, A. Frhr. v.: *Studium über die inneren Zustände Russlands* (3 vols., Hanover, 1847–52).
Haydu, Julius: *Russland 1932* (Vienna, 1932).
Helbig, Herbert: *Die Träger der Rapallo-Politik* (Göttingen, 1958).
Helfferich, Karl: *Das Geld im russisch-japanischen Kriege* (Berlin, 1906).
Herberstein, Sigmund Frhr. zu: *Rerum Moscoviticarum Commentarii* (Vienna, 1549).
Herder, Joh. Gottfr. v.: *Ideen zu einer Philosophie der Geschichte der Menschheit* (1791).

Hermann, Ernst: *Das Nordpolarmeer—das Mittelmeer von morgen* (Berlin, 1949).
Herzen, A. (ed.): *Katharina II, Kaiserin von Russland: Memoiren* (Hanover, 1859).
Hiehle, Kurt, in *Umschau*, 1950, pp. 105 *ff*.; 1954, pp. 129 *ff*.
Hildebrandt, Walter: *Die Sowjetunion, Macht und Krise* (Darmstadt, 1955).
History of Russian Art (Moscow, 1957). In Russian.
History of the USSR (Moscow, 1947–50).
Hodann, Max: *Sowjetunion, gestern, heute, morgen* (2nd ed., Berlin, 1931).
Hodgman, Donald R.: *Soviet Industrial Production 1928–1951* (Cambridge, Mass., 1954).
Hölzle, Erwin: *Russland und Amerika* (Munich, 1953).
Holzhausen, Paul: *Die Deutschen in Russland* (1812).
Ilin, I.: *Welt vor dem Abgrund* (Berlin-Steglitz, 1931).
Ischchanian, B.: *Die ausländischen Elemente in der russischen Volkswirtschaft* (Berlin, 1913).
Jackson, W. G.: *Seven Roads to Moscow* (London, 1957).
Jenkinson, A.: *The First Voyage made by Master Antony Jenkinson towards the Land of Russia* (1557).
Jordan, George R.: *From Major Jordan's Diaries* (New York, 1952).
Jungk, R.: *Brighter than a Thousand Suns* (London, 1958).
Just, Artur W.: *Russland in Europa* (Stuttgart, 1949).
Kennan, G. F.: *Soviet-American Relations, 1917–1920* (vol. 1, 2, London, 1956, 1958).
Kerner, R. J.: *The Urge to the Sea* (Berkeley, Los Angeles, 1946).
Knickerbocker, H. R.: *The Soviet Five-Year Plan* (London, 1931).
   Soviet Trade & World Depression (London, 1931).
Koch, Hans: *Sowjetbuch* (Cologne, 1957).
   5,000 Sowjetköpfe (Cologne, 1959).
Koestler, Arthur: *Sowjet-Mythos und Wirklichkeit* (Hamburg, 1947).
Korff, Baron: *Russland* (Berlin, 1901).
Kostylyov, V.: *Iwan Grosny* (2 vols., Berlin, 1953).
Krause, Helmut: 'Marz und Engels und das zeitgenossische Russland', in *Marburger Abhdlg. zur Geschichte und Kultur Osteuropas* (Giessen, 1958).
Krypton, Constantine: *The Northern Sea Route and the Economy of the Soviet North* (New York, 1956).
Lacroix, Frédéric: *Les Mystères de la Russie* (Paris, 1845).
Lange, M. G.: *Wissenschaft im totalitären Staat* (Stuttgart, 1955).
Lansdell, Henry: *Russian Central Asia* (London, 1881).
Laserson, M. M.: *The American Impact on Russia (1784–1917)* (New York, 1950).
Lavater-Sloman, Mary: *Katharina und die russische Seele* (6th ed., Zurich, 1941).
Lehrfreund, L.: *Die Entwicklung der deutsch-russischen Handelsbeziehungen* (Leipzig, 1921).
Lenin, V. I.: *The Development of Capitalism in Russia* (Vol. 3 of his collected works, London, 1961).
Litt, Theodor: *Wissenschaft und Menschenbildung im Lichte des West-Ost-Gegensatzes* (Heidelberg, 1958).
Lubimenko, I.: 'England's part in the discovery of Russia', in *Slavonic Review* (London, June 1927).
Lukyanov, P. M.: *History of the Russian Chemical Industry up to the Beginning of the 19th Century* (4 vols., Moscow, 1948–55). In Russian.
Lysenko, T. D.: *The Situation in Biological Science* (Moscow, 1951). In English.
Margeret, Jacques: *Estat présent de l'Empire de Russie* (Paris, 1607).
Matthaei, Friedrich: *Die wirtschaftlichen Hilfsquellen Russlands* (2 vols., Dresden, 1883–85).
   Die Industrie Russlands in ihrer bisherigen Entwicklung und in ihrem gegenwärtigen Zustande (2 vols., Leipzig, 1872–73).
Mavor, James: *An Economic History of Russia* (2nd ed., 2 vols., London, 1925).
Mayerberg, Augustin: *Relation d'un voyage en Moscovie, 1661* (Paris, 1858).
Mediger, Walther: *Moskaus Weg nach Europa* (Brunswick, 1952).
Mette, Hans Joachim: *Russische Geschichte* (Bonn, 1949).
Migulin, P. P.: *Unsere moderne Eisenbahnpolitik und Eisenbahnanleihen* (Kharkov, 1903).
Milyukov, P.: *Essays in the history of Russian Culture* (Paris, 1930). In Russian.
   'The influence of English political thought in Russia', in *Slavonic Review* (London, Dec. 1926).

Minden, Gerold von: *Europa zwischen USA und UdSSR* (Bamberg, 1949).

Mitchell, M.: *The Maritime History of Russia, 848–1948* (London, 1949).

Moorehead, Alan: *The Traitors* (London, 1952).

Müller, Marianne, & Egon Erwin: . . . *stürmt die Festung Wissenschaft!* (Berlin–Dahlem, 1953).

Nestor Chronicle, The (The Russian Primary Chronicle, Laurentian text, transl. and ed. Samuel H. Cross & Olgerd P. Sherbowitz-Wetzor. Cambridge, Mass., 1953).

Nolde, Baron B. E.: *Yuri Samarin and his Time* (Paris, 1926). In Russian.
La Formation de l'Empire russe (2 vols., Paris, 1952–53).

Nötzel, Carl: *Das heutige Russland* (2 vols., Munich, 1915–18).

Ocherki istorii Leningrada (Essays on the history of Leningrad; 3 vols., Leningrad, 1955–56).

Ordega, S. von: *Die Gewerbepolitik Russlands von Peter I bis Katharina II* (Tübingen, 1885).

Olearius, Adam: *The Voyages and Travels of the Ambassadors sent . . . to the Great Duke of Muscovy*, etc. (London, 1662).

Oudard, Georges: *Peter the Great* (New York, 1929).

Paléologue, Maurice: *The Enigmatic Czar. The Life of Alexander I of Russia* (London, 1938).

Pankratova, A. M., K. V. Bazilevich & others: *A History of the U.S.S.R.* (1947).

Pantenius, Th. H.: *Geschichte Russlands von der Entstehung des russischen Reiches bis zur Zeit vor dem Weltkriege* (2nd ed., Leipzig, 1917).

Pares, Bernard: *A History of Russia* (London, 1958).

Parry, Albert: *Whistler's Father* (New York, 1939).

Paszkiewicz, H.: *The Origin of Russia* (London, 1954).

Perry, J.: *The State of Russia under the Present Czar* (London, 1716).

Pierling, P.: *La Russie et l'Orient, Mariage d'un tsar au Vatican: Ivan III et Sophie Paléologue* (Paris, 1891).

Platonov, S. F.: *History of Russia* (London, 1925).

Plattner, Felix A.: *Pfeffer und Seele* (Einsiedeln, 1955).

Poniatowski, Michel: *Histoire de la Russie, d'Amérique et de l'Alaska* (Paris, 1958).

Possevino, Antonio: *Moscovia* (Antwerp, 1587).

Putnam, Peter: *Seven Britons in Imperial Russia 1698–1812* (Princeton, 1952).

Rambaud, A.: *History of Russia from the Earliest Times to 1882* (Boston, Mass., 1886).

Ramo, Luciano: *Storia del Varietà* (Milan, 1956).

Rappard, William E.: *A quoi tient la supériorité économique des Etats Unis?* (Paris, 1956).

Rauch, Georg von: *A History of Soviet Russia* (London, 1957).

Reading, Douglas K.: *The Anglo-Russian Commercial Treaty of 1734* (New Haven, 1938).

Réau, L.: *L'art russe des origines à Pierre le Grand* (Paris, 1921).
L'art russe de Pierre le Grand à nos jours (Paris, 1922).

Reddaway, W. F.: *Documents of Catherine the Great* (Cambridge, 1931).

Revelations of Russia (Grimma, 1846).

Rhamm, K.: *Germanische Altertümer aus slawisch-finnischen Urheimat. Die altslawische Wohnung* (Brunswick, 1910).

Richter, L.: *Leibniz und sein Russlandbild* (Berlin, 1946).

Roberts, Henry L.: *Russia and America* (New York, 1956).

Russian Engineers (Moscow, 1953). In Russian.

'*Russland*', *seine Gegenwart und Vergangenheit* (St Petersburg, 1900).

Rüstow, Alexander: *Ortsbestimmung der Gegenwart* (3 vols., Erlenbach-Zürich, 1950–57).

Sartorius Frhr. v. Waltershausen, A.: *Das volkswirtschaftliche System der Kapitalanlage im Ausland* (Berlin, 1907).

Schäfer, Dietrich: *Osteuropa und wir Deutschen* (Berlin, 1924).

Schaffer, Gordon: *Russian Zone* (London, 1947).

Scheffer, Paul: *Seven Years in Soviet Russia* (London, 1931).

Schleuning, Johannes: *Die deutschen Siedlungsgebiete in Russland* (Würzburg, 1955).

Schmid, H. F.: 'Die slawische Altertumskunde und die Erforschung der Germanisation', in *Zeitschrift für slawische Philologie* I, 1925.

Schulze-Gaevernitz, G. von: *Volkswirtschaftliche Studien aus Russland* (Leipzig, 1899).

Schuman, F. L.: *American Policy toward Russia since 1917* (London, 1929).

Schwartz, Harry: *Russia's Soviet Economy* (2nd ed., New York, 1954).

Seeger, Elisabeth: *The Pageant of Russian History* (New York, 1956).
Semenov, V.: *Geschichte des Mittelalters* (Berlin, 1952).
Seraphim, Ernst: *Führende Deutsche im Zarenreich* (Berlin, 1942).
Seton-Watson, Hugh: *The Decline of Imperial Russia 1855–1914* (London, 1952).
Skrine, F. H.: *The Expansion of Russia 1815–1900* (3rd ed., Cambridge, 1915).
Smith, W. Bedell: *Moscow Mission 1946* (1949).
Sommer, Erich Franz: *Die Einigungsbestrebungen der Deutschen im Vorkriegs-Russland (1905–1914)* (Leipzig, 1940).
Spirin, I.: *Die Eroberung des Nordpols* (Leipzig, 1955).
Staden, H. v.: *Aufzeichnungen über den Moskauer Staat* (ed. F. Epstein, Hamburg, 1930).
Stählin, K.: *Geschichte Russlands von den Anfängen bis zur Gegenwart* (4 vols., Stuttgart-Königsberg, 1923–39).
   Aus den Papieren Jacob von Stählins (Königsberg, 1926).
Stevens, Leslie C.: *Life in Russia* (London, 1954).
Stieda, W.: 'Die Anfänge der Kaiserlichen Akademie der Wissenschaften in St Petersburg', in *Jahrbücher für Kultur und Geschichte der Slaven* (Breslau, 1926).
Storost, G.: *Litauische Geschichte* (Tilsit, 1921).
Struys, Jean: *Les voyages de J. S. en Moscovie, en Tartarie, etc.* (Amsterdam, 1681).
Stumpp, Carl: *Sammlung Georg Leibbrandt, Gemeindebericht der Schwarzmeerdeutschen 1848* (Leipzig, 1941).
   Berichte der Sammlung Georg Leibbrandt (Berlin, 1943).
Sumner, B. H.: *Survey of Russian History* (2nd rev. ed., London, 1947).
Talbot Rice, Tamara: *Russian Art* (West Drayton, Middlesex, 1949).
Tarsaidzé, Alex.; *Czars and Presidents* (New York, 1958).
Thomsen, V.: *The Relations between Ancient Russia and Scandinavia and the Origin of the Russian State* (Oxford, 1877).
Tolstoi, I. I.: *The First Forty Years of Intercourse between England and Russia, 1533–1593* (1875).
Tompkins, S. R.: *Russia through the Ages. From the Scythians to the Soviets* (New York, 1940).
   The Varangians in Russian History (Chicago, 1937).
Tooke, W.: *The Life of Catherine II, Empress of Russia* (3 vols., London, 1800).
Tugan-Baronovsky, M.: *Geschichte der russischen Fabrik* (Berlin, 1900).
Turel, Adrien: *Russlands und Amerikas Wettlauf zur Eroberung des Jenseits* (Zurich, 1950).
Die UdSSR, Enzyklopädie der UdSSR (Leipzig, 1959).
UdSSR—Unser Wissen über die Sowjetunion (Berlin, 1957).
Vossler, K.: 'Russische Zustande am Ende des 17. Jahrhunderts', in *Archiv für slawische Philologie* (Berlin, 1924).
Waliszewski, K.: *Le berceau d'une dynastie. Les premiers Romanov* (2nd ed., Paris, 1909).
   Peter the Great (London, 1897).
Wallace, Henry A.: *Soviet Asia Mission* (New York, 1946).
Webb, Sidney & Beatrice: *Soviet Communism: a New Civilization* (2 vols., London, 1935).
Wegweiser v. St. Petersburg, Neuer illustrierter praktischer (3rd ed., St Petersburg, 1897).
Wetter, Gustav A.: *Der dialektische Materialismus* (3rd ed., Vienna, 1956).
Willan, T. S.: *The Muscovy Merchants of 1555* (Manchester, 1953).
Winckler, A.: *Die deutsche Hansa in Russland* (Berlin, 1886).
Winter, Eduard: *Halle als Ausgangspunkt der deutschen Russlandkunde im 18 Jhdt.* (Berlin, 1953).
Witt, Nicholas de: *Soviet Professional Manpower* (Washington, 1955).
Wittram, Reinhard: *Drei Generation, Deutschland—Livland—Russland, 1830–1914* (Göttingen, 1949).
   Peter der Grosse, Der Eintritt Russlands in die Neuzeit (Berlin, 1954).
Zarychev, G. A.: *Reise durch den Nordostteil Sibiriens, das Eismeer und den Östlichen Ozean* (Gotha, 1954).
Zeman, Z. A. B. (ed.): *Germany and the Revolution in Russia 1915–1918* (London, 1958).
Zimmer, Ernst: *The Revolution in Physics* (London, 1936).
Ziska, Antonin: *Weltreise* (1954).
   Asien (Oldenburg, 1950).

Periodicals, etc., consulted: *Deutsches Handelsarchiv*, 1885–1910; *Discovery*, London; *Der Flieger*, Munich; *Newsweek*, New York; *Osteuropa-Naturwissenschaft*, Stuttgart; *Der Russisch-Deutsche Bote*, 1899–1905; *Russische Revue*, St Petersburg, 1872; *Science et Vie*, Paris; *Science News Letter*, Washington; *Sowjetwissenschaft, naturwissenschaftl. Abtlg.*, East Berlin from 1950; *Die Umschau in Wissenschaft und Technik*, Frankfurt a.M.

Sources of Illustrations

The Architecture of Leningrad, State Publishers of Literature on Buildings and Architecture, Moscow, 1957 (4). Archiv für Kunst und Geschichte, Berlin (6). Art Achive, The Hague (2). Associated Press, Frankfurt (2). dpa, Frankfurt (5). Historia-Photo, Bad Sachsa (1). Historisches Bildarchiv Lolo Handke, Bad Berneck (5). Keystone, Munich (3). *The Kremlin, Moscow*, State Publishers of Literature on Building and Architecture, Moscow (5). *Leningrad*, State Publishers of Fine Art, Moscow, 1956 (4). *Mediaeval Russian Churches*, The Mediaeval Academy of America, Cambridge, Mass., 1949 (1). *Moscow*, State Publishers of Fine Art, Moscow, 1956 (1). Österreichische Nationalbibliothek, Vienna (2). Presseabteilung der Botschaft der UdSSR, Bonn (1). Süddeutscher Verlag, Munich (5). Ullstein, Berlin (12).

For the text figures the Picture Archive of the Osteuropa Institute, Munich, placed contemporary pictures at our disposal; many of these were redrawn by Oskar Sixt and Horst Hennig of Munich.

Index